A FINE KIND OF MADNESS

A FINE KIND
OF MADNESS

Ronnie Scott Remembered

Rebecca Scott
with Mary Scott

HEADLINE

First published in 1999
by HEADLINE BOOK PUBLISHING

10 9 8 7 6 5 4 3 2 1

British Library Cataloguing in Publication Data

Scott, Rebecca with Scott, Mary
A fine kind of madness : the biography of Ronnie Scott
1. Scott, Ronnie, 1927–96 2. Jazz musicians – Great Britain –
Biography 3. Saxophonists – Great Britain – Biography
I. Title
781.6'5'092

ISBN 0 7472 2199 5

Typeset by Avon Dataset Ltd, Bidford-on-Avon, Warks

Printed and bound in Great Britain by
Mackays of Chatham plc, Chatham, Kent

HEADLINE BOOK PUBLISHING
A division of the Hodder Headline Group
338 Euston Road
London NW1 3BH

www.headline.co.uk
www.hodderheadline.com

You left this world too soon.
You left me alone too soon.
I need you back with me . . .
But the cards were dealt.
And all is said and done.
Now I'm lost and I must find my way home.

I miss you and I love you Dad.

CONTENTS

ACKNOWLEDGEMENTS

The authors would like to express their special thanks to John Fordham for his invaluable help, generosity, support and encouragement.

Our grateful thanks to Rabbi Guy Hall for his wisdom, generosity, support and encouragement; to Andrew Simon and Paul Wilson of the National Sound Archives for their patience and dedication; to James Codd and the staff at the BBC Written Archives, for their dedication in producing essential documents; to David Nathan, National Jazz Foundation Archive, Loughton Library for the hours spent in researching the *Melody Maker* polls; to Dan Morganstern and staff of Rutger's University Jazz Archives, New Jersey, USA for their interest and kindness and making so much research material available; to Dennis Matthews at *Crescendo* for his help and support and permission to quote from the many personal interviews done with Ronnie over the years; to all at the *Melody Maker* for allowing us to use quotes from their many interviews with Ronnie; and to the Julliard School of Music Library in New York for the kindness of their staff and their vast resources of British Jazz.

Thanks are due to all of the people who so willingly gave of their time to help us tell this story, especially the following: Rose Krane (Rose Schatt), Alex and Thea Zwern, Blanche Zwern, Ella Laine, Sydney Levy, Josie Barber, Cousin Betty, Alfie Summers, Rabbi Sonny Herman, Alf Shaw, Ray Cook, Harry Pitch, Cynthia Gordon, Joe Greene, Tony Crombie, Lennie Bush, Laurie Morgan, Kenny Harris, Peter Ind, Allan Ganley, Vic Ash, Cab Quaye, Harry Gold, Stan and Jackie Tracey, Alan Skidmore, John Dankworth CBE, Chips Chipperfield, Jim Godbolt, David Redfern, Mike

Carr, John Critchinson, Martin Drew, Barbara Jay, Kenny Napper, Marge Ellison, Louise Simms, Hilary Totah (Hilary McNair), Jack DeJohnette, George Coleman, Chico Freeman, Françoise Venet, Jill O'Doherty, Tony Middleton, Derek Everett, Dr Sydney Gotlieb, Walter Houser, Pete King, Sonny Rollins and Sir Paul McCartney.

Love and thanks to Spike Milligan for the foreword and to Judy and Amber Scott and Frances Jackson for their constant support and forbearance.

So many people gave so generously of their time to help us tell this story as accurately and honestly as we were able and to *all* of you we extend our heartfelt thanks and sincere appreciation.

Picture Credits

All pictures from the collection of Mary and Rebecca Scott, apart from numbers 5, 6 Ella Lane; 7 Cynthia Gordon; 8 Alf Summers; 9 Michael Ochs Archives/Redferns; 10 Chuck Stewart/Redferns; 12 William Gottlieb/Redferns; 20 Mike Carr; 33 David Redfern/Redferns; 34 Mick Hutson/Redferns; 36 Roy Campbell/AAPS Photography (UK) Ltd.

FOREWORD

Writing a foreword to a book about Ronnie Scott is very difficult. He was a complex man. He had two failings, gambling and women, and he had mixed fortunes with both.

One woman who stayed constant and faithful in his life is Mary Scott, and I am glad that their daughter Rebecca is now writing this book with Mary about him.

Everything else apart, he was a magnificent jazz musician. His improvisation was beboppish and he would take an old tune and give it a new life. I will never forget when he played an old Irving Berlin waltz, 'I'll Be Loving You Always'. For the first ten minutes I didn't recognise it then suddenly I got the drift. He went on to play for another hour and a half without stopping and finally, like all great musicians, he returned to the tune which I recognised.

Yes, Ronnie was all things to all men, and I never met anybody that disliked him apart from his bookie.

Spike Milligan, August 1999

CHAPTER ONE

THE DARKEST HOUR

My father often said, 'I'm a musician, and that's my excuse for being here.
What's yours?' Although delivered with a wry smile, this remark summed up the
very essence of his being: without his music, life was meaningless.

I T IS INDISPUTABLE THAT 1996 was the worst year of our lives. Dad's illness, which had been creeping up on all of us for about four years, had turned into a roller-coaster ride of terror and euphoria. He suffered from depression, which was exacerbated by physical illness. He had been troubled with thrombosis, which is excruciatingly painful, and had needed a couple of operations on his legs. This, together with major problems he was having with his teeth, which prevented him from playing his saxophone for nearly two years, spelled disaster. To compound the problem, his latest affair, a tempestuous relationship with his girlfriend Jo, who now lived in California, had once again come to an end. Their relationship had been an on-and-off situation for about three years, and I couldn't bear the thought of him being alone.

I knew that he couldn't lose himself in his music any more, for by now he had reached the conclusion that he would never play again – he was such a perfectionist. But I really believed I would be able to lift his spirits that Christmas and that we would have a good time, as always.

I was planning on travelling to London to spend the holiday with Dad, and I telephoned him to talk about the impending trip. He told me not to come. He said, 'I'm not in the mood for Christmas, Rebecca. I will not be able to do the things we usually do.' But I thought that I was invincible. I was convinced that if I came I'd cheer him up. I decided to come, because I had joined him for so many Christmases, and they were always a great success. Dad had talked to Mum and told her: 'I've told Rebecca that I'm not well. I'm not sure if I can handle the visit, Mary.' Mum reassured him, as always, and we discussed it. Mum said to me: 'You'll have to make Christmas for Daddy this year, Rebecca.' And so I arrived in London on 16 December 1996. My father tried to put on a good face, and when he wasn't able to he would do everything he could to get me to leave the flat so that I wouldn't see him at his worst. I bought Christmas decorations and put them up, but they seemed only to make things worse for him. One after-noon, after I had just taken a bath, I looked into the living room and Daddy was sitting there watching TV, but he had taken all the decorations down. I don't know what he did with them; I guess he threw them out. I started to glimpse the depth of his unhappiness, suddenly realising that he really did not want to celebrate Christmas and that seeing it all around him was incredibly painful.

Losing his ability to play was catastrophic for my father. Playing was his reason for being, and it was also his refuge. He had shown tremendous courage, fighting to overcome everything that was happening to him, but nothing seemed to work, and the beginning of 1996 was the beginning of the end. During the course of the year my father started to drink heavily, trying to use alcohol to numb his pain. By the time I arrived he was losing control. I had never seen him drink like that. Not ever. Not in front of me, not even in June when he was so ill. This time it was different. Dad struggled to keep it away from me, sometimes causing an argument to get me to leave the flat. He had major mood swings and went from being gentle and of generous spirit to plunging into deep sadness, when he would become intensely frustrated with everyone and everything, finally ending up in a rage. That whole week was fraught with tension.

23 December 1996

We went out for dinner, Dad, myself and Dani (Jo's daughter). Dad was very nervous and edgy all evening. When we were in the restaurant he kept asking me to leave the table so he could talk to Dani about Jo, so I did. I went to the ladies' room and gave them as much time as I could. When we left the restaurant Dad wanted to go to the 161 club, but it wasn't open, so we walked on to Dad's club. Dad had told me that Dani would talk to him about Jo only if they were alone, so when we went in the club he asked me again to leave them alone, because he wanted to talk to Dani in the downstairs bar, so I went to his office to wait for them.

I was alone for about two hours. By then I had really had enough. I thought, Dad has been drinking brandy and ginger ale one after the other. He shouldn't be doing this; it isn't fair to Dani and it isn't fair to me. So I'm going to put my foot down. I'm going to say: 'It's time to go home.' I went to look for them, and that's when everything spun out of control. I said to Dad: 'Look, Dani lives here. You can see her any time you want to. All you have to do is just pick up the phone and she can be with you in fifteen minutes. I live three thousand miles away, and I have to go back to New York in a couple of days. Let's just spend some time together. Let's just forget about Jo. Let's forget about things that are happening right now. Let's think about other stuff.' Dad flew into a rage and told me I was being selfish. When I look back on it, I realise I didn't handle things the right way. I got caught up in his rage. He said some hateful things to me that night. I couldn't believe my ears because he had never ever said anything mean to me in my whole life. If I did something stupid he would tell me, but this was totally different and I wasn't expecting it at all. We were all in the cab on the way home, and he kept going on and on. I didn't have any words to say to him, except: 'Shut up, you don't know what you're saying.' I knew his rage wasn't directed towards me. It was an anger that he had to get out. He wanted to vent off to people that had really hurt him, but I was the closest one to him so I got it all full blast. By the time we got to Chelsea I was in such a state I didn't want to hear any more that night, so we dropped him off and I went to spend what was left of the night with Dani.

The first thing I did when we got back to the flat was call up my mum. I told her that Dad and I had had a row and she said: 'You have to call him, and you have to make it up with him.' I said: 'No, no, no. You don't understand. This wasn't just a little tiff, this was a huge row. Nothing like this has ever happened between us: it was really bad, I can't bear to hear any more tonight. You need to call him, I don't want to talk to him again tonight.' Mum tried to calm me, she told me she would call Dad and talk to him and that we both needed to get a night's rest and cool off. She said: 'Tomorrow when you talk everything will be all right. Even though he's ill, Daddy never holds grudges. He's probably already really sorry for everything he said. He's been trying to reach you to apologise.'

Dad had called Mum. He was very upset and had been trying to reach me by phone. Finally, at about 4 a.m., I picked up the phone and told him I didn't want to talk any more tonight, and he said: 'Look, Rebecca, either you speak to me now or this is going to be the last time that you ever talk to me.' I thought: Well, what the hell is that supposed to mean? You're going to disown me as your daughter? But I said: 'Daddy, you're upset, I'm upset. We'll talk about this tomorrow when we both have clear heads. We'll get a good night's sleep, and I'll talk to you about this tomorrow. I'm going out to do some Christmas shopping and I'll probably be home around 3.30 to 4 p.m. We'll sit down, have something to eat, and talk about this rationally. I'm going to hang up the phone now. I'm going to bed and I'll see you tomorrow.' And I hung up the phone.

Dad kept calling Mum back, and they had about five conversations throughout the early hours of the morning. He calmed down and was able to discuss the whole situation without rancour. He told her that he knew he shouldn't have but he had left a message on Jo's machine. Then he said he was going to turn his phone off and go to bed, and anyone who called him could leave a message, he would get back to them the next day. He told her not to worry, that everything would be all right, and they said goodbye to each other.

I'll never forget when I came home that afternoon, at about 4.30 p.m. When I was walking through the large wrought-iron gates that front the entrance to the courtyard at Elm Park Mansions, I saw the caretaker sitting in the office. I thought: Oh, he's a bit late. Then I thought to myself: Daddy usually goes to the club about this time. I wonder if he's already left. If he has I'll go and meet him at the club later on, for dinner. Then I thought: Last night we discussed that I would be home around this time. I figured, Well, he was drunk, and I'm sure he won't remember a lot of what transpired, and the things he said. He's probably at the club right now.

So I'm trucking up the five flights of stairs with my shopping, and I get to the front door and this feeling came over me as I was sticking my key into the lock: Don't go in here Rebecca, *don't* go in here. It was just so weird, this voice in my head saying: Rebecca *don't* go into the apartment. *Don't* go into the apartment. When I look back on it now, that feeling, it was almost like he was in the doorway, like you see in the movies, the spirit saying: *No! No! No!* But you just walk right through it because it can't stop you. I turned the key in the lock and opened the door. Dad always turned off all the lights before he left, but if he was at home, no matter what he was doing – he could be sitting in the bedroom, making tea in the kitchen, in the bathtub with his radio on – the TV in the living room would always be blaring loud. He always had the TV on constantly so he could catch the horse racing, car racing, tennis, snooker, football, all the sports he liked. When I came in, the hall light was on but the dimmer switch had been turned to a low setting. I thought: Hmm, this is funny, why are there lights on? I called out his name: 'Dad. Da-ad, are you here?' and I was thinking my first thoughts about that feeling of don't go in here. Probably because I thought he was going to yell at me because I'm late or whatever. I thought we were going to have another row because he was going to be upset, or I was going to be upset because of the things he had said to me, and I was going to have a kind of an attitude, a bit of a chip on my shoulder just to let him know how much the things he had said had upset me. I would say: 'Well, how could you say those things to me? No matter what state you were in, you shouldn't have said stuff like that to me.' These things were all quickly going through my head, and then I thought: No, I don't want to fight with him. I'm just going to be calm, and I'm just going to sit him down. I'm sure he doesn't remember half the things he said. And I started to walk down the hallway . . .

I opened the living room door . . . and that's when I found him. I didn't know what to do. I was transfixed. I didn't want to walk into the room because I didn't want to see his face, and I didn't want to feel the coldness of his body. I wasn't sure if he was dead or if he had just passed out. The table that was normally by the side of his chair was knocked over. His chair had fallen on its side, and he was lying on the floor by the couch. I don't really remember what the whole room looked like, because all I could focus on was him lying there. The phone was in the living room, where he was, and I thought: What's the number for the ambulance? All I could think of was that in America it's 911, but I didn't know what it was here, and I didn't know what to do. I thought: Should I run over and check for a pulse? Should I sit him up? At the same time I just kind of knew – I could almost feel the lifelessness and I didn't want to touch the cold body. I didn't want to have that last . . .

All these thoughts were running through my mind. I had these stupid big shoes on; they were really high and clunky. I remembered that the caretaker was downstairs, and I thought: Let me go to him first. He'll help me. He'll help me. And I was running down the stairs with these stupid shoes on, trying to run as quickly as possible, my heart beating a mile a minute, and me thinking: Oh, my God! *Oh, my God*! This *can't* be happening, this *isn't* happening. He wouldn't do this with me here, he *wouldn't do this*. I just kept thinking: *No! No! No! No!* He just *must* have passed out. I was trying to convince myself that he was fine, that everything was going to be OK. Then this feeling of guilt came over me, a sickening empty but heavy feeling in my stomach that somehow got into my veins, and the feeling travelled all through my body: This is my fault. If I hadn't had a row with him he wouldn't be so upset. I'm going to be blamed for this. If I'd just let him do what he had to do, and yell at me for whatever he had to yell at me for. If I hadn't said anything back to him . . .

Then I reached the caretaker's office and ran in. By now I was half-crying and stumbling over my words incoherently as I burst through the door all out of breath. The caretaker, Mr Smith, was a gentle, kindly man. Taking my hand in his, he said: 'Try to be calm. I'll help you. Now, tell me again. What's happened?' I managed to say: 'You have to call the ambulance . . . I've just found my dad—' Mr Smith was very calm and sympathetic, and he at once took control of the situation. He rang for the ambulance and said: 'All right, now, let me go upstairs with you and check on everything.' When we reached the flat, he said: 'Don't come into the room. I want you to wait out here. I'll go in and check for you and see what the situation is.' And he went into the living room, and that's when I knew . . . the expression on his face when he came back out confirmed my worst fears. He'd obviously felt for a pulse. Gently he said: 'Come, come. I think you should come downstairs to the office. Who should I call?' Of course I said: 'Call Uncle Pete – Pete King, Daddy's partner. I think he's at the club.'

I don't know how long it took Uncle Pete to come – it seemed like for ever – but he came straight to the office. Uncle Pete said: 'Becky, you should call your mother, you should call your mother.' I wished that he was the one to make the phone call, but I had to do it. I remember that as I was dialling I was thinking: Oh, God, everyone is going to blame me for this – this is my fault in a way. But at the same time I felt sure that if it hadn't been that day it would definitely have been another day, just because he had tried so many times. At first Mum didn't answer the phone and I was yelling into the answering machine: 'Mum! *Mu-um*! Pick up the phone. Pick up. *Pick up*!' Mum ran to the phone, and said: 'Rebecca, I was in the middle of doing the Christmas cakes. This time of year you must give me time to get to the phone . . .' I hardly heard a word she was saying. I didn't know how to say it. I didn't even think of how she was going to react. I didn't say, 'Sit down. I have to tell you something.' The words just came out of my mouth: 'Mum, Daddy died this morning.'

CHAPTER TWO

FAMILY HISTORY

As I walked across the room towards my Aunt Rose, she looked up, saw me, her eyes lit up, her face wreathed in smiles, and delightedly she burst out: 'Rebecca! You're a Schatt! You're a Schatt! You're a Schatt!'

AMID THE STEADY FLOW of fleeing Jewish migrants headed for the West who were escaping from the 1880s pogroms in southern Russia and Poland was the Schatt family. My great-grandfather Morris and great-grandmother Betty arrived in London and settled into a new home in Broomehead Street off Commercial Road in the East End. My great-grandfather, who was tall and handsome with dark hair and striking features, was a tailor by trade and quickly established himself in his own business, eventually becoming tailor to Queen Victoria. During the course of the coming years their family grew in leaps and bounds: first came Philip, followed by Annie, Doris, Hymie, David, Mary, Rosie and Joseph. Joseph, nicknamed Jockie, later to be shortened to Jock, by his elder brother Philip, was destined to become a famous alto saxophone player and band leader and my grandfather.

The Schatt family flourished and the children reached maturity. The first-born son, Philip, who strongly resembled his father in looks, was the first to leave home. At twenty-four he received his call-up papers from the army. Shortly after he joined the armed forces they wanted to send him to India. Philip really did not want to go, so, feeling he had no choice, he made a radical decision and deserted the army, leaving England and his family for America, where he re-enlisted, this time in the American armed forces. Although neither of them knew it at the time, Philip was not to see his young brother Jock again for some thirty-odd years.

One by one the brothers and sisters married, setting up their own homes in London, with the exception of Rosie, who died at an early age from flu, and Annie, who married a Belgian piano player and teacher whose name was Max Zwern. Shortly after the wedding they moved to Belgium to be with her new husband's ailing father. After the birth of their first-born son Alias, known as Alex, the family moved to Frankfurt in Germany, where their second son Zigmond, known as Ziggy, was born. Later on, the move to Frankfurt would prove to be a fatal mistake.

By the time Jock Schatt was in his early twenties he had already firmly established himself as a highly respected musician and band leader who travelled widely. Jock was over six feet tall, with black hair and blue eyes that twinkled with laughter, and had inherited the same striking features of his father. In his home town of London, he met and fell in love with a beautiful young saleswoman whose name was Sylvia Rosenbloom, nicknamed Cissie by her family.

Grandma Cissie was descended from a family with a bloodline of Dutch and Portuguese heritage, which was reflected in her beautiful blue-black curly hair and sparkling deep dark brown eyes. Grandma Cissie did not know her father, Solomon Rosenbloom; he had deserted her mother, Rebecca Messias (Nanna Beckie), and her younger brother Mark (known as Uncle Markie) and herself when she was just a small child. However, my errant great-grandfather had four sisters, Annie, Debbie, Eva and Rose, all of whom stayed in touch with Nanna Beckie and Grandma Cissie, although they all moved to Canada, and later to California. After Solomon Rosenbloom left, Nanna Beckie, taking her two children with her, went to live with her father and mother, Benjamin and Betsy Messias. Benjamin Messias was an ethical, moral, very learned man, small in stature, a prolific writer, a toastmaster and orator who officiated at Portuguese synagogues throughout Britain and the City of London. He was also secretary of a benevolent society working with large companies organising the dis-tribution of coal to impoverished families, frequently travelling back and forth to Holland. The Messias family was orthodox, very religious and a large one. Nanna Beckie had three sisters and three brothers, some of whom were to remain in London, while others moved to Canada, the west coast of America and South Africa. Nanna Beckie left school at the age of eleven, and when Cissie was in school she told her that she had forgotten how to write, so my grandmother used to write all her mother's letters and cards for her, which she always signed Nanna Beckie, spelling Nanna with two en's instead of the customary single letter. When my grandmother

Cissie was in her teens, Nanna Beckie met and married a widower by the name of Samuel Less.

Uncle Markie had the same dark eyes and hair as his sister. Slim and wiry in build, he was a compulsive gambler and at first eked out a living as a bookie's runner. Great-Aunt Leah, Nanna's sister, was crippled by a fire in her father's fish shop and lived in a tenement nearby. She had a son who was a sailor and had been blown to smithereens in the Great War. Great-Aunt Leah frequently told the family that she saw him standing at the foot of her bed in his uniform. Her daughter Betty (known as Cousin Betty) lived with Grandma Cissie and the family on and off over the years, and they had a great affection for each other. Then there was Uncle Harry, who struggled to make a living at the Brighton race track. He was a really colourful personality who was of a somewhat dubious character, involved in illegal activities. Finally, it all caught up with him and he served prison terms for fraud and con-artistry. One of Daddy's favourite uncles was Uncle 'Gypsy' Rafie, who was olive-skinned with thick, jet-black curly hair, eyes so dark they were almost black, and wore a bandanna and a gold earring. He used to sell racing tips down Petticoat Lane for sixpence a shot.

Grandma Sylvia's nickname, Cissie, stuck and, although she didn't much like it, everyone called her Cissie until the day she died. At the end of August 1926, when Grandfather Jock was twenty-three years old and Grandma Cissie was twenty-five and four months pregnant, they were married in an East End synagogue. It was a splendid affair, the reception held at a well-known catering hall called Bonns in Great Prescott Street, Aldgate. Cousin Betty and Jack sat at a table with their parents, thrilling at the delights of the good Dutch cooking. The young children's eyes rested on, and their mouths watered for, such traditional favourite sweets as pastries, huge gâteaux and bolas (cakes made from almonds, demerara sugar, eggs and lots of butter), which were piled high on plates on the tables. The band that played at the reception was made up of Grandfather Jock's friends, and as the reception progressed Cousin Jack remembers Grandfather Jock borrowing the band leader's sax and sitting in with the band, much to the delight of all the guests who kept applauding and asking for more.

After the wedding my grandparents, Jock and Cissie Schatt, set up home in a little terraced house at 33 South Tenter Street, a short distance from Tower Bridge and London's Western Dock. They settled into their new home and just five months later, at the East End Mothers' Maternity Hospital, on Friday 28 January 1927, Grandma Cissie gave birth to my father, Ronald Schatt. At the time of Daddy's birth my grandfather was leading a Palais Band in Scotland, the Glasgow Plaza band. It was the roaring twenties and the era of the big bands, everybody dancing to the rich, full, pulsating sound of the popular tunes of the day. It was an elegant time, and my grandfather cut a striking figure, dressed in his dinner jacket as he fronted his band. Because of his high-profile profession, and the prevailing atmosphere, Jock Schatt, along with many of his generation, prudently decided to change his name to Scott, and was always known professionally as Jock Scott.

With the birth of my father, the house at South Tenter Street became a traditional Jewish home. My grandmother's mother, Nanna Beckie, who was the matriarch of the family, with her husband Great-Grandpa Samuel, and Grandma Cissie's brother, Uncle Markie, were frequent visitors to the little house, and steadfastly every Friday night the candles were lit for Sabbath. Dad's young cousin Jack (Nanna Beckie's sister Leah's son), who was fourteen at the time, clearly remembers the whole family gathered at 33 South Tenter Street for the religious ceremony when Dad was circumcised. It was a 'men only' occasion, with Dad's great-grandfather, Benjamin Messias, his grandfathers from both sides of the family, his father Jock, and all the uncles and nephews, dressed in dark suits, crowded into the little living room. As the ceremony progressed and the Moyail performed the ritual act, Cousin Jack, cringing in empathy, quickly turned his head away so he did not have to see the deed itself. After the ceremony, Ronnie was returned to the comfort of his mother's waiting arms and everyone celebrated and mingled, enjoying the traditional fare that had been prepared by Nanna Beckie and Grandma Cissie for the occasion.

Dad's maternal and paternal relatives were a highly resourceful, talented and gifted group of people. They were a blend of tailors, restaurateurs, hoteliers, musicians, actors, con-artists and very savvy businesspeople. My grandfather's brother Dave had taken up the violin, my great-grandfather Morris had initiated Philip into the tailoring trade, Hymie sold bales of all kinds of material off a barrow in Petticoat Lane. They all loved to gamble; it was a common thread that ran strongly through both sides of the family. My grandfather and his brothers and sisters all loved a wager here and there, at the greyhound tracks, the races, and so on.

Grandfather Jock's profession frequently took him away from their home in South Tenter Street. When Dad was little more than a year old, Jock was working in Glasgow and my grandmother decided to pay him a surprise visit, taking Daddy with her. When she arrived at the hotel she found my grandfather with another woman. The effect that this discovery had on my grandmother was devastating. Right there and then she told Grandfather Jock never to return home. Shortly after, Grandma Cissie divorced him, unable to respond to any of his pleadings for a reconciliation. Although Grandma had made an on-the-spot, irrevocable decision to end her marriage, she remained in contact with Grandfather Jock over the years, and Cousin Betty is one of many to recall that she never fell out of love with him.

Daddy was too young to remember the trauma of the break-up, or his father ever living at home. He lived with his grandmother Beckie, his step-grandfather Samuel, his mother and his cousin Betty. When she came to live with the family at South Tenter Street, Cousin Betty was fourteen years old and the youngest child of Dad's Great-Aunt Leah. Her memories of my grandmother are of a kind, gentle, generous woman who was like a mother to her. The family was tightly knit and often gathered at this little house to celebrate the high days and holidays. One of Cousin Betty's fondest memories of these gatherings is of how Grandma Cissie had the marvellous knack of making each person in a room full of people feel as though he or she was the only one there. Her natural warmth and jovial conviviality soon had the room filled with laughter and good humour, traits that my father definitely inherited.

Grandma Cissie left the house early each morning and did not return until seven or eight o'clock at night, working Monday to Friday as a saleswoman at Burstein's, the Aldgate department store that later became the Houndsditch Warehouse. She was extremely good at her job, very diligent and smart, and as time passed she was promoted to a managerial position in the sales department. Grandma Cissie supported the family at South Tenter Street, and although they never had much money her wages, in conjunction with Nanna Beckie's bargaining skills, ensured that they never went without.

While Grandma Cissie was working, Nanna Beckie looked after Daddy and took care of all the household duties and cooking. Cousin Betty used to help out by babysitting with Ronnie from time to time. She recalls: 'On one such occasion your dad was sitting in his high chair, just having finished his supper, facing a small coal fire that was shielded with a fire screen, watching the flames flicker while I was reading him a story. All of a sudden he reached down and took out his little willie, and with perfect aim let out a jet of urine straight on to the coals!' Cousin Betty clearly remembers Daddy, as he got older, following Nanna around wanting to do everything that she did. If she was scrubbing the floor, he would say: 'I can do that, Nanna, let me do it.' And because Nanna Beckie did let him he became very good at doing all kinds of chores around the house. However, Daddy did not carry these abilities into adulthood, or if he did he kept them well hidden! Dad often told me that Nanna Beckie and his mother 'spoiled him rotten'. As Cousin Betty says: 'Your dad was your grandmother's life. She doted on him, and within reason he got exactly what he wanted, and of course Nanna doted on him too. These early years were happy and secure ones for your father. He was surrounded by a lot of love.' At three years of age Ronnie started school at the Buckle Street Jews' Infant School in Aldgate. Nanna used to pick him up in the afternoon after the children had finished their nap.

Dad told me that his first memory of his father was about a year later. Grandfather Jock was in touch with my grandmother, and they had agreed to meet at a restaurant where he was playing. She and Dad sat at a table, and when he came off the bandstand he joined them there. Dad could not remember everything that went on that night, but he did recall that things got quite intense and that his father was saying everything that he could think of to persuade his mother to give him one last chance. My grandmother, for reasons known only to herself, was unable to do this, although Dad always said he was sure that she never stopped loving Jock. However, this was to be the last time that Daddy had contact with his father until he was in his teens.

While life moved forwards at South Tenter Street, Grandfather Jock vigorously pursued his career, by 1931 becoming a member of the famous dance band fronted by Jack Hylton. Later on he joined forces with Ennis Hylton's (Jack Hylton's wife) outfit, whose signature tune was 'This Is The Missus, Just Look Her Over'! During the ensuing years, Grandfather Jock and Ennis Hylton became close companions. Although they never 'officially' lived together, they each had a flat in the same building, and their relationship lasted until the day she died in the early 1950s. All of Daddy's cousins who knew her always addressed her as Mrs Hylton.

Nanna Beckie's second husband, Grandpa Samuel, was a favourite of my dad's, whose description of him was that he was a bit of an artful character who did not endear himself to everyone in the family because some of his activities were questionable, to say the least. However, he had one redeeming feature, which was that Grandpa Samuel used to take my father to a Portuguese synagogue as a small child. It was Dad's first window to the orthodox side of Jewish life, and he saw, to use his own description, 'Bearded old men all dressed in black, and the old synagogue was dusty and everything seemed very musty'. But Dad looked forward to and got much pleasure out of his excursions with the old man, which were destined to be short-lived. Sadly, Grandpa Samuel died suddenly in December 1935. The news of his death was brought to the family by a policeman's knock on the door. The shock was sharp and brutal; Ronnie was only eight at the time. I remember him telling me that this was his first experience of death. Grandpa Samuel was there one minute and gone the next. Ronnie had never imagined life without him, and found the harsh reality of his sudden and permanent disappearance very hard to deal with. Jewish culture has it that when a person dies he is alive for as long as there is someone left to remember him. Daddy never forgot Grandpa Samuel and now, because of Dad, neither will I.

When I started to get interested in horses, Daddy told me that when he was a little boy there were stables in the middle of the East End. He remembered them well; they were on Cable Street, next to a dairy, where he and Nanna Beckie used to take a jug to be filled up with fresh milk from the cows. Sometimes, as a special treat, Nanna would also bring an empty jam jar (an accepted form of payment) so that Daddy could have a ride on a horse-drawn roundabout which travelled up and down that street. Then there were the frequent excursions to Petticoat Lane and the jellied eel stand owned by Tubby Isaacs which is still there today. Jellied eels was a favourite treat, to be had when Nanna could afford it. Dad had many fond memories of going shopping with Nanna Beckie down Petticoat Lane. The thrill of listening to her haggle over prices with the many varied vendors, always wearing them down to the last penny, and always coming home with a bag full of bargains, was to remain a source of great pleasure to him for the rest of his life.

Sometimes I would ask him why he liked betting on the horses so much. Dad would look at me, laugh and say: 'I don't know, Becky. Who knows? Maybe it was because of Uncle Rafie.' 'Who was Uncle Rafie?' I would ask. Then he would proceed to tell me how Uncle Rafie used to go to Petticoat Lane, selecting a spot in a busy area, and with his quick line of patter, which had a rhythm and sense of momentum to it, offered racing tips for sixpence and was permanently surrounded by a constantly changing small crowd. Daddy loved to watch him keep the crowd going. The best part, though, was when Uncle Rafie, pretending not to recognise him, would call Daddy over and say: 'Hello, little boy. Go and get that gentleman's money and take him this for me.' Ruefully, and with a chuckle, Daddy would admit to me that he realised later that Uncle Rafie's business speeded up considerably as he ran back and forth exchanging tips for sixpences.

While Grandmother Cissie was working at the Houndsditch Warehouse Company she met Solomon (Sol) Berger. He was of medium build and height, a good-looking man and a tailor by profession with all the instincts and acumen to become a good businessman in his own right.

Sol came from a small family. His father was a presser in a tailoring firm and was a trade unionist and chairman of the Stepney Garment Workers' Union. His mother had died at an early age from diabetes, leaving four children. David, the eldest, died when he was twenty, then came Sol, followed by Anne, known as Auntie Anne Atkins, who lived in Golders Green, but they were not close. Harry, the youngest, known as Uncle Harry, was to become a frequent visitor to Sol's new home until he went to South Africa after the war.

Sol was a man as good as his word, reliable and affectionate and immediately got along well with Daddy. When Daddy was eight years old, in 1935, his mother and Sol got married. Dad often told me the story that when he was not allowed to go to the wedding he grumbled indignantly, and said: 'I bet all the other kids were allowed to go to their parents' wedding!' Although Daddy knew that his father was Jock Schatt, he did not remember what he was like, and for reasons known only to his parents Dad had not seen his father since the day Grandma Cissie took him to the restaurant. He was a part of a new family now and his mother and stepfather thought it would bring them all closer together if he were given the name Berger, and so my father became Ronnie Berger. Several months later, Grandma Cissie was pregnant with her second child. The family was completed when Dad was about nine years old, and he was very excited by the arrival of his sister Marlene. He was fascinated with the way his mother cared for and played with the new baby and used to watch her for hours. In later years my mother often told me that he watched and played with me with that same fascination, only this time it was mingled with that special thrill and pride that only a father has for his daughter.

What was to prove to be one of the worst nightmares in history, one that would change the lives of millions for ever, all over the world, had already developed into a monstrously efficient network of evil. In Germany Hitler had risen rapidly through the ranks to power; with the death of Hindenburg in August 1934 he assumed the functions of leadership, adopting the title of Führer of the Third Reich. Although other groups and institutions were persecuted by the Nazis because of their political unacceptability, one decree after another eliminated Jewish German citizens from their professions. The Nuremberg Racial Laws of 1935 deprived them of their citizenship. My grandfather Jock's sister, Auntie Annie, her husband Uncle Max and Daddy's cousins Alex and Ziggy were now living in very grave danger in Zurich.

In the early 1930s both Britain and America saw the rise of substantial anti-Semitic movements that physically threatened the Jewish communities. Sir Oswald Mosley, the head of the British Union of Fascists, the architects of a sustained campaign of hate, violence and intimidation, met massive resistance from the Communist Party and the Independent Labour Party, which had been actively engaging the Mosleyites in the streets with thousands of hostile demonstrators. Dad's stepfather Sol was a member of the Communist Party and played an active role in fighting the fascist movement. Mosley had targeted the East End to be the focal point of BUF activity – hence the birth of the now-famous Battle of Cable Street. These disciples of Hitler had special uniforms made for the occasion. Mosley himself arrived in a black sports car wearing a black military-cut jacket, grey riding breeches and jackboots. He had a black peaked military cap and a red armband and was escorted by a band of fascists on motorcycles. As he reviewed his troops they exchanged the Nazi salute. The march was to begin at Tower Hill and was scheduled to pass down the narrow width of Cable Street. The whole of East London's working-class population rallied: over a hundred thousand men and women came together that day. Jews and Gentiles, dockers and tailors, waitresses and cabinet-makers thronged the streets of the East End carrying signs that read: 'Mosley shall not pass.' They constructed a massive barricade at the entrance to Cable Street. Shops were closed and boarded, the narrow streets were completely impassable. They armed themselves with paving stones torn out of the pavements, broken bottles, chair legs wrapped with barbed wire and iron bars. Hurling stones, bricks and insults at the Mosleyites to drive them out of the East End, they shrieked demands that they leave England and go to Germany, stating: 'There is no room for fascism in England.' Shortly after this, my grandmother and Sol were married and the family moved out of South

Tenter Street just in time to avoid the racial riots that quickly followed Mosley's march.

Dad used to say that as Jewish families in London became more prosperous they made the trek from the East End to Stoke Newington, Stamford Hill, Edgware and Golders Green. For the Berger family Stoke Newington was the place of choice, and they moved into a flat at Bethnal Road.

Unknowingly, the family had moved into the same neighbourhood as Dad's first cousin Sydney, his Auntie Mary's son (Grandfather Jock's sister). Cousin Sydney used to attend the same synagogue as Daddy on Grove Lane (now named Lampard Grove). He told me how he and Daddy would occasionally bump into each other during the two years that the Berger family lived in the neighbourhood. They knew they were cousins and would exchange greetings and chat and often played football together in the yard in front of the synagogue, where everybody used to play during recess. On one such occasion Ronnie took Cousin Sydney home with him to meet his auntie Cissie; she gave him a warm welcome, and he and Ronnie played for an hour or two in the hallway. Grandma Cissie often ran into Auntie Mary when she went shopping; sometimes they would stop to have a chat and, although they did not see that much of each other, there was never any ill-feeling between them.

Dad was enrolled in the local elementary school, and at the same time he was becoming completely absorbed with aeroplanes. His love of racing cars was by now firmly established too. There were some hostile elements in their neighbourhood that Ronnie and his friends learned to fend off, such as the misguided and wayward bullies who were also anti-Semitic. Dad used to like to tell one particular story, and his eyes would light up and he would chuckle at the memory of it. His school used to hold boxing tournaments, and the sparring partners' names were drawn out of a hat. A ripple of electricity ran through the boys' hearts that morning as a slight Jewish boy drew the local anti-Semitic bully as his opponent. The young Jewish boy had taken his boxing lessons seriously, and, although much smaller than the brash, blundering bully, he expertly ducked and dived, dodging his ham-like fists and landing his own blows with swift, accurate jabs. Amid the ever-growing crescendo of shouts of approval and encouragement from Ronnie, his friends and a crowd of kids who had gathered, the young lad knocked the bully for six. This was a triumph for all concerned: the boy was the hero of the day, and a jubilant celebration followed.

My father was a good student, excelling in all his school work, and he was becoming an avid reader, a passion that was to stay with him for the rest of his life. He passed the Junior County Scholarship to the much-sought-after Raines Foundation School in Whitechapel Road.

While Daddy's attention was on aeroplanes and playing football, important events were taking place in another part of the world that in just a few short years would have a great impact on his life. The die was being cast and the foundations laid for the future that Daddy was born to become an integral part of and a major influence in.

A new music had been born and was starting to flourish and grow in the United States. Coleman Hawkins, a young black man from Chicago, who can best be described as, to use my father's own words of a much later time, 'the man who invented the jazz tenor saxophone', was busy honing his craft. He was to become one of the major influences in my father's life, as was Lester Young, another formidable tenor saxophonist, completely unique in every way, also a black man but from Kansas. Although this period in the history of the United States was known as the Great Depression, if you were a patron of the Hey Hey Club in the 1930s you were oblivious to its existence.

Everybody who was anybody in the world of jazz – big bands, trios, quartets, soloists – you name it, they were there, all together, every time they were in town, from 7.30 at night to the same time the following morning, and sometimes even later if the punters were still there to listen. It was an explosion of a musical adventure and discovery expressed in legendary jam sessions, featuring what was then called 'cutting contests', the most famous of which was being played out by Coleman Hawkins and Lester Young as they set each other one riff after another, each one surpassing the one that went before it, building to a climax of thrilling, highly charged excitement mingled with awe among punters and listening musicians alike.

Musicians from this era will tell you that Kansas City defined the word 'swing'. In New York, clubs had opened, and 52nd Street had become the midtown home of great black jazz, although it was not until 1938, with the appearance of the Count Basie Big Band at a club called the Famous Door, that 52nd Street got its reputation as the 'jumping-off place for jazz in New York City'. All the great giants and legends of jazz were born, the light of that golden era was lit and sent out beams that were to span the world and never be extinguished.

My grandfather had established himself with Ennis Hylton and her band, and they were busy with national and international tours. They went to India: to Bombay, where they played at the best hotels, and to New Delhi, where they played at the magnificent palace for the first viceroy, Archibald Percival Wavell.

Dad's Uncle Philip was married and raising a family in New York; he had a son, Joseph, and a daughter, Rose. Auntie Rose told me that when she was a little girl she noticed on his forearm a tattoo of a tiny bird holding a letter in its mouth. It was most unusual in those days to have a tattoo, so she asked him about it. She noticed sadness in his eyes as he replied: 'Every time I look at it, it reminds me to write home to my mother and family in England.' Auntie Rose made herself a promise, there and then, that when she grew up she was going to make a lot of money so that she would be able to go to England and meet all her relatives – and that is exactly what she did.

In Germany, Hitler and his hideous regime were sweeping through the country, systematically rounding up and shipping off the Jewish population to concentration camps. On 8 November 1938, the night before the horror of Kristallnacht, Daddy's Auntie Annie and Uncle Max and their two sons, Alex and Ziggy, were all arrested by the Nazis. With thousands of other Jews they were herded into freight trains and shipped off to a ghetto in Cracow. They had to go through the Nazi selection process of 'This one goes to a concentration camp' and 'That one dies'. The Zwern family once again were herded into freight trains, this time all going in different directions. Auntie Annie and Uncle Max were packed off to Auschwitz and were separated into different barracks, young Alex was shipped out alone to Hassag, and little Ziggy, also alone, was sent to a camp just outside Cracow, called Skarzysko.

Grandma Cissie, Sol, Daddy and Marlene were taking a holiday in September of 1939 in Bognor, enjoying all the pleasures of the seaside before returning home to London. Grandma Cissie and Sol were very proud of the fact that Daddy was about to begin his first year at Raines Foundation School. However, it was not to be: with the announcement that war had been declared, everything changed. Sol and Grandma Cissie, unnerved by the news, realised that it would be better not to return to London under the circumstances and instead decided to take their family to stay with Auntie Annie and Uncle Muchie at their hotel in Brighton.

Daddy was twelve at the time, and he had good memories about his year in Brighton. He used to joke about Brighton to me, saying: 'You want to have a good time, Rebecca? Let's go to Brighton.' We never did actually go to Brighton, but for him that was a good year. He had a great love of the ocean and the sun, and for the rest of his life they would remain his favourite means of escape from the rest of the world. Dad went to school there and quickly got himself in the rugby side, becoming captain of the school's second team. By now his fascination with aeroplanes had developed to the point where he wanted to become the rear gunner in a bomber. Dad told me that back then he wanted to learn to fly more than anything else in the world.

The family decided to return to London in 1940, moving into a rented three-bedroom house, with a large garden at the back, in Edgwarebury Gardens, Edgware. Daddy always said that everyone in the family was convinced that it was no coincidence that on that exact same day the blitz started, an event that was to become the butt of family humour.

In those days Edgware was a quiet little outer-London suburb surrounded by woods and fields, and there was a farm at the end of the next street, Edgwarebury Lane. The cosy little house had two double bedrooms. Grandma Cissie and Sol had one, and Nanna Beckie and Auntie Marlene had twin beds and shared the other. Daddy had his own small room, which looked out over the garden, with a single bed in it. Sitting on top of his chest of drawers, along with a tin air-raid warden's helmet, was his prize stash of 'best shrapnel' pieces, which he and his friends collected by scrambling among the bombed-out ruins. They had developed their own special criteria to distinguish the 'best' pieces from the ones of lesser worth, and there was serious competition among the boys as to who had the largest collection of those cherished 'best' pieces. The little room was filled with his school books and projects, along with his favourite comics like *Hotspur* and *Wizard*, and an occasional coveted magazine with pictures of racing cars.

Grandma Cissie kept his room for him, just as it always was, long after Daddy left home. These were his most cherished memories. He loved to reminisce about how he could come home at any time he wanted. His visits were regular, and each time Nanna Beckie and Grandma Cissie would make a special fuss of him, preparing his favourite foods, doing his laundry and immaculately ironing his shirts and suits, anxious to hear his stories about his latest escapades and accomplishments. This little home, filled with laughter, warmth and love, not to mention the welcoming smell of wonderful food, was a safe refuge, a gentle haven, in contrast to the harsher reality of life in the outside world, in the fast lane, creating a sense of balance, an anchor, in his eclectic lifestyle as a touring musician.

Sol and Grandma Cissie were very proud of Dad's accomplishments in school, and even though the outbreak of war had prevented him from attending Raines Foundation School, they encouraged him to keep up the good work at Edgware High School. Once again he fitted in easily and maintained his already established high standard of school work, so much so that during the shortage of teachers he was selected to take care of the younger classes, keeping them happy with Richmal Crompton's *Just William* stories. He had the knack of being able to really bring the characters to life for the listening children, and consequently these sessions were a great success. Dad excelled in English, and Miss Henderson, his English teacher, tried to encourage him to become a writer, recognising that he had a natural talent and aptitude for the written word. But Daddy decided that a career in this area required far too much work for his liking, and his interests lay elsewhere, although in his maturity he was to prove that his teacher's observations were correct, and actually over the years wrote several articles for various publications. Kenny Harris, a good-looking young man who was to become a drummer in a few short years, was in the same class as Dad and clearly remembers how quickly he was made school captain and had the responsibility of making out the schedules for the school prefects, of which Kenny was one.

The Jewish community was bereft of men, who were conspicuous by their absence. Those who remained had either been rejected by the services for health reasons or were simply too old. Daddy's stepfather Sol enlisted in the Eighth Royal Army Medical Corps in 1940 and was a nurse, stationed in Alexandria, Egypt, during the African Campaign. When he came back from Africa he was based in Southampton, working on the trains coming up the coast carrying the injured to the military hospitals. With very few men left at home, the children had lots of freedom. There weren't many cars, and everyone was too busy making ends meet to watch the children, so they all played together. Auntie Marlene remembers playing in the fields for hours with the neighbourhood children, catching newts and tiddlers in the ditches, while Daddy went off with his friends searching for the 'best' pieces of shrapnel to add to their collections. There were the Posner boys who lived in Edgwarebury Lane. Leon, the eldest, was Daddy's friend, and in later years they would visit New York together; Henry, the youngest, played with Auntie Marlene. Leon and Daddy practised the art of gurning, making faces at each other, and spent hours crafting their repertoire of facial contortions, a source of great amusement to the rest of the family. Daddy became an expert at it, and from time to time would practise it for the rest of his life. Grandma Cissie was working three days a week in a dress shop. Nanna Beckie did all the cooking, and between them they kept their home immaculate – it was always sparkling clean.

With the blitz raining daily devastation and destruction on London, people devised their own means of shelter within their own homes, so that they had some way of diving for cover, even if it was just under a bed, a table or an upturned bathtub. Grandma Cissie had allocated the dining room of her home as the central place of refuge. This was a large room, situated at the back of the house, with French windows leading out into the garden. A special bed called a Morrison shelter was set up for Auntie Marlene: the sides of the bed were open with sturdy poles at each corner supporting a metal 'roof'. There were several large couches which at night were used as beds for friends as well as family, a large heavy dining table and chairs and some small end tables. When there were air raids, which was most of the time, everyone congregated in this room.

Uncle Markie's girlfriend Daphne practically became a member of the family at this time. Of Irish descent, she was a tall, pretty girl with shoulder-length glossy brown hair. Uncle Markie had deserted from the army and was on the run, showing up at the family home only once every six to eight weeks. If anyone came looking for him, Daddy and Auntie Marlene were instructed to say that they had not seen him and did not know where he was. Daphne worked at Fortnum & Mason in Piccadilly, which was as celebrated an establishment then as it is today. Auntie Marlene has fond memories of Daphne, a vivacious girl and quite a character but terrified of the bombs and of being alone, so she regularly slept on one of the couches in Grandma Cissie's dining room. Grandma Cissie and she became lifelong friends, and Grandma loved to tell stories about Daphne, who talked in her sleep. She was haunted by the thought of being 'called up' by the army and of having to wear a uniform and constantly had nightmares about it, crying out in her sleep, 'I'm not going to wear those great big boots'.

Auntie Marlene was a little girl, and even though the dining room was full of people she was put to bed in the middle of them all. The sounds of the calls when they played cards, and the adult chatter and bantering, acted as a source of comfort as she slowly dropped off to sleep. Grandma Cissie and Nanna Beckie, Julian and Anne Kovler, who were Sol's and Grandma's best friends – Daddy and Auntie Marlene used to call them Auntie Anne and Uncle Julian, and their son was Cousin Roy – would play their favourite game of Solo, a simplified version of bridge where each player called out bids. The call names were a mixture of French and English words: 'solo', 'abundance' or 'misère', and so on. Ronnie learned all the card games, and he played bridge, one of his favourites, into adulthood. Nanna used to take him to local whist drives. About thirty or forty people attended, four people sitting at each little card table, which had a green felt top, with score cards on each table, the winners of each game playing each other until a champion emerged, winning a small prize.

The family went on with their daily lives, Nanna Beckie and Grandma Cissie never showing any sign of fear, with no cowering in corners. Although some neighbours and other people in the community were evacuating their homes, Grandma Cissie told her family that they were going to stay put and stick it out. She said that on a private's pay, in a strange place, they would be very badly off and thought it better to remain in a nice, comfortable house and take their chances. Daddy and his friends found it very thrilling and exciting, each one becoming an authority on the different types of planes and bombs. Auntie Marlene told me that the closest the family ever came to a hit was when a bomb dropped on the next street. She said: 'Edgwarebury Lane ran parallel to our street, Edgwarebury Gardens, and during one of the air raids a house to the back and to the right of ours was flattened to the ground. It was right at the end of our garden. It was quite odd to see one house suddenly disappear. After the shock wore off, Ronnie and I used to like the fact that we could see the buses come down Edgwarebury Lane.'

Dad, still enamoured of aeroplanes, decided to move on to Hendon Technical College, where he studied aeronautics, at the same time joining the local air training corps, with his eye on learning to fly at Hendon Aerodrome. His childhood dream of learning to fly and becoming a rear gunner in a bomber constantly eluded him and was never to be fulfilled.

CHAPTER THREE

TEENAGERS IN THE BLITZ

It was an absolutely ruthless period, which of course left its mark on all of us. With the bombs dropping all around, we became fatalistic. We had a 'hell for leather' attitude. It was every man for himself, and you lived every moment as though it were your last. TONY CROMBIE

MUM AND I HAD just seen Daddy off at the airport, after he had spent a week with us in New York. I was about thirteen at the time, and I asked my mother if she knew how my father had become a musician and she told me the story.

Each morning on his way to school, Daddy passed an old junk shop and often lingered at the window. This particular morning he saw a very old cornet propped up and held together with black tape. Thrilled with his find, he thought about it all day and decided to buy the instrument after school. On his way home he stopped in the shop, paid his five shillings and the cornet was his. Very proud of his purchase, he could hardly wait to get home and try it out. The black tape did not hold up well; the instrument was actually falling apart, and to his great disappointment he was unable to get anything out of it. Although disappointed, he did not give up his thoughts of playing an instrument and kept his eyes open for something that would serve him better. After some time had passed he saw a soprano sax in the same window. It was in better condition than the cornet, so he brought it home. Dad always said that he believed the instrument must have been the original prototype soprano saxophone, as invented by Sir Charles Soprano. He described the instrument as having a double octave key, several pads missing and a hideously mangled reed. Dad said: 'I didn't know anything about reeds then, but I managed to get some sound out of it, which sounded like a severely constipated hyena! And when my mother heard me play a few faltering bars of some tune or other, she was as proud and delighted as only a mother can be.'

With Sol still away from home, Grandma Cissie was busy trying to make ends meet. Because of the shortages she would alter the clothes they had to make them fit, especially for Nanna. Auntie Marlene was luckier, because their cousins in California were girls and they sent care packages of their hand-me-downs to her, so she was very well dressed. Daddy also benefited from this because he got his sister's clothing coupons and some of Nanna's as well as his own and always looked smart in his suits, with freshly pressed shirt and tie. With the restraints of rationing, most of the food available was very plain, and the family even ate bacon because there was no decent alternative, and it was something that Daddy never lost the taste for. There was one Jewish deli in Edgware, but it was too expensive except for the occasional black market egg. Even with these shortages, Nanna Beckie was such a marvellous cook she somehow or other managed to improvise and produce flavoursome meals that would stay in Daddy's memory for the rest of his life. He loved Nanna's cooking and now and then whimsically wished for the warmth of her kitchen filled with love and tantalising aromas of often succulent and always delicious appetising treats to tease his senses again.

Dad enjoyed all types of sports. He loved cricket and tennis and was very keen on ice hockey, his colourful descriptions of what went on during a game fascinating Auntie Marlene even though she was just a little girl at the time. Seeing how much his stories excited his little sister, Ronnie agreed to take her to see her first game of ice hockey.

The family life was not a religious one; it was more cultural in that traditions were still followed. Grandma Cissie kept up lighting candles every Friday night, even though no prayers were said. The high days and holidays of Passover, Rosh Hashanah and Yom Kippur were celebrated with the gathering of family and friends and the serving of appropriate foods, although the religious meaning was somehow lost. Uncle Julian and Auntie Anne Kovler and Cousin Roy always came for Christmas, staying for two or three days. Ronnie took Roy with him to meet his friends, and Roy was fascinated by Ronnie's soprano sax, egging him on to play some tunes. Auntie Marlene told me the story of how one Christmas they were all sitting round the table with paper hats on, eating their chicken soup for

Christmas dinner. Ronnie was clowning around, and the Glenn Miller band was playing on the radio. She said: 'Uncle Julian pulled Mum up and said, "Come on, Cissie, let's dance", and Mum said, "Let me sit down. I want to suck my feet!" She loved to suck the chicken feet cooked in the soup!'

By now Daddy's passion for reading was well developed. He had a serious interest in architecture and read every book he could get his hands on pertaining to this subject. He told me that at this time in his life he was thinking seriously about making it his career, and had things turned out differently there was a distinct possibility that he would have become an architect. Everyone in the family used the public library a lot, although there were books on the shelves at home, such as Eugene O'Neill's plays and J.B. Priestley's books, along with John Steinbeck's writings which came from Sol. Before he met Grandma Cissie, after the death of his brother David, Sol went to New York intending to start a new life there, but because of his previous affiliation with the Communist Party in London he was never able to get his work permit in the US and as a result he was deported.

There was a wind-up gramophone in the dining room and sometimes records were played, tunes such as 'Begin The Beguine', but most of the time the radio was on and the family listened to plays and comedy shows – the latter were Dad's favourite. But these days my father was spending more and more of his spare time in his room with his newly acquired soprano sax. Grandma Cissie and Nanna began to realise that his playing was becoming more than just a hobby, and there was no mistaking his natural talent and affinity with the instrument. Even though Sol was miles away from home, he and Grandma wrote to each other regularly, and she told him everything that was going on at home. When he heard about Daddy's progress on the instrument and how serious he had become, even though a private's pay was not that much, he told Grandma to see what she could find out about getting Daddy a good instrument so that he could learn to play properly, and somehow he would find a way to pay for it.

Grandma Cissie went to Archer Street in the West End where musicians gathered in search of work. All of Grandfather Jock's friends and associates were to be found here, a number of them musicians from the dance bands that she had known from the early years. They were more than happy to give Grandma Cissie some advice about the instrument she and Sol wanted to buy for Daddy. Sol was home on leave, and he and Grandma Cissie went together and bought Daddy a Pennsylvania tenor saxophone, which was silver-plated with a golden bell. Daddy's expression would soften, his eyes would twinkle and he would get that little curl to his lip as he chuckled as he talked, remembering his surprise at receiving the gift and his intense pleasure as he ran his fingers up and down the pearl keys, which were responsive and subtle to his touch. He was always able to recall the thrill and awe he experienced that day, a feeling of sheer exultation and pure joy. This instrument was the real McCoy, and, he hardly dared believe it, it was really his. He had made the initial connection with the true love of his life.

The world of music had been changing and shifting as though preparing a special place for Ronnie Scott and his contemporaries. The new music from America had already filtered across the Atlantic and made its mark on the British scene. Grandfather Jock, along with his fellow musicians, would have heard the marvellous melodic and romantic phrasing of Sidney Bechet's clarinet when he appeared in London in the 1920s. Later, in the early 1930s, when Duke Ellington, the first of the big 'swing' bands came to London, it was because Jack Hylton brought them over, and British fans and musicians heard the first live performance of the Duke Ellington Orchestra. One of the originators of jazz, the great trumpet player Louis Armstrong, also came to London in the 1930s. Arnold Shaw was one of the first messengers spreading the word. He wrote a column on the New York jazz scene for the English magazine *The Gramophone*, which covered the worldwide record scene. In the early 1930s Arnold Shaw joined forces with *Melody Maker*, the magazine that originated in London in 1926, reporting on the regular music business and jazz. They had requested that he focus on the American black musicians, who, of course, were the originators of first the blues, then Dixieland (hot jazz) and the big band swing of the 'New Deal Thirties', along with small groups playing bebop, and modern jazz. Musicians and punters alike wanted to hear the music for themselves, so everybody tuned in to the radio and listened to AFM (the American Forces Network in Europe), which played all the major big bands – Harry James, Artie Shaw, Woody Herman, Count Basie, Duke Ellington and Benny Goodman – along with the bebop quartets with Dizzy Gillespie, etc. A record shop called Levy's was the first to open its doors to the British public in 1928 specialising in records of the British dance band scene. After the war had ended the public demand was such that they imported records from America that exclusively portrayed the panorama of this great music. It really was the history of jazz in the making.

Grandma Cissie had asked Grandfather Jock to recommend a saxophone tutor for Dad, and this resulted in his going once a week after school for six months to Jack Lewis, who taught from the front room of his home in Stamford Hill. Jack's own son was a musician, and he was delighted to take such a keen youngster on. Dad had an excellent ear and was already a terrific mimic, and consequently he picked things up very fast. Other nights after school and on weekends Dad used to go to the Jewish youth clubs in the East End. He was a member of the Oxford and St George's Club, which was on Berner Street at Commercial Road. There he met up with a group of boys who were also budding musicians and were to remain friends for the rest of his life. There was Alfie Summers, who played the drums; Sonny Herman on trombone, who went on to become a rabbi and psychologist; Harry Pitch on trumpet, who in later years took up the harmonica and today can be heard playing the theme tune for the television programme *The Last of the Summer Wine*; Alf Shaw on guitar; Benny Lang, trumpet; Harold Simmonds, who played clarinet; and Harry Morris, who was not a musician but was always on the scene. The Oxford and St George's Club was known as the Settlement, with a basement that was actually an air-raid shelter. They had games rooms where you could play snooker and billiards, and there was a dance hall with gramophones, records and radios. But the sacred room for Ronnie and his friends was the basement, where the walls were lined with bed bunks that were three high. This was Mr Allen's domain, and here they learned how to play their instruments under his instruction.

Mr Allen was from Kneller Hall, the British Military Academy of Music, where he taught professional musicians who had signed up for a couple of years in the army. It was his job to teach them to play the music played by brass bands. None of them was particularly interested in what they were playing, so there was a distinct lack of enthusiasm in these classes. Quite the opposite to the young boys at the Settlement, who were hungry to learn and bursting with enthusiasm, and with his guidance they learned to play all sorts of brass band pieces. Alf Shaw remembers how they used to listen together to bebop on the radio. They would listen to Dizzy Gillespie, Coleman Hawkins and Lester Young, and would memorise the tunes they heard and try to reproduce them on their own instruments. Sonny Herman recalled that Mr Allen got caught up in their enthusiasm and the new rhythms and extraordinary syncopations they were trying to play. He was a great help because as a teacher he was a stickler for breathing techniques and keeping tempo. Sonny said: 'He taught us how to stay together. We were making music together with joy, and that was important to Mr Allen. Ronnie was amazing. It really was incredible how quickly he caught on and could play the tunes he heard. When Vic Ash, the clarinet player, first came along to hear us he was a young boy, and listening to Ronnie and being enthused by his music was a major influence on him becoming a professional musician.'

The Settlement was run by Basil Henriques and his wife. He was known as the Gaffer, and his wife was known as the Missus. The Missus was in charge of all the girls and taught them ballet. She was also very strict with the girls, instilling in each of them a strong foundation of morals. The Gaffer was in charge of the boys, and he was an imposing presence, about six feet three inches tall, with an Oxford education and a marvellous accent to match. He was also a magistrate dealing with juvenile delinquents and did a thorough job of getting the boys 'back on track'. Later on he was knighted for his contribution to society and Berner Street was renamed Henriques Street in his honour. The Gaffer couldn't understand the music that Ronnie and his friends were playing and referred to it as 'Something strange that was imported, brought over by those American GI people, you know'. Of course, he was a prize candidate for Ronnie to mimic, which he did with great alacrity, to everyone else's amusement.

On Saturday and Sunday nights they held dances at the Settlement, and Ronnie and the boys formed a band for these occasions. Among the regulars at the dances were two extremely pretty twin girls named Cynthia and Lorna Gordon. They were not identical twins. Cynthia had dark hair, which she wore with bangs, and Lorna had blond hair, and even though facially they did not look alike they were both very petite, with terrific figures; they were fourteen years old. All the guys in the Oxford Club knew that Ronnie had an eye for Cynthia. The night that they met, electricity was in the air! Everybody else was already in the club when Ronnie arrived, a slender figure with his raincoat over his arm. He was, as always, immaculately dressed in a suit and collar and tie. Cynthia had heard through the grapevine that Ronnie was interested in her and knew that the next time he saw her he was going to make an approach. It was as though everyone was waiting to see what would happen. He walked over to her and his first words to her were: 'Can I have your autograph? My life has only just begun!' This was the first flush of love and the beginning of his first real romance that was to last for four years.

Harry Morris was a real character, small in stature, of slight physique, with thick dark hair that he wore slicked back with a distinct widow's peak, and a very wide smile. Often a casual dresser but smart, with sports jacket and grey flannels, an open-neck shirt and sweater, he also had an enviable wardrobe of tailor-made suits. As a young boy he already had a great knack for putting the right people together. He used to travel between the Oxford and St George's Club and the Stepney Jewish Boys' Club, which was in Mile End and where he met Tony Crombie, a young drummer. Harry took Tony to the Settlement one night and introduced him to Ronnie and the lads, and this was the beginning of another lifelong union. Another lad who was a member of the Stepney club was Vidal Sassoon; he and Tony both lived in that neighbourhood. Then there was the Stepney Girls' Club, where dances were held on Sunday nights. Ronnie and the boys used to play there some Sundays because they wanted to meet the girls. Vidal was an extremely good-looking young man, and one of Sonny Herman's earliest memories of Vidal is how he and Ronnie and the rest of the gang used to make sure that the girls could see Vidal. They would 'put him on show', Sonny said. 'It never failed. Two by two the girls would come over to our group, all wanting to meet Vidal. Once we were surrounded by girls, one or the other of us would send Vidal on an errand. We always managed to find something for him to do, and we got the girls!'

Dad was rarely at home for any length of time those days, although he and Auntie Marlene used to enjoy meeting up in the kitchen and picking at food together before it was properly prepared for a meal. She remembers how he used to love raw chips! Since everyone in the house got up at different times, breakfast was a solitary meal eaten in the kitchen by each member of the family. What time Dad did spend at home was taken up practising in the evenings, much to the distaste of the elderly neighbours, who complained frequently to Grandma Cissie. But she made a few enquiries and quite quickly found out that as long as he didn't play after 10 p.m. they couldn't do anything about it. So Dad was able to continue practising his scales at home and learning new tunes from the stock arrangements that he bought from the sheet music shops for a shilling each. Sometimes, Victor Feldman, the youngest son of the Feldman family, who at that time had a business called Feldman Music Publishers, used to get his brother Robert to drive him over to Dad's house complete with his drum kit. They would play jazz together on the upstairs landing. Victor was without doubt a child prodigy and was playing professionally at the age of seven. While he grew up he learned to play several instruments, among them the piano and vibes, and he excelled on all of them.

Many of Dad's friends had already left school and were working by now.

Tony Crombie, who was a good-looking young man, about five feet eleven inches tall, with broad shoulders and dark hair, was working with his father at a furrier's. His father was an accomplished fur cutter, and Tony had the task of stretching the skins, not a job he particularly enjoyed, but it put money in his pocket while he honed his craft as a drummer and pianist. Later on he went to work for Adolph Elkin, who owned an enormous tobacco warehouse, and pretty soon he discovered that Harry Morris worked for the same company, packing cigarettes. Tony could never understand how Harry could afford to dress the way he did. Harry's father had died some years before, and his mother was left to bring him up and provide for him on her own, and everyone was poor in those days. One day Tony and Harry were chatting as they worked, and Harry pocketed a pack of cigarettes. Tony made a remark, so Harry confided that he did this a couple of times a week, selling the cigarettes to friends. Then he saved up the money until he had enough to buy himself a tailor-made suit, which in those days cost about eight pounds.

In the summer of 1941 Dad left school and joined the ranks of the working class. Although he was still only fourteen years old, all his energies were focused on his saxophone and listening to and playing as much music as he could. Consequently, it seemed logical that he should get work with a company that was involved with the business of music. So he went to the Keith Prowse Organisation, which was the largest company in London dealing in instruments, sheet music and records. They started him off in the packing department in the basement of the Coventry Street branch, but he found this very confining and – sin of all sins – the epitome of boredom. Fortunately for him, the staff took pity on him and he was transferred to the Kensington High Street branch, where he was put on the records sales desk. This was much more appropriate to Dad's needs and nature, and he was able to listen to a lot of music. Although quite shy, his manners were impeccable; he was softly spoken, and his enthusiasm for music connected with the customers so he sold lots of records. The first records that found their way to the gramophone at home were Tommy Dorsey swing discs and Benny Goodman's Band.

Later on he moved to a dance band instrument supplier in Soho's Rupert Street called Lou Chester, which was run by an ex-dance band trombonist. It meant that he was back in the storeroom again, but the fact that Cynthia worked as a hairdresser in a shop off Leicester Square in Cranbourne Street brought some light relief for Ronnie, who used to walk over to the shop and pick her up at lunchtime. He never had any money, so if it was a nice day they would go to Green Park and stroll hand in hand, chatting along the way, eventually picking a spot to eat their sandwiches. They would sit together on a bench, he with his arm around her shoulders, gently twisting her shoulder-length dark hair around his fingers, sometimes playing with her ear, but he would never kiss her. Softly, with his lips gently brushing her ear, he would whisper: 'I hope you don't mind, but I have to be very careful because of my embouchure!' He was still very young and was ultra-sensitive about his developing embouchure, fearing that if he kissed Cynthia it would somehow affect his playing. Fortunately for Ronnie, Cynthia's family life was very regimented and that, combined with the strong moral ethics that the Missus at the Oxford and St George's Club had instilled in her girls, made it easy for her to be understanding and quite happy with the progress of their relationship.

However, Dad's position as clerk for Lou Chester was to be short-lived and the last day job that he would ever have. His musical prowess was developing in leaps and bounds. People were now talking about the young saxophonist who played at the Jewish youth club dances, and other lads who were also budding musicians came to hear young Ronnie Scott playing. Grandfather Jock's brother, Uncle Dave, who was a violinist, got him his first real job with the Felix Mendelssohn's Hawaiian Serenaders when he was fifteen. They were mostly fiddle players, playing at weddings, Bar Mitzvahs and dances.

At home, the gatherings of friends and family in the dining room were very much a part of daily life as everyone continued to cope with the ongoing trauma of bombs dropping daily on London. Winston Churchill's now-famous speeches sustained the resolve of every British subject to win the war in any event, and production of weapons, uniforms and aeroplane parts boomed. The Queen became a familiar voice on the radio, encouraging everyone who had a garden to grow vegetables. One of the ballrooms in Buckingham Palace was turned into a teaching facility for women, presided over by the Queen herself, who gave the women step-by-step instructions on canning, pickling and preserving foods, while Princesses Elizabeth and Margaret looked on. At Sandringham, the golf courses and gardens were turned into farmland, producing wheat, oats and rye for the nation. The land all across the country was worked by women, who were known as land girls. The Queen played a major role in hands-on public relations, bolstering the morale of those left behind while their men were fighting the war. Salvage centres were organised to recycle waste paper, tins and bottles. The British Legion set up a poppy fund for the armed forces, and Queen

Elizabeth was spokesperson for each of these organisations and was often seen wearing the red silk poppies herself. Hitler said, 'The Queen is the most dangerous woman in Europe', because her ability to raise morale wherever she went was unsurpassed.

London had converted schools and some business buildings into feeding and clothing centres for the homeless, who grew in staggering numbers daily as the relentless bombing persisted. Much of the East End of London was a blazing inferno, with flames pouring out of windows and thick black smoke forming surreal and ominous clouds. After the palace itself had been bombed for the ninth time, the Queen said that now she could look the people of the East End in the eye again. During the course of the war the Royal Family made more than one visit to that part of London in an effort to boost people's morale.

Tony Crombie, who was slightly older than Ronnie, was already hanging out with young guys who were sitting in or working at some of the clubs in the West End. Tony used to carry the drums for 'Flash' Cecil Winston, a short, stocky boy with well-greased black hair combed straight back and bird-like features, with eyes so dark they were almost black with a permanent twinkle in them, as though he were inwardly always laughing at something. The first paying gig that Tony had was at the Mazurka Club in Denman Street, owned by Joe Rubini, who could afford to hire only a drummer and pianist. Tony used to travel by bus from the East End, stowing his drum kit under the stairs of the double-decker.

The Mazurka Club was situated up two floors of steps, and to gain entrance you had to knock on the door, which was answered by the opening of a six-inch-square panel. You would find yourself looking into a pair of eyes peering out over half a nose, and if the guy did not know who you were, he would not let you in.

Alf Summers used to carry his drumsticks in his pocket, Sonny Herman had his trombone and Ronnie, of course, had his sax. Harry Morris was known as a 'moody' trumpet player, because he did not play an instrument but used to carry an empty trumpet case with him so people would think he was a musician! Alf Summers told me: 'Clubs like the Mazurka welcomed guys like Ronnie because they would sit in and play for nothing and, of course, they augmented the band. We all had a great time. All we wanted to do was play, and all we wanted to play was bebop.'

A wide selection of small drinking clubs hired pianists and drummers, and the boys went from one club to another, sitting in wherever they went. Sometimes the owners would be confused by the fast-tempo bebop and would say: 'Can't you play something we all know?' They refused to play anything that sounded remotely like the popular music of the day, and because of it occasionally were asked to leave, so they would move on to another bottle party club like the Jamboree, in Wardour Street, or the Nuthouse Club in Regent Street.

Dad, Tony Crombie and their clique of teenage musicians would make their way to Lyons Corner House in Coventry Street, along with the professional musicians who hung out there at 4 a.m. after work was over. The Corner House was open all night and always so packed with customers that the lads inevitably had to queue up in the street. It was an unnerving experience, with the constant drone of the bombers flying overhead, seeing some buildings suddenly burst into flames and others being totally obliterated, while fire engines and ambulances with their sirens blaring were coming and going in all directions. Tony Crombie vividly remembered this gruelling experience and said: 'After several nights of this we finally discovered a side door guarded by a Lyons security guard who was an exact replica of the towering bully used by Charlie Chaplin in *Easy Street*. We were successful in humouring him into opening the door for us to slip inside by dropping half a crown into his ever-receptive palm.'

Those hours between 4 and 7 a.m. were magic to the teenagers, surrounded by the comforts of a warm restaurant and hot food. The open-air unofficial labour exchange of Archer Street had now been transferred to the comparative safety of the Corner House, which was thronged with musicians looking for gigs. Dad found himself quietly thinking more and more about his father, and as he moved among the circle of professional musicians he began to look for him. While sitting in the crowded Corner House he searched the faces of older musicians looking for features that might resemble his own, wondering what he would do or say if he actually saw Jock. While he travelled on the top decks of buses he looked down on the West End streets searching for an older man carrying a saxophone case. He imagined that Jock Scott would be an elegant, well-dressed, grey-haired man.

For Dad there was something awe-inspiring and irresistibly exciting about the dance band world of the 1940s, and he said: 'I was desperately eager to get into a band uniform, climb behind a music desk and wait for my turn to stand up and take a booting tenor solo. When I say that I was desperately eager, I mean that I couldn't even wait long enough to master the barest rudiments of playing the saxophone.'

In 1943 Carlo Krahmer, an active, jazz-orientated band leader of the time who had been playing professionally since 1936, ran the band at the Jamboree Club and was also resident at the Feldman Swing Club, which was originated by Victor Feldman's father for his sons. The Feldman Club was open only on Sunday nights; during the rest of the week it was a restaurant, the forerunner of today's 100 Club in Oxford Street. By this time Dad and the guys had a repertoire of several tunes that they had learned, and while they were hanging out around the bandstand listening to the professionals, if the band played 'Honeysuckle Rose' or 'Lady Be Good', they were allowed to sit in. Dad had completed his six months of lessons with Jack Lewis (who was Vera Lynn's father-in-law; he used to say: 'That's still one of my principal claims to fame!'). Dad had been playing for about a year when Carlo Krahmer offered him a job with his band for two weeks. His tenor player, Len Wood, was leaving the band and his replacement, Jimmy Skidmore, couldn't start for two weeks. Dad said that he would love to do the gig but felt that his playing was not up to it. Carlo explained that he was contracted to present a six-piece band and told Dad that all he had to do was sit on the stand and go through the motions for two weeks. Most nights, several musicians came into the club and sat in, among them Johnnie Claes, the fine Belgian trumpet player. When this happened Dad would join his mates at a table and sit and listen with them. The rest of the time, to use his own words, 'I tossed off a few notes here and there just to reassure myself, but for most of the time I might just as well have been a cardboard cutout'. This was his first professional gig, and it was a great learning experience. But once the two weeks drew to a close, he went back to the semiprofessional life of playing at weddings and the East End youth clubs.

By now, Cynthia and Ronnie had become an item and she fondly reminisces: 'Ronnie was very different from the other boys at the club. He had a very dry sense of humour, but he was never aflame with happiness; he always seemed a little sad. He was very well read and had a way with words. He was very romantic and even then he had class; he was a gentleman. It was a lovely encounter for young people, it really was, even though the war was on and the air raids were going every day, it was a great time. The Oxford and St George's was a wonderful club it was like an oasis in a desert, and that's where all our youth was spent.'

During the week at the Oxford and St George's there was no dancing because the young musicians were learning their craft in the basement, and the rest of the club's young population were involved in other activities. So after the club closed at about 10 p.m., Ronnie and the boys frequently walked with Cynthia and Lorna to their mother's house on Albert Square. There was generally quite a crowd of them. The twins' father had died when the girls were only three, but Mrs Gordon was a very hospitable and warm-hearted woman who always welcomed the group with open arms, plying them with endless pots of tea and plates of biscuits. They would all sit around in the living room and listen to their latest V discs and discuss the music; the 'V' stood for 'victory', and the discs were made for American servicemen to help boost morale, the music a combination of show tunes and jazz. Sometimes they would tune in to the American Forces Network or Midnight in Munich and spend the evening listening to Duke Ellington and others. When the time came to go home, Cynthia would often walk Ronnie and two of their friends, David Gunstock and Basil Fitterman, who also lived in Edgware, to Aldgate Underground Station for them to catch their train home.

It was no secret that Cynthia was a very spiritual young girl. She and her brother Wally and Lorna were all psychic, a fact of life they had lived with from as early as they could remember. Seances were often held by all three in their living room with members of local families who had lost loved ones. Many a bereft mother, brother or sister sought and found great solace from these three gifted young teenagers. It was not a subject that Cynthia and Ronnie discussed. He simply accepted that this was an integral part of who she was and that she had become a very important part of his life.

Night after night everybody danced at every opportunity they got; it was their way of escaping from the harsh reality of the blitz. In the East End the owners of warehouses set up gramophones and played records in the basements of the buildings, which were air-raid shelters. One such place was the Spice Mill, where the dancers jitterbugged and whirled on the wooden floor, which was carpeted with spilled ground peppercorns that made a marvellous swirling sound as their feet flew over the boards to the pulsating rhythm of the music of the big bands. The sound of their shoes on the spices made their adrenalin race even faster, spurring them on so that they danced until they dropped. As the pepper was kicked up by the dancing feet, onlookers were prone to sneezing fits, and sometimes it made their eyes run too, but no one seemed to care. They made jokes among themselves and laughed about it, grateful that families and friends were together making good times out of bad.

Every hall and all the churches used to hold dances, and Dad and his mates played all of them, including Bow Church in the East End. One night after playing there, he and Alfie Summers were riding the Underground to the West End when one of the passengers spotted Dad's saxophone case and said to him: 'What have you got there?' Dad said: 'It's a saxophone.' The passenger was joined by everyone else in the carriage, all saying: 'Give us a tune, then! Come on, play something for us!' So he took out his saxophone and played for them all the way to the West End.

Alfie and Dad headed for a club called the Rainbow Corner in Piccadilly, which was a club where American servicemen used to hang out. There they met up with the rest of their friends; they all used to play at the club. By this time Johnny Dankworth (now CBE), alto player, had joined the scene. The sergeant in charge of the entertainment would give the boys lots of V discs featuring the Tommy Dorsey Band, Duke Ellington's Band, Artie Shaw's Band, Glenn Miller's Band. The discs were 78 RPM about 12 inches across with usually two bands on each disc. These discs were worth their weight in gold to the young musicians, who learned Duke Ellington's and others' tunes straight off them.

From here they would go to an American officers' club in Hans Crescent where American bands would come to play. Not only would they hear the music but in between sets would play themselves. The officers here were also generous and gave the young musicians V discs too. Another enticing attribute that this club had to offer was the fact that there was always a tremendous amount of food, which was presented as a sumptuous buffet. This alone was a great magnet for the teenagers, suffering the stringent rationing of wartime. The promise of such a feast was irresistible. The only way you could get into the club was if you were a musician, and, suddenly, instead of six musicians the numbers would swell to ten or twelve, some of the guys, like Harry Morris with his empty trumpet case, 'moody'. For instance, when the bass player left the stand, one of the guys would jump up and hold the bass, acting as though he could play. Sonny Herman did this on more than one occasion, saying: 'I was a trombone player and couldn't play the bass at all, but when the bass player left the stand to get a beer or something, I would jump up, hold the bass as though it were my own and pluck a few strings. I'm not quite sure what came out! But this was the only way to legitimise the reason why we were in the club.' Mission accomplished, the boys would eat to their hearts' content and before they left would fill their pockets with food – and for those who had empty instrument cases some would be stashed there too!

The American servicemen had the resource of the PX, which was a huge duty-free shop carrying a vast variety of foods, clothes, silk stockings, chocolate, toiletries, in fact anything and everything that you could normally purchase in peacetime, plus the coveted V discs, all at very low prices. This facility provided a great source for quite a healthy black-market business with the GIs, who could buy from the PX and then sell the goodies that were scarce if not nonexistent to the British. Harry Morris would get all kinds of things from them and then sell the items on the streets of London, making himself a small profit.

Life for Dad and his cohorts from the East End had already entered the fast lane. Each day was lived to its maximum and not one minute slipped by unoccupied. Sonny Herman remembered this period in their lives as being 'Quite fantastic! Most of the time life was just one great big humorous gathering, music was made, but in between times it was great fun, there was so much to enjoy. There was this dimension of humour where we sought out the funny side of almost every situation we had gone through. We were still in the midst of some extremely strenuous, difficult and psychologically complex times, and a lot of our humour was based on this fact. We enjoyed being alive, and we didn't allow the death that was all around us to penetrate our consciousness. One of the things that made us so carefree was that already we had lived through so much of the bombardments in London and all the ramifications that came with them.'

Every now and then, Dad, Sonny Herman, Alfie Summers, Alf Shaw and a couple of other mates from the East End used to escape from London and go to a little seaside town called Cliftonville in Kent. They used to stay at a boarding house that was owned by the wife of a trombonist, Charlie Fox. Charlie would say to the boys: 'When you go down there, go to my wife's place. She'll look after you very well, fellers.' When they arrived, Charlie's wife would open the door with a cigarette hanging between her lips. She was a chain smoker, and all her fingers and even her lips were permanently stained with nicotine. The standing joke between the lads was: 'Charlie Fox's wife every night!' Alf Shaw remembered: 'As soon as we arrived, before we were all through the door, she would turn to Sonny and say: "Can you give me ten shillings so I can go and get some bacon and things for breakfast?" Everybody was so hard up then she had to get a sub before she could take care of us.'

Ronnie and the boys all piled into the attic, six of them in one room with mattresses on the floor. It did not take them long to discover that the house next door was also owned by Charlie and his wife, and that all the waitresses slept in the attic. Even though the attics were on the fourth floor of each house, the boys used to open the window and scramble along the parapet until they reached the girls' window, and a few gentle taps on the glass would gain them entrance. Alf recalls: 'There was a constant traffic along the parapet, and, blimey, it wasn't half high, and it was only a foot wide! I was lying in the bed one night and there was this knocking at the window. I looked at the window and it was Sonny Herman, and he was pressing his nose against the glass, and he's calling: "Fellers, fellers, come on, let me in!" So I stuck my head out from under the blanket and said: "Come on, it's freezing cold out there, and he's got next to nothing on." He was just in his underwear, but the fellers all said: "Listen, Shaw, if you let him in you'll be the next one out there!" So I stayed in bed and minded my own business.'

There was a large hotel in Cliftonville, along the lines of a Grand Hotel, with never any guests staying there so the place was always empty. The young musicians, ever keen to hone their craft, used to set up on the bandstand in the ballroom. They jammed, practising the art of staying together while keeping up the extremely fast tempo of the new bebop tunes that they had listened to on the radio and the V discs. They tried to catch and develop those tunes, all the time exploring the new and vast horizons of improvisation. Even for these energetically enthusiastic young musicians, playing music to a spacious and empty ballroom would take its toll after a few hours. The need for the appreciation of and the communication with an audience would see them all pack up their instruments and head for the beach, where there was literally an audience waiting for them.

Several hundred people were seated in deck chairs, and the lads set themselves up on the boardwalk and launched into an up-tempo number. Some of the folks on the beach turned their deck chairs around so they could watch the band in action. The boys quickly received the gratification they craved as applause broke out, rippling across the beach, accompanied by cries of: 'More, more! Bravo! Give us another one, then!' After playing a few serious numbers, just for the fun of it Ronnie and Alfie stepped down on to the beach and collected a few handfuls of sand, which they threw down on the boardwalk. By this time Sonny had dressed up as an Indian with a towel around his nether regions, and accompanied by Alf on the guitar and with all the guys clapping out the beat and chanting he did an Egyptian dance. His long, lean body, with skinny arms and legs flailing, performed a multitude of strange gyrations with facial expressions to match. The crowd yelled out, 'More sand! More sand!', and threw handfuls of sand under Sonny's dancing feet. There was a lot of banter back and forth, everybody laughing a lot and thoroughly enjoying themselves.

It was not long before Dad was playing professionally again, this time at the Bouillabaisse Club, a West Indian bottle party club in New Compton Street owned by a man named Bah, who was West Indian and enjoyed a little notoriety because he had half an ear bitten off in a fight. The band leader's name was Clarry Wears, and Tony Crombie was the drummer. At last Dad was working as a full-time professional musician, and for the first time felt that he was really a part of the West End scene. Tony Crombie introduced him to Denis Rose, a pianist and trumpet player. He was very tall and angular, with high cheekbones set in a long face, his bony countenance making him look somewhat gaunt, the one softening feature his eyes, large, round, dark brown and luminous, looking out from under bushy eyebrows.

Tony and Denis had previously met in Petticoat Lane listening to the latest American discs at the record stand on Sunday afternoons, and Denis often stopped by the Bouillabaisse to play. Denis not only became a lifetime friend of Dad's but was to play a major role in his development. Dad was gifted with an incredible musical ear and an amazing ability to memorise and play the most complex solos from such innovative creators as Coleman Hawkins, and he was already a powerful player. Denis, however, brought a whole other perspective and dimension about the music to Ronnie, and indeed to all the guys who were caught up in bebop. Harry Pitch enthusiastically recalled: 'Denis had a fantastic range on the trumpet and he played piano. On the piano he showed us all the chord changes, and he was able to explain the intricacies of the music and show us at the same time what was going on.' Denis was able to listen to a Lester Young solo and then transcribe every note of it, breaking it down into a format that enabled Ronnie and the others to understand the structure as well as the mechanics of the music. He was a veritable wealth of musical knowledge, spending entire days in the Keith Prowse record shop playing disc after disc and patiently transcribing the music into his manuscript book. He was also a streetwise East Ender, but he was a natural teacher who brought inspiration as well as knowledge to the young musicians. My father said that his comprehension of music grew in leaps and bounds when he met Denis, and all through the years he conferred with him about the subtleties of composition.

The romance with Cynthia was now quite steady. Ronnie often used to meet her from work and they would go to the movies, and even though he was no longer working at the record shop he would still pick her up at lunchtime. More often than not Cynthia would buy him a cup of tea and a packet of cigarettes because he was short of money. In October of 1943 Ronnie made a point of stopping by the hairdresser's shop at lunchtime. It was Cynthia's sixteenth birthday, and he said: 'Come on, it's your birthday. Let's go and get our picture taken.' On the way they ran into Harry Morris, who tagged along with them and ended up in the birthday picture too.

Gigs came in, sometimes one-night stands arranged by Ronnie or his friends. They would call up the club owners, who would book a piano player and sometimes a drummer, then the rest of the guys could sit in and play all night. When the guys booked the gig they would always ask: 'How's the piano?' The owner would respond: 'The piano's great! I just had it painted last week!' There was nearly always a problem with the piano because the club owners had no idea how to take care of the instrument and never called in a professional piano tuner. Consequently, the piano players all carried tuning tools in their pockets and became pretty adept at a quick tune-up.

The musicians still used to congregate at Archer Street during the daylight hours, and now that Dad was a professional he started to hang out there too. It was with some level of trepidation that he moved among the established older musicians, keenly aware that the likelihood of his running into his father was close to becoming reality. Seeing an older man carrying a saxophone case always quickened his heartbeat, and he would surreptitiously edge around him until, unobserved, he could see the man's face. If it turned out to be Jock, what would he say? He went over it a thousand times in his mind: 'Excuse me, is your name Jock Scott?' If he said yes, then what? 'My name's Ronnie. I'm your son.' What if his response was negative; how would he live with that? He comforted himself with the thought that at least he would know who his father was and it would put an end to his silent search of a hundred or so faces every time he was in the West End. Also what of Jock's friends? Dad was bumping into them all the time, musicians who played with his father; soon he would know who they were. He considered the likelihood that they already might know who he was, which presented another possibility: what if Jock came up to him one day and asked him if his name was Ronnie and announced that he was his father? Then what would he do and say? Would he feel relieved, happy, angry or all three?

Dad never mentioned his growing concerns about his father to Grandma

TEENAGERS IN THE BLITZ

Cissie, but she must have had her own thoughts on the subject. Knowing the circles that Dad was moving in, she had to ponder the possibility of father and son running into each other. Also, Jock was highly respected and had so many connections in the world of music that he could be a help to his son. Finally, she made the decision to set up a meeting between my father, who was now seventeen, and Jock in a café in Archer Street.

At long last the guessing games were over, the long-awaited dreamed-of day had come: Dad was on his way to meet his father. As he rode the Underground from Edgware to the West End, Dad was filled with anticipation of what lay ahead. The mere fact that they were to meet laid a number of ghosts to rest, and he thought about how he would ask Jock's advice about his joining a dance band at the Cricklewood Palais. Somehow, in the light of this, all his other questions faded away.

When I saw pictures of my grandfather in his forties and pictures of Dad when he was young, I couldn't help thinking that it must have been like looking in a mirror when those two looked at each other for the first time. Dad said that when he saw his father he was exactly as he had imagined him. He was quite tall, handsome and distinguished-looking, with grey hair, immaculately dressed in a suit with a beautiful shirt and tie. Once they started talking it was quickly apparent that they both shared the same sense of humour, and Jock was at once charming and intelligent, putting Ronnie at ease so that gradually his shyness at meeting his father slipped away. Dad was not really aware of it at the time but later on realised that Jock had kept his ear to the ground and was aware of his son's progress in the music business. It was really out of deference to Grandma Cissie that my grandfather had maintained an extremely low profile, communicating with her, and now Ronnie, only when she initiated it.

When Dad asked Jock his advice about joining the dance band he was slightly taken aback when his father said to him: 'Just read the parts, Ronnie, and don't try to lead the saxophone section.' At that time Dad had no such thoughts, one of his main concerns being that he could barely read the music, but his developing prowess as a bebop musician and that he was rapidly learning the art of improvisation had preceded him, and Jock knew that Ronnie had the strong will and focus that were the essential ingredients of a natural leader, and was concerned that Ronnie was running before he could walk.

When they weren't playing their own gigs, Ronnie and Tony used to sit in wherever they could, and one of their stopoffs was the Royal

41

Tottenham Dance Hall. It was 1944, and Lennie Metcalfe, a budding young piano player, was hanging out at the dance hall when Ronnie and Tony walked in. After the band took its first break, Ronnie and Tony sat in for the next show, and Lennie remembered: 'This was the first time I heard Ronnie play. He played a Coleman Hawkins version of 'Body and Soul' that was mesmerising. We were all a little bit in awe of Ronnie, and I was thrilled that I got to meet him that night, albeit briefly.'

After the dance was over, Ronnie and Tony headed for the Fullado Club, where Laurie Morgan was playing with the Don Rendell Quartet. The Fullado Club, which was just off Charing Cross Road, was primarily a black club that was an interesting interchange of cultures in the days when the black population of London was much smaller than it is now. Sonny Herman and the rest of the gang from the youth clubs were there: Pete Chilvers and Dave Goldberg, some Scottish guitar players, Lennie Bush (bass) and Johnny Dankworth. Sonny remembered their first impressions of Johnny: 'Johnny Dankworth was a very thin, hungry-looking alto player. He always looked as though he needed something to eat. We always thought we would take him home and give him some nice chicken soup!'

John Dankworth, from Highams Park in Essex, began his musical life as a classically trained clarinettist. Like all the other guys, he used to tune in to the radio and one day was listening to *Radio Rhythm Club* on the BBC when he heard Charlie Parker playing 'Cherokee'. This experience changed the course of John's life. Infused with and inspired by what he had just heard, he changed his instrument to alto saxophone and became a disciple of bebop. Ultimately, his role as band leader in postwar British jazz was to be as significant as my father's.

CHAPTER FOUR

AT LAST – AT LONG LAST – V-E DAY!

It was the best of times, it was the worst of times, it was the age of wisdom, it was the age of foolishness, it was the epoch of belief, it was the epoch of incredulity, it was the season of Light, it was the season of Darkness, it was the spring of hope, it was the winter of despair.

CHARLES DICKENS, *A Tale of Two Cities*

FOR RONNIE AND ALL his friends it seemed as though those long days and nights, drawing into weeks which became months, and the months years would never end, years of picking their way through the ever-increasing rubble of demolished buildings accompanied by the acrid smell of burned-out fires. Then there was the singular sound of the buzz bombs followed by the sudden deadly silence, which seemed louder than anything else that was happening as people dived for cover, never knowing where or exactly when the thing was going to come down and explode. When the boys were on the bandstand playing, there was many a night when the building they were in would shake with the impact of a nearby explosion, but they kept on playing anyway, their music a reflection of the earnest desire not just to survive but to live – and every moment was lived as though it was the last, everyone playing as though there was no tomorrow, and the result was electrifying. Searchlights streaked and crisscrossed the sky, highlighting the strange, yet now familiar, forms of the gigantic helium-filled barrage balloons with wires hanging from them that floated above the tops of buildings. Their purpose was to protect the population from the bombers, which had to stay above the balloons. Even so, it was a civilian war really, and it took its toll. Laurie Morgan remembered: 'We were all up in the air, shell-shocked; none of us were normal. You couldn't be normal in a situation like that. But there was the music, this incredible music, which lit up everything. We were transported by it, and through the music we were able to interpret life and express all our experiences, feelings and emotions. Our outlooks, attitudes and reactions developed from the music.'

They all helped each other in every way they could. For the men and women who worked in factories making everything from weapons and bullets to aeroplane parts, parachutes and uniforms for each branch of the services, a radio programme was developed called *Music While You Work*. The selection of music was always up-tempo so that the workers' hands would fly faster and produce more, in an effort to keep up with the insatiable demands of war. Ronnie and the guys played for ENSA, going to factories and playing for the workers. On one occasion Tony Crombie couldn't make the gig, so Ronnie asked Alf Summers to take his place. The group was a quartet with a girl singer, and the arrangement was for everyone to meet at the ENSA headquarters, the Theatre Royal, Drury Lane, from where they shared a cab to the factory in Ealing. When they walked into the factory about three hundred girls were sitting at sewing machines making uniforms. No one looked up as they entered and climbed on to the little stage. They began playing, and the girl sang a few songs, but all the time the factory girls kept sewing, their machines whirring nonstop, until after a few more numbers Ronnie turned to Alf and said: 'Do you think they can hear us?'

Ronnie and his mates often checked in at the Theatre Royal to see if their services were needed. ENSA had removed all the seats from the Theatre Royal, exposing a vast expanse of floor. Whole orchestras, in fact every musician in London, came to the theatre, and while they attended to their business with ENSA they put their instruments on the floor. Consequently, the whole floor was full of hundreds of instruments. This particular afternoon Harry Morris, the witty wiseguy and extremely likable rogue, who by now had become Ronnie's shadow, was as usual in tow. Ronnie had finished his business with ENSA and everybody was chatting away as they left the theatre. As they stepped out into the street Ronnie turned to Harry as he was speaking and in the same breath noticed that Harry was carrying a huge accordion! Stopping in mid-sentence, Ronnie said: '*What the hell* are you doing with that accordion, Harry?' Still in stride, Harry replied: 'This thing is so big *no one* would ever think it wasn't mine.' Harry was incorrigible.

One Monday afternoon after hanging out in the café on Archer Street and playing a couple of games of snooker in Windmill Street, Ronnie stopped off at Mac's Rehearsal Studio, where his father was rehearsing with Ennis Hylton's band. Ronnie arrived in time to hear a couple of tunes before the band broke up. While he was waiting for his father, Ronnie started chatting to Harry Carr, who doubled on tenor saxophone and clarinet. He said to Harry: 'I don't think I'll ever be able to play as well as you.' As he packed his saxophone in its case, Harry replied: 'You will, Ronnie, you will.' As indeed he did. This was one of the few occasions when Ronnie sought out his father. He wanted to exchange ideas with him, seeking his reassurance and his advice but sadly Jock had another appointment to rush off to and barely had the time to say 'hello'. Small as this incident appears, at the time to my father it was another example of Jock not being there for him when he was needed, and it felt like rejection.

My father had several British influences, a major one being a local tenor player whose name was Reggie Dare. He was a tall, blond, charismatic man who could charm the birds out of the trees and possessed a magnetic quality as far as women were concerned. Reggie was an adventurous musician and one of the first tenor players to lead a quartet, breaking away from the big dance band format which was all the rage. Dare and Johnny Claes led the bands for two ritzy West End restaurants, the Potomac in Piccadilly and the Princes in Jermyn Street.

The Johnny Claes band was a nine-piece unit with an exciting sound. Claes, whose trumpet playing echoed the sound of Roy Eldridge, led the group with a driving, energetic force, incorporating the intricacies of the new American music into his band's repertoire. A sharp dresser himself, he believed firmly that the band's image was of great importance. Ronnie was impressed with Claes' diverse leadership abilities and the musical direction of the band. Johnny was a friendly man, and he and my father had a common interest in racing cars (in later years Claes drove at Le Mans). One night he invited Ronnie to sit in at the Potomac. It was an experience that Dad never forgot. He found himself way out of his depth: the music was very complicated and his music reading skills were poor at best, so he was not able to bluff his way through. Johnny quickly realised how defeated Dad felt by the embarrassing experience and tried to reassure him that his problem was one that could be rectified.

My grandfather was keenly aware of Dad's inability to read music and was highly concerned about it. After his recent experience, Ronnie was ready to accept any help he could get. So Jock went to Harry Gold, a fellow musician who played bass saxophone, and asked him if he would give Ronnie some lessons. Harry responded to Jock's request by saying: 'I can't teach him anything, Jock. He's already a very good player.' Jock replied: 'Harry, I want you to help him with his reading. It's holding him back. He has to learn to read properly.' So Harry agreed to help and Ronnie went to him for a couple of months. Harry gave him some scales and exercises to practise which would help Ronnie associate the note he was seeing on the manuscript with his fingering on the saxophone. Harry said: 'The lessons went very well, and he became a good reader. I worked with Ronnie several times over the years. The first time was in the 1950s, when he sat next to me in the London Philharmonic, playing the Festival Hall. He had become a good reader by then. We were rehearsing a very difficult part in a piece called "Saxophone Tripart One", written by the famous Canadian composer Robert Farnon. Ronnie turned to me and said: "Am I playing this right?" I said: "Yes, you're playing it perfectly." It was brilliant, but Ronnie was a perfectionist, and anything less wouldn't do – he would berate himself. In a situation where the band held rehearsals, Ronnie was a good reader, but when it came to sight-reading [seeing music for the first time in front of an audience] he wasn't so good.' Harry went on to form his own very famous group called Harry Gold and His Pieces of Eight, and, now ninety-two years young, he is still playing and doing radio shows on both sides of the Atlantic, internationally recognised as an important influence in the world of bass saxophonists.

My father, who excelled at school, was insecure when it came to reading music. Even though Harry could see clearly that he was learning fast and reading well, Dad was always slightly unnerved when he had to sight-read a piece of music. He was playing regularly now. If he did not have a gig, he sat in every opportunity he got, travelling around the West End with his mates from the Oxford and St George's. Harry Morris by now had added another dubious activity to his agenda. He was known among his East End friends as a 'smudger'. Harry would patrol the West End armed with a camera and would stop people and say: 'I'll take your pictures. Just pay me, give me your name and address and we'll post them on to you.' But he never had any film in the camera! He was, however, a legitimate photographer on occasions, producing work and getting paid for it. My father loved Harry and found his escapades highly amusing, but Grandma Cissie was not so taken with him and considered him to be a bad influence on her son.

Harry made up for his indiscretions in other ways as far as Ronnie and the lads were concerned. He always had a nose for bringing musicians together, and one night after Ronnie had finished playing at the Oxford and St George's Harry took him to the Orchard Club in Wigmore Street and introduced him to Cab Quaye. Cab worked with his quartet, which was called Cab Quaye and His Ministers of Swing, as the resident band at the club. Cab let Ronnie sit in and said: 'When I heard him, I knew immediately that he was far advanced, a good reader, and absolutely immaculate. So I hired him, and he played with me for about a year.' Norman George (subsequently Susan George's father), who occasionally depped for Ronnie, met a young piano player called Roy Cook and brought him to the Orchard Club. He introduced him to Cab, and a few weeks later Cab hired him. Roy recalled: 'I was most fortunate to be there because there were better piano players around, but they had all been called up, so it gave me a chance to meet and play with Ronnie. I played there solidly for three months before getting called up myself, and it was one of the most exciting times of my life, actually.' The band used to play 'A Train', 'Doggin' Around' and 'Don't Be That Way'. On other numbers, such as 'Swanee River' and 'My Blue Heaven', Cab used to sing as well as play the drums and the rest of the band had to join in chanting the chorus. Their instructions, written by Cab on the lyric sheet, were, 'To be sung short and neat'.

Some well-known musicians used to come to hear Ronnie play and sometimes sit in. Aubrey Frank, who had been voted several times top tenor player in the *Melody Maker* polls, used to like to sit in. Roy chuckled as he remembered: 'Aubrey was quite a good tenor player, but even at that age Ronnie used to blow him off the stand! Ronnie was so outstanding, it was unbelievable really.' Sam Donahue from the American Naval Band was a frequent visitor, and so was Johnny Claes. In August 1944 *Melody Maker* gave the band a small write-up with a picture of the quartet. Grandma Cissie was so proud and pleased that she could hardly wait to show Sol when he came home on leave.

By the autumn of 1944 Johnny Claes asked Ronnie to join his band. Ronnie later learned that Jerry Alvarez, the alto player, had been responsible for bringing Johnny Claes to the Orchard Club so he could hear Ronnie play again. Johnny was impressed with my father's rapid growth, and since his current tenor player was leaving the band the timing was perfect. My father was now on a roll, about to embark on a new adventure that would expand his experience in more ways than one. Denis Rose was a member of the Claes band and spent a lot of time off stage as well as on with Ronnie. They were to spend many hours practising and discussing the finer points of music. Freddie Crump, Tony Crombie's favourite drummer, was also in the group. He was a small, slight, black man from Richmond, Virginia, who had come from the US in the early 1930s with the Blackbirds show and decided to make England his home. Dad was just as fascinated with his playing and showmanship as Tony was, and they agreed that his incredible display of unleashed energy and the flamboyant execution of his performance rivalled even those of the American prodigy, Buddy Rich.

Claes was preparing to take his band on the road, which was to be Dad's first experience of touring and leaving home for any length of time. The hours spent in buses and on trains were passed with the exchange of jokes and limericks, some of which were made up on the spot. Ronnie further honed his craft of mimicry, doing exaggerated impressions of eccentric characters they met on their travels and dissolving the rest of the band in hysterical laughter. The more seasoned members of the band exposed him to some other joys of life on the road, and he had his first taste of 'available young women'. They stayed in small, cold hotels with only a tiny electric heater for warmth, and no food or drinks of any kind were available when they finished their gig. Sometimes they stayed in digs run by landladies who were more homely and welcoming, but everything was hampered by the limitations and restrictions of war.

When Ronnie came home from touring he would go down to the East End to see all his mates and more often than not they would all end up back at Edgwarebury Gardens, including Cynthia and Lorna. Nanna Beckie and Grandma Cissie always managed to prepare something tasty for everybody, making them all very welcome. Sonny Herman recalled: 'Ronnie's Mum was a very stylish lady – she always looked elegant. She and his grandma Beckie made us feel very at home. I think she was pleased that Ronnie had a nice group of friends. She enjoyed our fairly frequent visits.' Grandma Cissie had also taken a liking to Cynthia and was supportive of their growing relationship. People got married young in those days, and Grandma Cissie really looked forward to the day when Ronnie would settle down and get married. But touring with the band caused some changes in Ronnie's relationship with Cynthia.

The romantic side of his nature, which she had been so attracted to, flourished as he wrote her beautiful letters from all over the British Isles. Ronnie was masculine in every way. He was also maturing, and he became more demanding in their relationship, trying to persuade Cynthia to explore the physical aspect of love. Much to his frustration, Cynthia was not forthcoming. 'Nice' girls did not indulge until they were married in those days, and difficult though it was she stuck to her principles. Cynthia was aware of the fact that there were girls who made themselves readily available to the musicians while they were on tour, and she saw this as a way of Ronnie relieving his frustrations and taking some of the pressure off her.

Ronnie still played at the Stepney Girls' Club with his mates from time to time on Sunday nights. The band would be playing and the boys and girls would be dancing, everyone having a good time, when all of a sudden somebody would shout out: 'Look out, fellers, the MPs are about.' The MPs were the military police. The Americans were called 'Snowdrops' because they wore white hats; the English soldiers wore red caps. The police were looking for people who should have registered for military service and hadn't done so. The guys would beat a hasty, surreptitious retreat off the bandstand, through the back door, leaping four steps at a time down the back staircase in their haste to get out. Harry Pitch remembered: 'They would come in and ask to see our papers. I had papers because I was working in a factory making aircraft parts, but Denis Rose got caught once and they took him away.' Denis getting caught resulted in his being called up for the Medical Corps, which turned out to be a short-lived experience, because after a couple of weeks he deserted, returning to Soho (where he hid) and his friends and life of music.

Always mindful of his friends, during his tenure with Johnny Claes and the Clay Pigeons, much to the surprise and delight of everybody at the Stepney Jewish Girls' Club, Ronnie persuaded Johnny and the band to play there one Sunday night. It was a wonderful evening for all concerned, especially for the younger members and visitors to the club, who were into the music and who otherwise would not get to hear a band of this calibre live. Working with the band filled Dad's life with new experiences of all kinds, some of key import, such as broadcasting for the first time. Although when playing in the studio the only apparent 'audience' was the crew and the microphones, there was nevertheless an exhilarating feeling, coupled with mild awe that the music was actually being heard by thousands of listeners. The realisation of this made its full impact when friends and strangers commented on the programme later. Grandma Cissie and Sol were so proud of Ronnie that inevitably they told their friends to listen to the broadcasts. There was no doubt now in Grandma Cissie's mind that her son's feet were firmly planted on the road to making a name for himself.

Tony Crombie had a gig as a drummer in Ray Ellington's band at the Bag o'Nails. Ronnie was a frequent visitor, because one of his early idols, Reggie Dare, was on tenor sax. One morning, after the Bag O'Nails closed, Tony, Ronnie, Denis Rose and the lads were all gathered in Lyons Corner House when Harry Morris walked in with a group of musicians from the Artie Shaw US Navy Band, which was led by tenor saxophonist Sam Donahue. He brought them over to the table where the lads were sitting. The guys leaped to their feet and room was made instantly for the Americans to sit down, introductions were made and a lively exchange ensued. Tony remembered: 'Ronnie was really impressed by Sam, who played driving up-tempo numbers which gelled wonderfully with the tight four-in-a-bar work of the rhythm section. Ronnie played in that mode for a good while.' Although the American bands were restricted by the musicians' union to playing for only the American armed forces, there was nothing to stop them from sitting in with the British bands. The following evening the American stars showed up at the Nuthouse Club and sat in with the ubiquitous Carlo Krahmer. It was a special treat for the young musicians and punters who were lucky enough to be at the Nuthouse on nights such as this. The Americans had a ball, basking in the glow of the reverence bestowed on them by the young British musicians and welcoming the opportunity to hang out and play in the relaxed atmosphere of a club again.

The Feldman Club had become a favourite spot for the visiting musicians to hang out in. Several of the guys from the Glenn Miller Band, really good jazz players, liked to sit in at the club when they had time off from entertaining the American troops. The BBC had been evacuated to Bedford, where the Glenn Miller Band was stationed (making it easy for the band to do broadcasts and recordings for Europe) but some of the recordings were made in London, and the guys would look for an opportunity to play after their gig was over. John Dankworth chuckled as he remembered: 'These guys were gods to us. I first heard them when I was about sixteen in 1943. All we had to listen to were the seventy-eight records, so when the guys from touring American bands sat in at the clubs it was manna from heaven for us!'

One night the Glenn Miller Band was playing at the London Palladium and Ronnie got a couple of tickets. He had made arrangements to meet Cynthia that night and would not tell her where they were going. She remembered: 'We were walking and talking and all of a sudden he stopped and said: "Would you like to see Glenn Miller play?" I said: "You can't be serious ... Of course, I'd *love* to." And he took the tickets out of his pocket. It was so lovely the way he did it. We had a fantastic evening.' Sadly, it was during this period that Glenn Miller took off from Bedford to Europe and his aeroplane went missing, a major loss for fellow musicians and fans alike.

In April 1945 the Claes band was written up in the *Melody Maker*, and this time my father's musical prowess was prophetically noted: 'Scott is undoubtedly one of the tenormen of the future.' Grandma Cissie and Sol could not have been happier, these words endorsing their dreams for Ronnie. Just a month later, on the morning of 8 May 1945, the prayers, hopes and dreams of millions of people on both sides of the Atlantic were realised with the announcement that the Second World War was over.

My father, even then, hated to be woken up for *any* reason. Waking him up without bringing the wrath of the universe on your head was a gentle art that had to be learned by all of us who lived with him. This particular morning Grandma Cissie saw no reason to exercise the usual caution and ran up the stairs calling his name as she went: 'Ronnie, Ronnie! The war's over!' She flung his bedroom door open and shook his shoulder, saying: 'Ronnie, Ronnie, wake up! Wake up! It's V-E Day! The war's over!' This was a day to be filled with unrivalled rejoicing and relief: at last, at long last the bombing was over. The people of London flooded into the streets. They gathered at Buckingham Palace, Downing Street, Piccadilly and Trafalgar Square, where Ronnie and Denis Rose marched together playing their horns. The city of London, from north to south and east to west, had become one enormous party.

The East End had been on the receiving end of a relentless and brutal pummelling during the war. On this day, the Royal Family visited the neighbourhood, to show their respects to the valiant residents. Ronnie and Denis went down to Ronnie's old childhood haunt, Petticoat Lane in the East End, meeting up with Flash Winston on their way. The locals wheeled a piano out on to the street with a couple of chairs. Denis sat down at the piano and Flash Winston set up his drums, Ronnie fronting the trio with his saxophone. The East Enders were laughing and at the same time tears poured down their faces as they hugged each other, sang songs and danced, so great was the relief and the realisation that all the deadly explosions, engulfing fires, droning bombers, and long nights spent in tube stations, basements and bomb shelters were finally over. It seemed to stop as suddenly as it had begun six long years earlier. During the celebrations, Winston Churchill and his principal colleagues appeared on the balcony of the Ministry of Health in Whitehall and made two brief speeches to the vast crowd. After Churchill spoke the words, 'This is *your* victory!', the crowd roared back: 'No! It's *yours!*' It was an unforgettable moment of love and gratitude.

Although the war was over, and, as Churchill put it, 'We can all take a night off today and a day off tomorrow', the country was faced with the awesome task of coping with its losses of both life and finance and turning the gigantic piles of rubble back into homes and businesses. The Second World War wrought many major changes in the way life was lived, and influences from America left an indelible mark on society. The whole face of music had changed. The young generation loved and wanted to hear jazz; everyone still wanted to dance, so the dance hall business escalated to new heights. New boundaries had to be carved out since the old ones, particularly those left over from the Victorian era, no longer fitted into the new world. Two months after V-E Day, Britain went to the polls and the Labour Party was voted into government, winning with a large, absolute majority. This was the first Labour Government that held both office and effective power. Clement Attlee was now Prime Minister of Great Britain, much to the surprise and great disappointment of Winston Churchill and his administration. Churchill had led Britain through its darkest hours and had hoped to lead the country through recovery and beyond. On that Declaration Day, 26 July 1945, at Chequers, Churchill signed his name in the visitors' book and after his name wrote *finis*. There was a different kind of independence developing, especially within the young generation. People wanted to have more control of their own destinies, which manifested itself in all walks of life. The young musicians were no exception and were determined to have a say in the policies of the bands they played in.

A great homecoming was on its way. Servicemen were soon to be demobbed and sent home to their families. Other families had relatives who had been incarcerated in Hitler's death camps. Now those were being liberated and the inmates who had managed to survive were desperate to find their families. Grandfather Jock was anxious about the whereabouts of his sister Annie and her family. He had not heard from her for so long that he feared the worst. Before the war they had visited Jock and his parents and Ronnie had played with Ziggy and Alex at his grandfather's house. Jock remembered how strict his father had been about the children eating sweets, and how he, Jock, had given young Ziggy and Ronnie some money and shooed them out of the house to buy a penny's worth of whatever took their fancy.

Jock and his family's fears were well founded. The day the Russian army liberated Skarzysko Ziggy was lying next to a woman on boards covered with straw, both of them nothing more than skin and bone. He was just a boy, and she could have been his mother. Her name was Natalie Rubin, and she spoke to Ziggy as a mother would speak to her son, comforting him. They kept each other alive by talking about survival. Chaos reigned in Poland, people pouring out of the concentration camps, ill, weak, some of them barely alive, heading on foot for the nearest town, which for Ziggy was Czestochowa. Hungry and freezing cold, he was forced to trudge through the ice and snow for mile after mile. In the crush of hundreds of people Ziggy and Natalie lost sight of each other, neither one knowing that life was going to bring them back together again in the not too distant future. So many had been killed. Ziggy wondered if his brother Alex was alive and heading for Czestochowa too. And what of their parents, Annie and Max? He had no idea which camp they had been sent to. London and his grandfather's house, with all his aunts and uncles and cousins, seemed a universe away. Hardly able to put one foot in front of the other, Ziggy felt so terribly lost that he longed to see just one face he recognised, for just one warm embrace from someone he had loved telling him they were pleased he was still alive.

In the summer of 1945 Uncle Mark returned to London. He had spent the war hiding out and working in a gambling casino in Leeds, Yorkshire. He brought his new girlfriend with him, Rosie, who was the catering manageress at the club where Mark had worked. She was a young woman of English descent, not Jewish, who quickly became known as Auntie Rosie to Ronnie and Marlene. She was a warm, generous, fun-loving young lady and madly in love with Uncle Markie. They moved into a flat in Oxford Street, above Bond Street Underground Station. Auntie Rosie had been living in Leeds with her husband and young daughter Josie when she fell in love with Uncle Mark. Josie remembers: 'My father left us when I was eight. My mother told me, "This is Uncle Markie, and he's going to take care of us now." But when Mum and Uncle Mark moved to London I was sent to live with my aunt and uncle in Leicester, and they brought me up until I was twelve.' Uncle Mark was not ready to move back to London and take on the responsibility of a family; neither was he prepared to marry Auntie Rosie. During the ensuing years Uncle Mark was *never* able to make the commitment of marriage to Auntie Rosie. Periodically Uncle Markie would break off the relationship but always ended up going back to Auntie

Rosie. Ultimately, they lived together for thirty years until the time of his death in 1973.

Auntie Rosie always believed that Uncle Mark would settle down and soon she could send for Josie to come to join them. It did not take long for Uncle Mark to get a job. He worked for a gangster who owned a chain of gambling clubs. He was very fond of Ronnie and gave him an open invitation to come to the club and play a few hands of poker whenever he felt like it. Uncle Mark was hooked on horse racing, as was my father, who by now was placing bets on the horses. They shared a love of gambling. The thrill of risking everything on the roll of a dice, a game of cards, a dog at the greyhound track or a horse at the races was their greatest high. Uncle Markie used to say: 'My Ronnie and me, we'd bet on two flies climbing up a wall!'

On 16 February 1946 *Melody Maker* ran a piece under the heading HEATH CAPTURES SCOTT AND SHAND. The report stated: 'Biggest break of his short career has just come to young London tenor saxist Ronnie Scott, who joins Ted Heath and his band this weekend.' Among other things, the write-up went on to say that 'The eagle eye of Ted Heath has already detected the touch of brilliance in his playing'.

My father was nineteen and ready for a change, although he had his own ideas about what he wanted to play. Some musicians in Heath's band were just as interested in and involved with bebop as he was. One of them, Jack Parnell, who cut a dashing figure, was a sensational young big band drummer and later on formed his own big band and became very well known. He and Dave Goldberg, a Scottish guitarist, had recommended Ronnie to Ted Heath. Ronnie did not bestow the same accolades on his playing as did the musicians who worked with him and listened to him. Somehow he did not recognise the full extent of his ability and potential, so when things went well for him there was always an element of mild and pleasant surprise in his reaction to the situation. This was an integral part of who he was. He was very rarely completely satisfied with what he played and spent his life working at being a better player.

When he auditioned for the band, my father really was quite nervous, most concerned about his ability to read the arrangements, fearing that he might not be good enough. Needless to say, everything went extremely well, although at the time he could hardly believe that Ted Heath hired him, not quite accepting that he was ready for a band of this calibre. He loved to tell me the story of when he went to sign up at the band's office and Ted Heath told him that the money would vary from week to week.

Dad wondered what was coming next when Ted said: 'But you will never earn less than £20 per week.' Dad said: 'Rebecca, you have to understand, I was only nineteen at the time and £20 was a small fortune. This was the big league. It was fantastic!' There were weeks when Dad made much more than that, which was soon to be of critical importance for the rest of the family.

Ronnie went straight on the road with Ted Heath, doing his first tour with the band that February. In the meantime Lennie Metcalfe had received his call-up papers and had opted to go into the mines in Nottinghamshire. He lived in Mansfield, and in the evenings played piano at a lounge bar. One night a fellow musician came up to him and said: 'Listen, the Ted Heath band is playing in Nottingham next Sunday.' So when Sunday came around Lennie and five of his friends got together and decided to take the bus into Nottingham, which was about fourteen miles away from Mansfield, to go to the concert. When they got to the cinema where the concert was being held, there was a queue of people all the way up the street. They got in the queue and while they were standing there waiting to get in they saw a group of guys all dressed up in their dinner jackets heading towards the cinema. Lennie happily reminisced: 'I recognised Ronnie among them, so I called out to him: "Hey, Ronnie." He came over to me and said: "Lennie, how are you?" Then he said: "Why don't you come with me and I'll get you in the musicians' entrance." I said: "No, it's OK. I'll stay here and go in with my mates." Ronnie replied: "OK, but if you have any trouble, let me know and I'll make sure you get in all right." This was my first real introduction to Ronnie. I'd only met him a couple of times before, and all we said was hello. He really didn't know me at all, and here he was doing me a favour.' Lennie was thrilled that Ronnie had remembered him and had offered to get him into the concert. After such a marvellous evening the reality of the fact that he had to return to the dreary existence of working in the mines filled him with sadness.

On Monday nights the band used to play at the Hammersmith Palais. One Monday afternoon Ronnie went to meet Cynthia from work, and they met up with Tony Crombie and his girlfriend Gladys (who became his first wife) and all went to Ronnie's home in Edgwarebury Gardens. When they arrived at the house Cynthia suddenly realised that no one was home. They played records for a while, and Ronnie got very romantic, and increasingly persistent in his physical advances. But Cynthia once again stuck to her principles. This time Ronnie was really annoyed and became quite angry with Cynthia. She had persisted in resisting him, and time had fled, making him late for the gig at the Hammersmith Palais. It was a long journey on the tube from Edgwarebury Gardens to Hammersmith, and Ronnie was so mad with Cynthia that he did not speak to her on the train. When they got to the Palais it was just in time for him to rush straight on to the bandstand. As Cynthia now says, when the band came off for their break, 'He came over and sat with me, but he never said a word. It wasn't until we were on our way home that he started speaking to me again.'

It was only during this year that Cynthia realised that she really was in love with Ronnie, but she still could not do what he wanted. She said: 'During the first three years of our relationship there were times when I was snobbish, sometimes I was cold and snooty, standoffish. I think he liked that sort of thing because then he didn't feel that the relationship was too serious.' They were teenagers, and as is quite normal at that age were somewhat self-absorbed. One Sunday afternoon they were riding on the top of a double-decker bus, something they did quite frequently. Cynthia was looking down on all the people milling around and she turned to Ronnie and said: 'I feel as if I'm the only one alive on this planet. All these people around us, and I feel as though I'm the only one who's alive!' Ronnie replied: 'That's funny. That's the way I feel as well!'

When Ronnie was touring with the Ted Heath Band there were hordes of girls waiting for them as they came off the bandstand, like today's groupies with their rock stars. But this abundance of female company didn't take his mind off Cynthia. He still used to write her letters, and now he was earning more money he also telephoned her. The phone would ring at exactly 11.45 p.m. She could set her watch by it. Always very romantic, Ronnie would tell her: 'I can't read the music properly because I see your face in the arrangements.' When he came home from the tour the band was scheduled to do a live broadcast the following Saturday. He kept saying to Cynthia: 'Make sure you listen to the broadcast on Saturday.' He reminded her again on the Friday night. Cynthia had a little radio in the hairdresser's salon which she played all day, but she made a point of paying attention when the Ted Heath Band was announced. They played a couple of tunes, then Paul Carpenter, the singer, started to sing 'Cynthia's in Love'. Maybe it was this kind of romancing that sometimes made Cynthia a little wistful when she and Ronnie were out walking, and she saw a woman with a baby in a pram. Turning to Ronnie, she would say: 'Why don't we get married and have babies?' His only response was dead silence accompanied by an impassive expression on his face. Each time this occurred, Cynthia realised that her suggestion somehow scared him. He had no idea how to handle the situation; he just knew that he could not take that step, and so did Cynthia. As the reality of the fact that Ronnie would never marry her sank in, gradually Cynthia started the process of breaking away from her relationship with Ronnie and she began to date other people.

It was during this period that Sol was finally demobbed. Filled with enthusiasm to start a new life, he wanted to start up a business of his own. He and Cissie discussed the situation and decided to sell everything they could to raise the money needed to start up Gate Textiles, his wholesale tailoring firm. Sol decided on the name 'Gate' because the business was located in Aldgate. He began to travel regularly to Leeds to buy bales of cloth at the wool mills, and the little manufacturing company began selling to small men's outfitters all over the country. Ronnie, who had been working for Ted Heath for several months by now, was earning about £40 a week, and he made his contribution to Sol's enterprise by supporting the family while Sol built his new business.

One Monday night when the band was playing at the Hammersmith Palais, Ronnie met a young girl whose name was Joan Crewe. This time it was love at first sight. Joan was sixteen years old, extremely pretty, with short dark hair, wide eyes and a smile to match, and she loved to dance. Ronnie, a dance band star, cut a dashing figure in his dinner jacket, and it was not long before they became lovers. Whenever the band was in town, Ronnie and Joan were inseparable. Even though she had to work she was right by his side in the all-night cafés after the night's music was over. Theirs was as complete as a relationship could be, and in the not-too-distant future Ronnie was to find himself trying to evade the issue of marriage with Joan just as he had done with Cynthia.

There were aspects of playing with an outfit like Ted Heath's that Ronnie did not really like. Sometimes when he took solos his musical intuition took over and he slipped into the style of the American swing era tenorists coloured with a touch of the intricate complexities of the new modernists, breaking away from the traditional Ted Heath sound. He was not alone. Jack Parnell was weighing up the pros and cons of leaving the band and starting his own outfit with a group of musicians who wanted to expand on what they were learning from the American musicians. Ted was aware of the restlessness among certain members of his band and of their passionate desire to explore new horizons, but for the time being he said nothing.

Financially Ronnie was better off than he had ever been. Even though he was supporting the family at home, he still had enough left for himself. Dad had always had a keen eye for clothes and the latest fashions from America. He used to buy his suits, shirts and ties from the GIs and American sailors, and he sported the wide-shouldered suits and the cutback shirt collars then in vogue. At about this time he decided he needed some form of transport for himself. Tiring of the long tube ride from the West End to Edgwarebury Gardens and the many nights when he missed the last train home completely, he decided to buy himself a motorbike. He bought a Tiger Triumph 100 and got himself a learner's licence. Grandma Cissie was a little nervous about this new means of transport, beseeching Ronnie not to ride too fast. Her fears were well founded. Riding home from the West End to Edgware in the small hours of the morning when there was very little traffic, Ronnie, lying on the pillion seat almost flat like a racer, used to ride full throttle, experiencing the thrill of travelling at speed.

One night after work, Ronnie, Laurie Morgan, Lennie Bush, Pete Chilver and Dave Goldberg all went to the Fullado Club to hang out. All the guys were friends with Horace, a black man who used to work in the cloakroom. Horace was also a piano player and a devotee of bebop. From time to time he would bring in records for the guys to play on the gramophone at the club. This particular evening the album was called 'Jazz at the Philharmonic', featuring Charlie (Bird) Parker, Lester Young (Prez) and Coleman Hawkins (Bean or Hawk). It was the first time the boys had heard Charlie Parker play, featured on 'Lady Be Good'. Laurie Morgan vividly remembered this milestone in their lives: 'It was Charlie Parker — his playing — that inspired all of us, even though Ronnie's first love was Coleman Hawkins. We were all ignited by the soaring passion of the original spirit and the emotional soul, coupled with an ingenious cleverness and technique. This music was an all-consuming blazing flame that engulfed us on this side of the Atlantic, never mind in America! Ronnie, through his gift, shared his love and great respect of many players as each one emerged by presenting their playing in his own. He was absolutely brilliant at interpreting their music for other people to hear, which was a demonstration of his respect and the greatest compliment he could pay to their craft.'

Up until now Ronnie and all the lads had been listening to other players who had already been influenced by Charlie Parker. But he was actually the originator of bebop. Dizzy (Birks) Gillespie met Bird in 1940 with legendary drummer Max Roach, when they wood-shedded the music (honed their craft) at Minton's Playhouse and Monroe's Uptown House in Harlem. As Dizzy said: 'Bird's influence is layers and layers of spirit.' When Charlie

Parker was asked about the origin of bebop, he said he had grown weary of playing the usual chord changes and was convinced that there had to be a different structure on which improvisation could take place. He said: 'I could hear it sometimes, but I couldn't play it.' Then one night in December of 1939, after he had finished work, Charlie Parker was jamming in Harlem, at Dan Wall's Chillie House on 7th Avenue at 139th Street, with a rhythm section led by a guitarist called Biddy Fleet. Running through Ray Noble's 'Cherokee', suddenly he could play what he had been inwardly hearing. There have been many descriptions written about Charlie Parker's musical revelation, but the words he chose to describe it are so simple. He said: 'Bop is no love child of jazz. Bop is something entirely separate and apart. It's just music. It's trying to play clean and looking for the pretty notes.' Charlie Parker was the 'messenger'. He was on a mission. And *everybody* was listening.

By the beginning of 1943 Birks and Bird teamed up and worked together in the Earl Hines Band. Bird referred to Dizzy 'as the other half of my heartbeat'. Dizzy's personality was huge. He was larger than life itself, vivacious and extrovert, with an incredibly quick wit, and in a few short years his name was synonymous with bebop.

Working with Ted Heath was a very prestigious job for a young musician, and my father began to receive recognition. In August 1946 he came fifth in the *Melody Maker* poll, beating his old idol, Reggie Dare, who came eighth, by three places. This really was a remarkable accomplishment, considering he had been playing the saxophone for only four years and this was his first year with a really big-time dance band outfit. That same year a book was published called *The Full Story of Ted Heath and His Music*. The authors, Edwin Charles and Alan Fletcher, referred to Ronnie as 'the "baby" of the band, but tenor sax player Ronnie Scott has already built himself a full-grown reputation and has a brilliant future ahead'. They went on to say: 'Sharing solos with the redoubtable Johnny Gray, young Ronnie amply demonstrates that his exalted position is earned and held by sheer, downright musical ability. More than once I have seen Ted standing in the wings with a look of real wonderment on his face at the things this boy can do with a saxophone.'

There were, of course, copies of the *Melody Maker* at the house in Edgwarebury Gardens, and on occasion in the articles Ronnie was referred to as 'the son of that well-known alto sax player Jock Scott'. Auntie Marlene was growing up and was keenly interested in everything that went on around her. One afternoon when she came home from school she went into the kitchen for a snack and found that someone had left a copy of the *Melody Maker* on the kitchen table. Curious, she picked up the magazine and flicked through it until she came across a write-up about Ronnie, including the information about Jock. Puzzled by it, as soon as Grandma Cissie came home she confronted her with the article, saying: 'Mum, what does this mean? Ronnie's name is Berger, Daddy's Ronnie's father. What's going on?' Grandma Cissie made light of it, explaining it away by saying: 'Oh, it's nothing, Marlene. Don't take any notice of it. You know how the press are always looking for an angle. It's nothing more than a publicity stunt.' Auntie Marlene accepted the explanation and for the time being that was the end of it. She continued to believe that Sol was Ronnie's father.

Ronnie was becoming more and more restless within the confines of Ted Heath's Band and was unable to contain himself when he took a solo. He was evolving musically at a rapid pace. His head was full of Bird's soaring, unfaltering improvisations, and he could not stop himself from experimenting with and incorporating some of what he had heard into his own playing. For the first time playing double time for at least part of his solo, the experience was both electrifying and invigorating. He had tasted a new kind of freedom. Ted Heath did not really like what was happening but said nothing.

It was in 1947 that the blizzard of all blizzards swept across England and Wales. People who lived in rural areas were snowed in for months that winter, forced to melt the snow as their only source of water. In February the band was playing in Liverpool, and everybody was booked on the overnight train to London for the show the following day. My father, in retrospect, considering the weather conditions, marvelled at his own folly when he told me the story: 'I felt like having some excitement, and it seemed like a good idea at the time.' He chuckled. 'Anyway, it wasn't snowing that night, so never having flown I decided to book myself on a flight back to London the next day. I stayed in a hotel overnight. The only trouble was, you see, when I got up the next morning, there was the biggest bloody snowstorm you ever saw in your life, and of course the airport was closed.' Obviously there was no way he could get back to London in time for the show and Tommy Whittle was brought in to take his place. Shortly afterwards, Ted Heath wrote Ronnie a note, saying: 'Your services are no longer required.' *Melody Maker* noted the arrival of Tommy Whittle and the departure of my father from the band. They were soon to run another story announcing that Dad had joined the band of trumpeter Jack Jackson, which was the resident band at Churchill's, a restaurant in the West End.

His friends Laurie Morgan and Pete Chilver were also in the band.

The young musicians regularly congregated on Archer Street even if they had a gig. Monday was the big day if they were out of work. Everyone was identified by the type of instrument case they carried, and the drummers either had drumsticks sticking out of their pockets or they carried a snare drum under their arms. They all knew the Windmill girls, who hung out in the street before and after their shows went on. Sometimes the lads went into the Windmill to catch a show. The girls were allowed to be topless but they had to stand completely still while on stage. Only those girls who were clothed — albeit scantily — were allowed to perform to the packed house. Then there were the girls who hung around the musicians; today they would be called groupies. Comedians and actors were often seen in the street too, as were the Mafia, who controlled the London gambling joints, among other things. There was Jack Spot and Albert Dimes, each of whom had his respective 'family'. Ronnie used to play poker with Albert's crew, never being able to resist a wager. The lads gathered in the Harmony Inn for cups of tea and endless discussions about all their American idols, Charlie Parker having become a major topic of conversation, with Denis Rose going over his latest transcriptions of Bird's music. A need was growing in the boys to hear the music live, to see the musicians perform, to feel themselves a part of the ambience that only a live performance can produce. Disconsolately, they acknowledged that due to the current situation with the musicians' union they would all be old and grey before their cherished mentors would be permitted to perform on this side of the Atlantic.

CHAPTER FIVE

THE SEED IS SOWN

We were high on American music and I remember I was still exulting in the tremendous impression that the Three Deuces had made on me. The idea of presenting modern jazz in that intimate kind of atmosphere kept recurring in my mind with accelerating frequency. I had plenty of time to reflect on it, too, because the voyage home took nine days.

RONNIE SCOTT, *Some of My Best Friends Are Blues*

IN NEW YORK BLACK musicians had been confined until the mid-1930s to playing in Harlem in the uptown clubs such as Minton's Playhouse and Monroe's Uptown House, which is where the groundwork for the music was developed. As Dizzy Gillespie once said: 'It was a wonderful time, but 52nd Street was better. We were just experimenting. By the time we came downtown our ideas were beginning to be accepted. Oh, it took some time, but 52nd Street gave us the rooms to play and the audiences.'

After Prohibition was repealed in 1933, by the middle of 1934 clubs were once again permitted to sell hard liquor legally, and by late 1934 and early 1935 52nd Street had already become the downtown home of great black jazz as well as the route to public recognition for white artists like Woody Herman, Buddy Rich, George Shearing and a host of others. As Marion McPartland (pianist) was heard to say: 'On 52nd Street you could walk through the history of jazz. In several hours, nursing a few drinks, you could travel musically from New Orleans up to Harlem and bop.' There was a strong rapport between performer and audience; people did not talk while the music was playing, but when a solo was completed or the tune came to an end, the musicians were greeted with shouts, whoops of approval and thunderous applause. Artie Shaw recorded Billie Holiday and Teddy

Wilson (pianist extraordinaire) at the Onyx. At the same time the Three Deuces was presenting Art Tatum, a phenomenal young pianist, a black man with a chubby, wide-open face filled with humour. Art was blind in his left eye and had very limited vision in the right. He walked with a lopsided gait and loved his pint of beer. By the time the 1940s arrived, Art Tatum represented the apotheosis of jazz improvisation. Whenever Art played, every pianist who was in town, from Duke Ellington to George Gershwin to Vladimir Horowitz (the last of the romantic classicists), was held in rapt attention by his unparalleled technique and totally brilliant flow of ideas executed at breakneck tempos with both delicacy and finesse. Along with many of the other great founders of this music, his influence is alive and well to this day.

By now bebop had completely permeated the souls of Ronnie and all his friends. Sonny Herman, who saved every penny he could to buy the American musicians' albums, had struck up a friendship with a petite little brunette who was a jazz fan and worked in Levy's record shop. She would give him a ring when the latest shipment arrived so he and his friends would have the choice picks of the new arrivals. But listening to the albums and radio and reading about their American mentors in *Melody Maker*, *Downbeat* or *Metronome* was no longer sufficient to satisfy their voracious appetites for a deeper experience of the music.

The kindred spirits frequently met at the Fullado Club, and on one such night Pete Chilver, Laurie Morgan and Ronnie, who had finished their gig at Churchill's, were hanging out talking with all the guys. They were immersed in their usual conversation about the various American giants of jazz, when Pete said: 'Let's all go to New York.' The seed was sown, and everyone enthusiastically concurred that this was the *only* thing to do. Ronnie and Tony Crombie were the first to turn this dream into a reality, scraping their meagre savings together and planning their New York holiday. Ronnie had very little money saved because he was still helping to support the family at Edgwarebury Gardens. In an effort to improve their finances, Tony managed to work out an arrangement with the editor of *The Musical Express and Accordion Times* (a forerunner of *NME*). The magazine was enthused by the idea of getting some first-hand impressions of the New York scene written from the perspective of visiting British musicians.

Since each of them was in a desperate hurry to get to New York, they agreed to make the outward journey by air and to travel back by sea. On Sunday 27 April 1947 Ronnie and Tony climbed aboard an Icelandic

Airways aeroplane headed for New York. Even though the flight took twenty-two hours because of detours to Shannon, Reykjavik and Gander, the young men did not care, their heads and hearts flooded with anticipation of the music that awaited them. The awesome possibility of meeting their jazz idols in person was almost overwhelming.

Dumping their bags at an inexpensive small hotel in Greenwich Village, they headed towards legendary 52nd Street between 5th and 6th Avenues. Had they had the money for a cab they could have hailed one and simply asked the driver to take them to 'the Street'; just as today in London you can jump into any cab and ask for 'Ronnie Scott's Club', no address required. On each side of the street were clubs: the Three Deuces, Jimmy Ryan's, Onyx, and next door to the Yacht Club (formerly the Famous Door) was a burlesque strip joint called the Club Samoa, the only club that was non-union, which meant that musicians who got into scrapes with the union played there. Ronnie's and Tony's first port of call was the Three Deuces, a small smoky place with a terrific ambience, where people sat at tables with a drink and listened to the likes of Charlie Parker and Miles Davis. Dad said: 'It was a *fantastic* experience for us. We'd never really heard an American group in a club before. Although the recordings we'd heard were marvellous, nothing compared with being a few feet away from someone like Miles Davis. Seeing as well as hearing them perform in that atmosphere was an exhilarating and inspirational experience beyond our wildest dreams.'

It was outside the Three Deuces that Ronnie and Tony first met the man who became known as 'the mayor of 52nd Street'. His name was Gilbert Pincus, a mere five feet nothing in height, with a fat cigar stuck in the corner of his mouth. On his large bald head he wore a black doorman's cap, sometimes the peak seeming almost to rest on the bridge of his very large nose. He wore a long black-grey coat, with a newspaper sticking out of the pocket, that came down to his ankles beneath which two very large, wide, flat, black shoe-clad feet protruded. Pincus was the self-appointed doorman for every club on the street. As Ronnie and Tony approached the Three Deuces, Pincus, with an elaborate bow and an exaggerated sweep of his arm, motioned them into the club, saying: 'Come on in, folks, you're just in time for the complete performance!' When telling this story, my father would say: 'It didn't matter if you arrived halfway through a set. Pincus would still say the same thing!' Among the musicians, Pincus was known as 'Yiz'll', because he would tell people blocking a club entrance: 'Yiz'll have to move on.' My father loved Pincus, who would get a cab for anybody. He was very fast. Suddenly excusing himself from a conversation, he would say, 'Pardon me!', dart across the street, nodding to a patron who came out of a club, flag down a cab with generous arm motions, open the door with a flourish and deftly accept the proffered tip. Then he would return to the conversation, picking it up exactly where he had left off, his black eyes carefully scanning the street for the next prospective punter.

Sleep was very low on Ronnie and Tony's agenda. During the day they explored the city, walking for miles, window-shopped, now and then stopping to buy shirts and ties. Wandering around midtown Manhattan one afternoon they came across Manny's Music Store on 48th Street near 6th Avenue. The shop was small – about twenty feet wide by forty feet long – with a narrow aisle and low ceiling but packed to the rafters with drums, flutes, saxophones, and all the brass instruments. They were greeted by Manny Goldrich, proprietor, a jovial, friendly man who had started out as a musician playing the violin, working as a salesman for Conn/Selmer to support himself. He enjoyed the company of musicians, loved selling instruments and went into business for himself in 1935. By the time Ronnie and Tony met him, Manny knew every musician in New York, becoming a close friend of many jazz musicians and extending them credit when necessary. The young men were made instantly welcome, Manny expressing interest in their being English. He showed Ronnie a selection of reeds, from which he selected several boxes, while Tony explored the drum kits and sticks. Manny was full of information about the New York jazz scene, and recognising their obsession with bebop he told them proudly: 'You know, every union day, upstairs . . . I'll take you up and show you! We have regular jam sessions up here featuring Dizzy Gillespie, Charlie Parker, Max Roach and all the guys. Oh, yeah, they all play here. Starts at two o'clock in the afternoon and runs until about six. You see that big counter there? That's our wrapping counter. I can't tell you how many times Charlie Parker after a jamming session just climbed on top of that counter and went to sleep.' Back downstairs, he put their purchases in a bag, saying: 'There you go, my man. Enjoy!' For Ronnie, this was the beginning of another lifelong friendship.

During the nights they walked the street, in and out of all clubs. Coleman Hawkins, Charlie Parker, Dizzy Gillespie, Billie Holiday, Sarah Vaughan, Woody Herman and Lester Young were among the truly incredible group of jazz artists and innovators that performed regularly on 52nd Street. Comics like Alan King and Joey Adams, among others, also got their start on the street. There has always been an affinity between musicians and comedians. All his life Dad had a great love and respect for American stand-up comics.

On his way to California, Laurie Morgan planned to spend a few days in New York with Ronnie and Tony, so he checked into the same hotel and the three of them, reunited, continued their musical adventure together, this time catching Thelonious Monk who, among others, played piano with Coleman Hawkins. Known as a 'modernist', Monk was one of the originators of bebop who had wood-shedded his craft along with Dizzy, Bird, Kenny 'Klook' Clarke (drummer) and Bud Powell (piano) and so on at Minton's and Monroe's. Monk was a unique and complex man whose compositions, like his famous 'Round About Midnight', would become classics. Dad, Tony and Laurie also caught Mercer Ellington, Duke's son, rehearsing the band at Nola's rehearsal rooms.

Dad and Tony were invited to dinner with Uncle Phil and family a couple of times during their visit. Uncle Phil was a gambling man and had lots of stories to tell the young men about how much money he had won on the horses. As he sat and listened, it seemed to Ronnie that his uncle was making more money on the horses than he was from his work as a tailor. Even though Ronnie was only twenty at the time, he was already a confirmed gambler himself, with a distinct preference for the horses, so he was an avid listener and much impressed with his uncle's stories. The conversation around the table was animated. My auntie Rose, also in her twenties, and her brother Joey (Uncle Phil's children) loved the thrill of putting down bets, and of course Dad had placed several bets himself during his stay in the city, much to everyone's amusement because he knew nothing of the tracks in America.

Uncle Philip was hungry for news of his brothers and sisters back in London, but Ronnie did not have much to tell because he had barely seen his auntie Mary and cousin Sydney since his family had moved to Edgware. Dad did not realise it at the time, but the family was keenly aware of the fact that he had always resented his parents not being together. Uncle Phil was anxious to hear about the meeting between Ronnie and his father. It brought him comfort to know that at last there was contact between Jock and his son. Philip knew how proud Jock was of Ronnie, and how he quietly observed his son's development and progress without intruding into the family's life at Edgwarebury. When Ronnie told him that he saw his father from time to time on Archer Street, this pleased him even more. Uncle Philip hoped that now Ronnie was a professional musician and moving in the same circles as his father the two of them would finally be able to overcome the void that had been created by the earlier years of Jock's absence.

Dad and Tony had booked open tickets for the boat trip back and planned to stay in New York until their funds ran out. Dad filed away the notion that Uncle Phil was making a fair amount of money on the horses, concluding that if push came to shove and he and Tony did get stranded in New York they could always get help from Uncle Phil. By the time mid-June came around, Ronnie and Tony had about twenty-five dollars left between them and decided it was time to book their passage home. When they went to the Cunard office they were mortified to discover that all the ships were fully booked for the next ten days. They cut back drastically on their expenses, limiting themselves to a couple of coffees and doughnuts each day. Every morning they trekked to the Cunard office in the hope that passengers might have cancelled at the last minute. Finally, in desperation, Ronnie and Tony went to see Uncle Phil, Ronnie saying: 'Listen, Uncle Phil, Tony and I are absolutely skint and we can't get a boat for some days. Would you help us out and lend us a hundred dollars? We'll send it back to you as soon as we get home.' Auntie Rose, remembering this incident, said: 'Times were hard for us in New York then, and Dad just did not have the money to spare.' Maybe Uncle Phil had had a streak of bad luck with the horses. Fortunately for the lads, the following morning they were told that they could get on the *Ernie Pyle*, a small boat with male and female dormitories and a self-service cafeteria – not exactly the lap of luxury for a nine-day journey, but neither of them cared. Ronnie was dreaming of how some day he would have his own club and bring all the American artists to England for everyone to hear, musicians and jazz fans alike.

When Dad arrived back in England it was to find his stepfather Sol, who was a very positive man, reflecting the spirit of hope and optimism that pervaded England at the time. Steadily building the firm foundations of his business, Sol spent any spare time he could find working for the Edgware branch of the British Legion. He was soon to become treasurer and vice-chairman of this organisation, setting about creating a system to raise money for ex-servicemen, focusing on those who had sustained life-inhibiting injuries during the war. It would not be long before Ronnie was to play an active role in helping Sol with his fundraising.

The reunion between Ronnie and Tony and all the guys anxious to hear a 'note-by-note' report of the two-month musical adventure was to say the least electrifying. Animated discussions and the exchange of new musical ideas flowed between them. However, not all the news came from New York: things were happening in London. The *Melody Maker* was sponsoring a public recording session at the EMI studios on Sunday 29 June. The responsibility of selecting a series of pick-up bands for the occasion was spread between 128 British musicians. They were to select whoever they considered to be the leading musicians of the day. The chosen tenors were Ronnie Scott, Reggie Dare and Tommy Whittle. For my father this was a special event as he was to play alongside one of his first heroes, Reggie Dare, and in his own group was George Shearing, the melodic and lyrical blind pianist who ultimately emigrated to America and became internationally renowned.

It was Monday – fixing day (slang for booking gigs) – and Archer Street was buzzing with activity. If there wasn't a gig to be had, the guys could be found in the café playing the football machine, or down the street shooting a game of snooker, maybe stopping off at Phil Rabin's Salt Beef Bar for a sandwich. Ronnie used to get his hair cut by a guy named Joe in the barber shop owned by Sid Seager, who had a barber the lads dubbed 'Yozzil the Executioner' because if you didn't watch out he lopped all your hair off. There was always a throng of musicians milling around. Tony Crombie remembers often chatting with Jock Scott. He said: 'Jock had a very dry sense of humour, just like Ronnie. He was always very smart, a good dresser, and they both were very intelligent. Ronnie and his father used to acknowledge each other, but they never had much to say. Jock let us know how much he admired the fact that Ronnie had achieved so much at such an early age, with Ted Heath at nineteen and making all the *Melody Maker* polls. He was very proud of his son.' The population of Archer Street was multifarious, some transient, some ensconced. Ronnie moved with a natural ease among all of them. Mob bosses Albert Dimes and Jack 'Spot' Comer, who owned the Modernaires Club in Old Compton Street, were part of the scene, and pedlars of pornography and prostitutes were nearby. The young musicians horsed around taking the mickey here and there, with Ronnie frequently practising his gurning skills, creating a laugh with his old friend Cecil 'Flash' Winston, drummer, pianist, stand-up comic and even a juggler if that was what you needed. When reminiscing with me about his friends there was a story of Flash's that Dad used to like to tell. He would say: 'Flash told me once that after his father died his mother wanted to find a medium so that she could talk to his father. And Flash said he asked her: 'He never spoke to you while he was alive. What makes you think he wants to talk to you now?' At the end of the banter, if there was no work they would stop by the Fullado Club to sit in.

It was on one such evening, a week or two after their return from New York, that Ronnie, Tony, Johnny Dankworth et al. were pursuing their favourite topic of conversation — bebop, Charlie Parker, Dizzy, Coleman Hawkins, etc. — and decided that they had to find a way of getting back to New York. Since none of them had any money, the only way they had any chance of getting there was to get themselves hired by a luxury liner. The *Queen Mary* was scheduled to make her first postwar voyage to New York and was taken out to the North Sea to test all her bells and whistles to make sure she was still seaworthy. In the meantime auditions were being held for first-, second- and tourist-class entertainment for the forthcoming voyage. Ronnie put together a band consisting of Tommy Pollard on vibes, Ken Moule, piano, Leon Calvert, trumpet, Johnny Dankworth, alto sax, who also did all the arrangements for the band, Ronnie on tenor and Bobby Kevin on drums. For reasons that John Dankworth can't quite remember, Bobby Kevin was elected to be the band leader. John remembered: 'We all went down to the audition and the tune that we played was "Time After Time". Incredibly, we got the job on the *Queen Mary*.' On Thursday 31 July they set sail for New York, minus Leon Calvert, who had developed appendicitis, and were booked to play on the transatlantic route until September of the same year.

When the *Queen Mary* pulled into New York harbour, all the tugs came out with flags and the fire float, sounding fanfares and sirens. The quay was swamped with reporters. It was a jubilant welcome and celebration for the postwar maiden voyage of the majestic vessel. New York was in the middle of a heat wave, and the high temperature and sopping humidity were things that the young musicians from England were not expecting and had never experienced before. With Ronnie at the helm, one of their first stopoffs was Macy's department store, where they arrived dripping with perspiration, to be surprised by the blast of cold air that greeted them at the entrance, never before having experienced the antidote to the heat called air-conditioning! After the privations of the war and the still extremely sparse supplies in London, the overflowing bounty that the New York department stores and shops had to offer presented itself to the boys like a veritable feast. There were many places where the prices were well within their reach, and all of them bought themselves suits, shirts, ties, socks and shoes. John fondly recalled: 'At that time I had no idea how to dress, and Ronnie took me under his wing. He had a great sense of style and of what went with what, so he supervised every purchase that I made. He really put my wardrobe together for me, and that's how I learned to dress.'

Laurie Morgan had been on the west coast for months now, having spent much of his time at the Westlake Music College studying and making lots of new friends. Charlie Parker was the focal point of interest for himself and the many young musicians whom he had befriended, and they spent many hours listening to his albums. Laurie purchased a formidable collection of Bird's albums to take back to London. He knew the lads were coming to New York and arranged his return journey to coincide with their arrival. That night, when Ronnie and the guys walked into the Three Deuces Laurie was there to greet them with Dizzy, whom he had met earlier. All the young musicians were in awe of what was happening: two seconds into the club and here they were being introduced to one of their gods, Dizzy Gillespie, by no less than one of their own! Dizzy was playing that night, and so began for my father what was to become a lifelong friendship, one filled with many common interests – humour, a love of chess and the sharing of stories – not to mention mutual respect and admiration. During the course of the ensuing years there were to be many such meetings and lasting friendships formed.

When they returned to London, and were sharing their experiences in Mac's rehearsal rooms with the guys who had been left behind, Laurie remembered: 'Ronnie had extraordinary powers of mimicry. He was almost like litmus paper: whatever came near him he could absorb and generate it out again, in comedy as well, in everything practically. He was an extraordinarily gifted man from a very young age indeed.' With Denis Rose at the piano, and Dad to his left, they played the new tunes that Dad had heard in the little clubs on 52nd Street. Denis, listening and transcribing the music to the piano, at the same time broke it down to explain to the insatiable young musicians gathered around him the structure, the startling rhythms, the complex chords and the fresh melodic lines that sprang from them.

Original compositions had been developed, like Dizzy's now-famous 'Salt Peanuts'. Diz and Klook had worked out what became known as the 'Salt Peanuts' triplet. Traditionally, in classical music, jazz or pop, triplets are accented on the *first* note of three, but Diz made the *second* note of the triplet an octave above the other two, and when they played the band used to sing out 'salt PEA-nuts', 'salt PEA-nuts'. When they were writing the compositions, the guys made up polysyllables like 'oo-bop-sh-bam', 'oo-pappa-da', and 'bu-DEE-daht'. They didn't know it then, but this method of identifying durations and indicating accents was to become extremely popular when singers like Ella Fitzgerald developed what became known as 'scat' singing, and Ella was unsurpassed at this unique craft, constantly improvising and producing new sounds.

In October of 1947 my father joined the Tito Burns sextet. Tito was a bebop accordion player and old friends Pete Chilver, Denis Rose and John Dankworth were also members of the band. When they went on tour, Ronnie and John not only had to share a room but they also had to share a bed! One night after everybody had gone to sleep Tito came creeping into the room and whispered to Ronnie: 'He's not awake, is he?' Then he said: 'You're playing so well, Ronnie, I want to give you a rise of two pounds a week.' John recalls: 'So Ronnie's money went up from sixteen to eighteen pounds a week. I pretended to be asleep, and I don't think Ronnie ever knew I overheard that whisper in the night!' Part of Tito's schedule was to do some broadcast dates, so for the first time since playing with Ted Heath Ronnie was on the airwaves again.

The band often played at Stoke Newington Town Hall, as did Jack Oliver's semi-pro band, a member of which was a young savvy tenor player, who was into boxing and had the build to match, full of humour and easygoing called Pete King. His meeting, albeit brief, with Ronnie was the start of a lifelong friendship and business partnership. Shortly afterwards *Melody Maker* ran a short biographical profile of Ronnie, ending the small piece with a list of Ronnie's 'favourites'. Listed as his favourite musicians were: Coleman Hawkins, Dizzy Gillespie and Charlie Parker. Composers: Ravel, Kern and Ellington. Right at the bottom was his hobby, which was: 'Talking about my trips to America.' This was one subject he never tired of, often referring to this period in his life from as early as I can remember until the last year of his life.

Alf Summers, who had been in the army for the past three years, was back in town and on the scene again. Harry Morris, who had learned that the Bouillabaisse Club had folded and that the little room was available, told Alf and together they went to see the landlord and came to an agreement. The club reopened with a new name – the Metropolitan Bopra House – for Sunday sessions from 3 to 6 p.m. The place was so small that the seating was around the side of the room so that people could jitterbug in the centre. They decided to sell bagels with fillings and had a big urn for tea. Posters were made up which read: 'England's Foremost Bop Club Presents Ronnie Scott & His Quartet.' This was my father's first gig with his own band, the quartet consisting of Tommy Pollard on piano, Lennie Bush on bass, Tony Crombie on drums and, of course, Ronnie fronting on tenor sax. Alf remembered: 'Ronnie wasn't too happy about the people dancing. He wanted to arrange the seating so that they would sit down and listen to the music.' My father's wondrous evenings spent at the Three Deuces had left an indelible print on his mind of presenting modern jazz in an intimate atmosphere in London. This was the first of many an opportunity to try out his dream in London.

By now Carlo Krahmer had founded the great Esquire Records label, which ultimately was a major contribution to the British jazz scene. On Tuesday 13 January 1948 Dad made his first of many recordings for the Esquire label with a group that Carlo put together called the Esquire Five. Recording was not to become one of my father's favourite occupations; in fact it was an area of performing that he was never comfortable with. When he discussed this subject years later, it was always with an element of regret, saying: 'I envy the guys like Stan Getz and Zoot Sims, who look forward to going into the studio and are always looking towards their next record. I really do. I wish I could feel like that. But for me it just doesn't work that way.'

Because of the situation with the British and American musicians' unions, which were still unable to work out their considerable differences, American musicians were banned from performing in Britain. My father and his fellow musicians had one goal in mind, which was to get work on the transatlantic liners and go to 52nd Street. The man who made it all possible was the same man who had given Ronnie and John Dankworth et al. their audition for the maiden voyage of the *Queen Mary*. His name was Geraldo (Gerald Bright), an East Ender who played the piano and formed his own dance band, which became one of Britain's most popular bands of the 1940s, 50s and 60s. He became Director of Dance Music at the BBC and was Director of Music for Scottish television. Geraldo gradually accepted jazz-influenced players into his own orchestra. After the war he also became the booking agent for the fleet of Cunard liners, supplying bands for the circa line cruises. This traffic of musicians back and forth to America became known as Geraldo's navy.

During the course of 1948 my father made several crossings on the

Queen Mary. Making these voyages was a reprieve in more ways than one; leaving the austerity, the rationing and the struggle against conformity of postwar London was in itself a great relief. The life on board had all the trappings of luxury. There was a strict regulation that there was to be no fraternising with the female passengers. However, this was a rule that was frequently broken, the young men being unable to resist the attention that was lavished on them by some of the beautiful young ladies aboard. Clandestine meetings were arranged on deck, and the couples snatched moments in each others' arms, stealing kisses between the rounds of the patrolling officers who policed the decks at night. On either side of the deck hung the lifeboats covered by huge tarpaulins, and the more daring thrill-seekers sought privacy in their dark, hidden confines. The musicians knew that if they were caught it meant instant dismissal, an interesting concept since the offenders were in the middle of the Atlantic Ocean on a liner!

Although playing the dance music was boring, it was a small price to pay, especially as the ultimate reward was a night on 52nd Street. As my father recalled in his book *Some of My Best Friends Are Blues*: 'We'd usually arrive in New York in the morning and leave the evening of the following day – which gave us a full night to do the jazz rounds. I'll never forget the night I heard the quintet of Charlie Parker with Miles Davis at the Three Deuces. And playing next door, incredibly, was Dizzy Gillespie's Big Band. Miles later sat in with Dizzy's outfit. It was a memorable night.'

Between voyages Ronnie could be found hanging out on Archer Street with his mates – like everybody else, looking for a gig. One afternoon not too much was happening, so Ronnie and Lennie Bush were having a cup of tea in the Harmony Inn discussing motor racing. This was an important day for the sport: a new racing track – Silverstone – had just opened and they were holding their first ever qualification tryouts. On the spur of the moment, Ronnie turned to Lennie and said: 'Come on. Let's go. Let's go to Silverstone. My bike's right outside.' Filled with enthusiasm and anticipation, they jumped on the bike, Lennie riding pillion. Lennie was a little nervous because when you rode a motorbike you had to pass a test if you were going to have a passenger on the back, otherwise the person on pillion had to hold a licence himself. Lennie had no licence and Ronnie had failed the test, the examiner declaring him to be too impetuous! There was something wrong with the bike and it was always very slow to start, but once Ronnie got it going it went like a rocket. And off they sped to Silverstone.

I learned about car racing from my dad when I was in my teens, and reminiscing with Lennie completed the picture. Silverstone was originally an aerodrome used in the war as an airbase. The racing track was a perimeter track running all the way around the airbase. The qualification tryout was about to begin in preparation for the first Formula One race ever to be held at Silverstone. The purpose of the qualification tryout is to determine the positions of the cars on the starting grid of the Formula One race. The car with the fastest lap of the day is placed first on the grid; the slowest guys are placed at the back. The drivers are all fighting to go as fast as they can. If their tyre pressure needs checking or if the car does not corner well or there are mechanical problems, they pull into the pit and the mechanics fix whatever's wrong. Each time the driver re-enters the race he is officially timed, and his fastest lap of the day determines his place on the grid. It was a thrilling day. Stirling Moss, at the beginning of his career, was there with a 500cc car (it had a motorcycle engine) called a Kieft. This was one of the first certified races he had ever been in. Some of the most famous drivers of the day were there, Gonzales, Alberto Ascari and Fangio among them. The average speed was between 140 and 150 miles per hour.

Ronnie and Lennie were completely caught up in the momentum, the unique sound of the racing cars' engines a combination of a very loud whirr, a whine and a buzz ringing in their ears. Quite a few pit stops were made. It was a bit of a hit-and-miss situation, this being the first race to be held on the old aerodrome. It was a wonderful day, and my father and Lennie stayed to watch all the drivers complete their laps and to hear the announcement that Alberto Ascari had secured first place on the grid. The master of them all was Fangio, who came from Argentina. He was nearing forty then and was World Champion for four years. As Lenny put it: 'He was the Charlie Parker of racing drivers.' Fangio, who went on to drive for another ten years, was an all-time favourite of Dad's. A short time later, when my father was presenting his quintet to the audience and introducing his musicians, he would announce his guitar player Louis Stewart as 'Louis Stewart, ladies and gentleman, the Fangio of the banjo'. He was the first of many guitar players to be announced in this way.

In between doing a short tour with Cab Quaye and his Ministers of Swing and broadcasting with the Ambrose Orchestra, Dad and all the young bebop enthusiasts were wood-shedding their craft at Mac's rehearsals rooms, which had been a club in earlier days; as well as the little individual rehearsals rooms there was a large one that in bygone days had been a club room, which was where they jammed. The sound of their music carried out into Archer Street and people started wandering in to listen. His 'shadow' and good friend Harry Morris, always looking for a way to make a quid or two, suggested to the guys that they should charge people to come in and listen. They thought Harry's idea was a good one, and a decision was made to have two bands to augment the programme: a sextet and a quartet. The sextet was Ronnie Scott, Denis Rose, Johnny Rogers (alto sax), Norman Stenfalt (piano), Lennie Bush and Tony Crombie. The quartet was Johnny Dankworth, Tommy Pollard (piano), Joe Muddell (bass) and Laurie Morgan. These were the ten musicians; Harry Morris, who started the club, was the eleventh man. As John Dankworth said, echoing the feelings that all the musicians had for Harry: 'Thank God for Harry. Without him there might not have been a Club Eleven!' Telling how the club was founded was one of Dad's favourite stories.

The Club Eleven was the first club in Britain to be run as a cooperative by musicians and became the place where every musician who was in town hung out, including any visiting American artists. Many new friendships were formed here. It was where Ronnie first met Harry South and his beautiful Swedish fiancée Harriet, a lifelong friendship developing with both of them. Harry was very quiet and laid back, with a great sense of humour, a very kind man. He was a reflective pianist with a soft touch, gentle in his approach, and was to become one of the giants of British jazz composition. An up-and-coming young drummer called Allan Ganley, who was in the air force at the time, used to go to the Club Eleven to hear the music. Ronnie and the rest of the musicians were his heroes, and he didn't dare approach them. Unbeknown to Allan, he was soon to meet all of them and have the time of his life.

The Club Eleven musicians learned that Charlie Parker, along with some of their other idols, was to play in Paris at the French Jazz Festival. They booked their passage on a boat, and Allan Ganley was thrilled to find himself on the same boat. Still too shy to say anything, he palled up with Jack Sharp, who had just started practising tenor and baritone. When they reached Paris, Allan and Jack shadowed the Club Eleven group to see where they were staying. Allan remembered: 'They checked into a real run-down old hotel called the Sphinx Hotel, so we booked in there too!' It was only a matter of time before they met Ronnie. Allan recalled: 'Ronnie was great. We got along really well. I remember one day we were walking down the street in Paris together and there was this terrible, filthy old woman huddled in a doorway. He looked at her and he said: "Oh, dear. That would put you off sex for life, wouldn't it?" I couldn't help laughing, although it was sad really, but there was humour in it, without any offence intended.'

John Dankworth recalled: 'We were in Paris so we went down the St-Germain Club, and we were playing a set when Charlie Parker walked in. Ronnie was taking a solo and I was standing to one side of the bandstand when Bird asked me if he could borrow my alto. I sat there mesmerised as I watched him play my horn, then he handed it to me and said your turn! It was amazing, we were actually playing with Charlie Parker!' After that night John felt that his alto had changed, that Charlie Parker had somehow 'opened it up'. He still has that horn to this day and would never part with it. The memory of this evening and the music pinnacled my father's memories of being in the presence of Charlie Parker. When he spoke about experiences of this nature years later, his voice was still full of the awe and inspiration he felt as a young man keeping company with the high priests of jazz.

In November 1949 *Melody Maker* noted: RONNIE SCOTT JOINS DAD'S LINER BAND FOR LONG TRIP. The report ran: 'On December 7 Ronnie joins the band led by his famous father, altoist Jock Scott, aboard the SS *Caronia* and will not be returning to this country before the end of March 1950.' The voyage was scheduled to include stops at New York, the Bahamas, the West Indies, South America, Africa, the Suez Canal, the Mediterranean, and Cherbourg on the way home to Southampton. My father told me this story many times, and the last time I heard it was the week before he died. The outcome of the trip was to be one of his greatest regrets.

My grandfather had invited Dad to join his band. This meant a lot to my father, who wanted to get to know Jock better. The thought of a world cruise was also very enticing, and what better way to get to know his father than working together? One of the problems was the distinct generation gap between himself and the rest of the band; the only players in his age-group were Pete Blannin on bass and Harry Conn on sax. Ronnie got bored and missed his fellow bebop enthusiasts. When they docked in New York he went to 52nd Street to refuel his appetite for modern music.

Then it was off to the Bahamas, returning to dock again at pier 90, but this time there was a letter waiting for him from Joan Crewe. Since they had met, Ronnie had either been working on the circa line or on tour with not much time in between for Joan. This four-month cruise was just too much; she was completely fed up with the whole situation. My father was really in love with Joan and set about finding a way to get back home. He contacted Grandma Cissie and persuaded her to send a wire from London stating: 'Grandmother dangerously ill. Come at once.' The *Queen Mary* was also docked at the quays, due for her return trip to Southampton. My father walked down the docks and sought out the tenorist on the *Queen Mary*. His name was Ray Feather. Dad offered him the opportunity to go around the world and, of course, he accepted. Now came the difficult part: he had to persuade the officers on both ships. It is an understatement to say my father was a very persuasive man – he had a way of getting what he wanted that was rarely, very rarely thwarted. However, the major challenge was in convincing his father. Dad told me: 'Of course, he didn't believe a word of it, quite rightly so, too.' My grandfather was absolutely furious. He knew he was being lied to and, as Dad grew to realise years after, was hurt and embarrassed that his son was putting him in this position. Dad said: 'I was young at the time, and hot-headed, and when my father said to me, "It's a matter of principle", I was wrong. I let him have it, shouting: "You can't tell me about principles! My mother's told me all about you. After what you did to my mother, you can't have a go at me!" The worst of it was, it wasn't even true. Your grandmother never, ever, said a bad word about my father. I've often wondered if things might have been different between us if I'd stayed and stuck out the cruise. Well, we'll never know now, will we?' Needless to say, my father came home.

Back in London, Ronnie slipped into the Club Eleven scene again. He was rapidly becoming a British musical celebrity, and in December 1949 came top of the *Melody Maker* polls. By now the Club Eleven had become so popular it was imperative that they find bigger premises. They moved into a deserted nightclub at 50 Carnaby Street, a much larger space in the hippest part of town. Dad had great memories of the Club Eleven. It was always packed, musicians and fans intermingled, the crowd was integrated, it served food, nothing fancy, people drank and played cards, it was happening. They explored the idea of trying to pick up visiting celebrities to perform at the club, but the musicians' unions on each side of the Atlantic were still at loggerheads.

Just a few days after the *Caronia* set sail with Jock and Ronnie on board, Ronnie's idol, Coleman Hawkins, was due to appear at the Princess Theatre. The Ministry of Labour had refused Hawk a work permit so at the last minute he offered to play at the concert for no fee. The unions made it clear that no British musicians under *any* circumstances were to play with him. Hawk had brought with him Kenny 'Klook' Clarke, who used to play drums with Dizzie, and two French musicians. Charles Delaunay, a well-known French impresario, suggested to the British organisers that Hawk go on with his Continental musicians. The massive audience in the auditorium had no idea of the dramatics that were going on backstage; it was a crowded bill that night and they were filled with the anticipation of seeing the great man play. Hawk was distraught, tormented by the problems that could materialise if he played. Fats Waller's manager, Ed Kirkeby, was backstage that night and joined Hawk, who asked him: 'Ed, what would dear old Fats have done?' Ed told him: 'Fats never disappointed an audience in his life.' Hawk said: 'OK, let's go.' There was no troublesome aftermath for Hawk to deal with. They had effectively sidestepped the unions ban, and the audience got the added bonus of hearing Kenny Clarke and the French musicians too!

Delaunay and the Wilcox organisation formed an alliance by which there would be an interchange of British and French jazz publications and records and was at the time working on a reciprocal exchange of bands and musicians. This meant that American musicians, such as Kenny Clarke and Bud Powell (an exceptional piano player), who resided in Paris, would be able to play in England.

In the meantime only the privileged few were able to go to New York and sample the musical bounty of 52nd Street for themselves, leaving the vast majority of fans and musicians in Britain feeling frustrated and deprived. It was several years before the disputes between the unions were resolved, and unbeknown to Ronnie and Pete King at the time they were to play a major role in opening the doors for American musicians to play in Great Britain.

My father and his fellow musicians were about to experience their first encounter with the repercussions of using drugs of any kind. It was one of a couple of stories on this subject that he would share with me during the course of our time together. It all began on the night of 15 April 1950. Dad said: 'I was on stage with my band, eyes tightly closed, blowing the last of nine choruses of Charlie Parker's "Now's The Time". The club was packed. I finished my solo, opened my eyes and got the shock of my life. A massive uniformed police sergeant practically filled my entire field of vision. I backed up, looked around and saw the place was full of coppers. Commotion, confusion and consternation. The copper barked out: "All right, stop the music and turn out your pockets." We were being raided by the drug squad. The music stopped and the ensuing silence was only broken by the sound of little packets hitting the floor.'

The crux of the matter was that they were all arrested and hauled off to Savile Row Police Station. My father recalled: 'We were all pretty naive apprentice pot-heads.' They spent the night in jail and the next day at

Marlborough Street Magistrates' Court were charged and to everyone's intense relief let off with fines of about £15. However, the press had a heyday with headlines declaring: POLICE SWOOP ON SOHO BEBOP CLUB. Grandma Cissie and Sol were beside themselves when they saw the newspapers.

Daddy told me: 'Your grandmother knew that I wasn't involved with hard drugs. When I was slightly younger, someone turned me on with heroin. It made me so violently ill for a couple of days it turned me off for ever.' Every time Dad told me this story he always stressed how fortunate he was. 'Rebecca,' he would say, 'some people are not so lucky. They try it, they like it, then before they know it it becomes a lifelong problem.' Out of the musicians' circle, his pianist, Tommy Pollard, was the first to become dependent on hard drugs.

Closer to home, Joan Crewe had also fallen into the heroin trap. Unfortunately for Joan, to use her own words, she took to the drug 'like a duck to water'. Joan tried to hide her habit from Ronnie. When he found out, he examined her arms constantly, looking for needle marks. One day Joan said to Ronnie: 'Marry me and I'll stop using drugs.' His response to that was: 'Stop for three months and I will.' Joan could not stop. There was no such thing as rehabilitation clinics in those days, and my father did not know what to do. He was so desperate to get Joan to stop that he even went to the police and asked if there was anything that the law could do.

The Club Eleven folded very soon after the episode in court, and my father's only other club venture was brief — in the basement of the Mapleton Hotel in 1953. It would be six years before he was to be involved in the jazz club business again.

CHAPTER SIX

BOTH ENDS OF THE RAINBOW

Crying is the same as laughing, except that it is at the other end of the same rainbow.   NIETZSCHE

Jazz is in the genes; it just needs the soil to grow in. Musicians totally immerse themselves in the music. Ronnie was really a great player.   SONNY ROLLINS

S OL WAS VERY IMPRESSED with the way his stepson had made a name for himself in the world of music and had himself always been very interested in the entertainment business. With Ronnie's help he produced a lot of Sunday concerts as part of his fundraising project for the British Legion. Ronnie, in full support of Sol's project, was able to persuade Peter Sellers and guys in the Jack Parnell Band, Ted Heath's band and other popular bands of the day to play the concerts, and he frequently performed himself. Sol created an interesting contrast by bringing in such people as actress Sybil Thorndike to perform and, of course, popular singers like Leoni Page. The Sunday concerts were very successful, raising substantial sums of money.

When in London my father's means of transport was still his motorbike, much to my grandmother's discomfort. She constantly worried about his safety. The bike was not very reliable, and sometimes Ronnie could not get the thing started at all. One afternoon on Archer Street, when he had finished playing several rounds of snooker with his friend Joe Green, who was a bass player, they decided to call it a day. Together they walked to the motorbike, and Ronnie tried to kick-start it but it was as dead as a doornail.

Joe gave it a try and had no luck either. Fortunately for Ronnie, Joe drove an estate car, so between them they piled the motorbike into the back of the car and took it to a garage. It was fixed just in time for Ronnie and Lennie Bush to ride out to Silverstone. On the way back from the racetrack, when they mounted the bike Ronnie forgot to put the metal prop back up before they rode off. Lennie remembered: 'We were going at a heck of a speed all the way, and when we reached London we were coming from Regent's Park around a right bend and wanted to turn left on Portland Place, going south. Ronnie leaned the bike right over as we made the turn, still going very fast. The prop stand was right down and struck the road. Sparks flew everywhere! We skidded all over the place. God knows how, but somehow Ronnie managed to right the bike and we didn't come off. It was a very scary few minutes, and we went much slower the rest of the way home!'

Rebuilding their lives was a long, hard struggle for the people of Britain. In some areas of the country rationing had still been part of daily life until recently, and even now there were still some restrictions. The government decided that an all-out effort of celebration and a positive projection of a thriving economy would help spur the people on to further enterprise. A huge festival was organised on the South Bank, and in 1951 the Festival of Britain was held. In London the Royal Festival Hall, designed by architects Robert Matthew and Leslie Martin, was opened to mark the occasion. A little later in the year a new jazz club, called Studio 51, opened its doors to the public.

My father's profile had grown considerably. He had a large following of fans and was consistently written about in the music press. The inevitable occurred, and my auntie Marlene, who was now fourteen, discovered the truth about her brother's father. It came as a huge emotional shock that was actually twofold. The fact that her mother had not told her the truth when she had first discovered the *Melody Maker* reference to Ronnie and Jock Scott was very painful and impossible for her to understand. Secondly, Auntie Marlene was very, very close to her father and loved him immensely, and the discovery that he was not after all Ronnie's father, too, created a chasm between her and Ronnie. My auntie told me: 'My mother was a wonderful person, very kind. She was always considerate of other people and their feelings, but she made some mistakes, and this was one. There can't be secrets like this within families. It ultimately causes too much pain.' Much as she loved Ronnie, this was a difficult time, and for her things would never be quite the same again.

Although Ronnie saw his father from time to time, the exchanges between them were more often than not brief. In an effort to relate to Jock, Ronnie had invited him down to the Club Eleven to hear his band, but Jock never came. To my father this felt like yet another rejection. Although Jock made it plain to other musicians and family members how proud he was of Ronnie's achievements, he was not able to communicate his feelings directly to Ronnie.

Ronnie's cousin Sydney clearly remembers Jock talking about his son, and he always got the impression that Jock would have liked to have had a closer relationship with Ronnie. He frequently spoke highly of Ronnie's musicianship, saying: 'Ronnie knocks me into a cocked hat as far as playing is concerned!' Sydney said: 'Jock was very charismatic, a bit like Cary Grant. He could be very charming, and women fell for him all the time.' Jock used to tell the story about an experience he had on one of his many cruises. A South American millionairess was chasing him all over the ship, so he had a system of spies, and the crew used to tell him where she was at any given time so he could keep out of her way. 'I loved Jock and his stories. He was my favourite uncle.' My father was the same way: he always had lots of stories to tell about his various trips, some of which were mercilessly mocking about the characters involved.

When Jock visited his brother Philip in New York, similar exchanges would take place. Auntie Rose loved her Uncle Jock and they looked forward to his visits. She said: 'When he left to go back to England we would all stand on the dock and cry.' When she grew up and he met her fiancé Bernie, they took Jock to the Bronx Zoo. He was a prankster and clowned around, shinning up a lamp-pole taking off the monkeys! But he couldn't stand being driven on the 'wrong' side of the road, Auntie Rose said. 'It made him very nervous, and we teased him unmercifully about it. But he always brought us news of Ronnie, through Uncle Jock we knew everything that Ronnie was doing. Not just on visits, but he wrote to us about all of his achievements, often sending clippings from one paper or another.' It was so surreal, somehow. Jock and his family were all around my father yet were never able to really penetrate the periphery. They all desperately wanted to draw him into their family circle, but somehow the timing was off, and the attempts made by both Ronnie and Jock to get closer to each other were thwarted either by outside occurrences or inner turmoil, and it never quite came off the way that everyone wanted it to.

Dad told me: 'Your grandfather would telephone me, and sometimes I would literally take weeks to get back to him. Then by the time I did he was involved with something, and we wouldn't see each other for months at a time. I remember once he was trying to get in touch with me and it was important, it was about the family, but I was young and headstrong. I didn't want to be bothered, I suppose. Who knows what the reason was? Anyway, believe it or not it was a very long time after the fact that I finally got the news about my father's sister Annie and her family.' Grandfather Jock had heard from his nephew Ziggy about what had happened to them all when the Russians liberated their concentration camp.

Ziggy had survived the long walk from Skarzysko concentration camp to the town of Czestochowa, where he had hoped to find family and friends who had survived the holocaust. He was there for a couple of weeks before he found his brother Alex, but neither of them had any news about their mother and father. They decided to go to Cracow, another town to which many survivors had fled; maybe they would have more luck there. Shortly after they arrived, they met a young Polish girl who told Ziggy that she had friends who had been in Skarzysko camp, too, and invited him to come to meet them. When Ziggy walked into the apartment there was instant recognition between him and the older woman who stood before him. They ran into each other's arms, this time with tears of happiness running down their faces. He had not found his mother but he had found Natalie Rubin, the woman who had treated him like her own son during their agonising time together in the camp. Natalie's daughter Blanche, who had escaped the horrors of the camps because of her false papers which portrayed her as a Roman Catholic, lived with her. Ziggy and Alex were from then on regular visitors, and it wasn't long before Blanche and Ziggy fell in love, and shortly afterwards they were married. But when the brothers finally unearthed the news about Jock's sister Annie and her husband Max, it was only to discover that they were among the thousands who had perished in the gas chambers at Auschwitz. When my father eventually heard the whole story from Jock, in that moment he felt sick to the pit of his stomach. Suddenly the full impact of what had happened to millions of Jewish people was narrowed down to his own family. He had, after all, played with Ziggy at their grandfather's house. All at once, trying to comprehend what had happened to them, how his cousins must feel, the tone of solemnity and sadness in his father's voice as he recounted the facts struck a deep chord in Ronnie. Whatever his reasons had been for not contacting his father, none seemed to mean anything in the face of what he had just heard. This was not something that my father spoke about. He told it to my mother before I was born, when she was reading Anne Frank's diary.

He had never read the book, but he had his own story to tell her.

The leaders were emerging from the circle of musicians. Jack Parnell formed his own band during this period, becoming very well known. So did John Dankworth, who rapidly established himself. My father signed his first exclusive recording contract with Carlo Krahmer at Esquire, making many recordings for the label. Ronnie played with Jack's first band and, on reflection, wondered at the fact that they were actually the pit band for a West End musical, *Fancy Free*, at the Prince of Wales Theatre, playing two shows a night six nights a week. This was a far cry from the kind of gigs they had envisaged themselves doing when Jack formed the band, and the fact they stuck with the monotony for a full year was even more amazing. The band was not actually in the pit but on a dais at the right-hand side of the stage, with the rhythm section upfront. The only thing that got them through was a multitude of pranks. Unfortunately for the piano player, Max Harris, he was the prime target when the saxophone section turned into a firing squad of paper pellet shooters. As Dad told it: 'I remember misfiring once and hitting Tommy Trinder full on his celebrated chin as he was coming off stage.' Needless to say, there was a big row about the incident. The show folded that November, and Jack reorganised the band, bringing in Jimmy Deuchar on trumpet who was also a marvellous writer and arranger. The band went out on the road, the highlight of their show a drum duet between Jack and Phil Seamen, who became a legend within his own right. Dad stayed with the band for a few months but once again Joan became restless, and he returned to London and the life of a tenor sax soloist.

In April 1952 the Ronnie Scott All Stars were invited with several other bands to play at the Salle Pleyel in Paris, the main attraction being Dizzy Gillespie. There were to be two concerts, one on Saturday night and one on Sunday. Ronnie and the band – which consisted of Tony Crombie on drums, Victor Feldman on vibes, Tommy Pollard on piano, Lennie Bush on bass and Jimmy Deuchar on trumpet – were all at Heathrow Airport preparing to board the plane when British officials informed Ronnie that his passport needed renewing. Because it was important that he be at the concert the following night they let him through but warned him that there was only a fifty–fifty chance that French immigration would let him through. But the French weren't so obliging. At 2.30 p.m. that afternoon Dad found himself at Le Bourget Airport heading back to London. My father said: 'I got back to England after the Passport Office had closed. I went to the police, then to the Home Office. I phoned all sorts of people.

Finally I got in a car and went right out to the home of a passport authority in the suburbs. By late Friday night I had a passport, but I dared not go to bed. I went to town and got ready to leave at 6.45 the next morning. All would have been well except for a blizzard that swept England, grounding every plane. I hung around the airport all day and at 7.30 p.m. an Air France plane decided to make the trip. Of course, I got there far too late.' The All Stars had to play the first night without Ronnie, and the *Melody Maker*, which recorded the whole story under the subtitle of 'Rough Passage', wrote: 'And the rough passage to which he and other passengers were being subjected in storm-racked skies was paralleled by that awaiting his All Stars at the hands of the French jazz fans.' They were out for blood, but Jimmy Deuchar saved the day: '. . . and the first applause for Britain welled out of the vast audience.' My father always had a special place in his heart for Jimmy, as a player, arranger-writer and friend. The Sunday night concert with Ronnie in attendance surpassed all previous efforts, and the audience went wild. Pat Brand wrote in the *Melody Maker* that 'probably for the first time in history, British jazz had made its mark in Paris'.

By 1953 Jack Parnell found he needed to become a little more commercial to get the kind of dates he wanted for the band. By doing this he would get more broadcasting dates, which subsequently would lead to more gigs. Bands of this nature brought on board singers to perform a couple of popular tunes, and Jack had made the decision that this was the way to go. His only problem was that his singer of choice had a husband who played tenor saxophone and she would agree to join the band only if he was given a job too. This meant that someone in the saxophone section was going to have to be fired, and that someone was no other than Pete King, who had turned pro since his first encounter with Ronnie, when he was playing in semi-pro bands. The firing caused a row, with Pete's fellow musicians expressing their disapproval to Jack, who felt he had no choice in the matter. The outcome of it all was that on the journey from Pete's last gig with the band at Colston Hall in Bristol, Phil Seamen, Ken Wray and Mac Minshull, trombonists, and Derek Humble and Kenny Graham, saxophonists, went to Jack, who was sitting in the front of the bus, and handed in their notice. By the time they arrived back in London the Parnell band was in shreds. For Pete, the staunch support of the musicians left him feeling profoundly moved, which is what he told the press when they reported the incident. This event for Pete and Ronnie was to be the beginning of not only a lifelong personal friendship but a business partnership in more than one capacity which, although my father is no longer with us, Uncle Pete still carries on to this day.

The expatriates of the Parnell band and Ronnie et al. all gathered in the Harmony Inn on Archer Street to have a cup of tea and consider what the hell they were going to do next. Cooperative bands were now openly discussed in the music press and were a focal point of debate between musicians. Financing a band was a very expensive proposition, but the cooperative approach spread the load between everybody and created the realistic possibility of their forming a band of their own. It was a mutual decision that Ronnie would be the leader and that Pete King would handle the day-to-day business, so in January 1953 the nine-piece band named the Ronnie Scott Orchestra was formed. During the course of its lifetime the line-up in that band was marvellous, my father, when reminiscing about those days, often referring to it as 'one of the best bands I ever had'. The saxes consisted of the terrific young alto player Derek Humble, Benny Green (who later became very well known as a broadcaster, journalist and author), Pete King and Ronnie. On trumpet was Jimmy Deuchar, who apart from being a marvellous player wrote highly original arrangements for the group, Ken Wray was on trombone, Norman Stenfalt, who also contributed arrangements, on piano, and Lennie Bush on bass. Tony Crombie, on drums, wrote several arrangements, all of which, such as 'Stompin' at the Savoy' and 'Flying Home', were specifically designed to feature Ronnie playing at a fast tempo. Tony remembered: 'Ronnie was an exceptionally exciting soloist. He was extremely proud of the band and demanded and got a consistently high-quality performance. He really loved fast tempos and would rehearse the band on certain arrangements, gradually increasing the speed until eventually we were playing jazz at tempos previously unknown to Western civilisation – around 104 bars per minute, and equalled only by street musicians in Calcutta, but they had the added spur of playing while hopping about barefoot on red-hot coals!'

The *New Musical Express* (*NME*) sponsored my father's new band, which held a public rehearsal. This revealed that a few rough spots needed to be ironed out, so the band took off to Manchester, where they rehearsed every day, honing their craft, and played every night to enthusiastic audiences. During the band's 'exile' in Manchester the *NME* kept up with their progress in every area, noting the following: 'Ronnie Scott's Orchestra went to Manchester to play the overture to its own birth. Nobody would have dreamed that, try as he might to disguise the fact, Tony Crombie cooks the best spaghetti west of the Adriatic, that Pete King wears the most outrageous flamboyant red and blue spotted underwear that anybody ever saw, and Ronnie Scott, with his hair ruffled by a night's sleep, bears an uncanny resemblance to the late Napoleon Bonaparte.'

Sol and Cissie were thrilled with the way Ronnie's career had burst into full bloom. Sol offered to make suits for the band, and his wholesale firm made up the special order. The suits were an immaculate blue gaberdine with check waistcoats. My father said: 'We had marvellous music stands in pale blue Plexiglas with a V-shaped base and a white scroll desk. Each man had his name inscribed on the scroll. The stands were lit from behind so that they glowed impressively. We really looked terrific on stage.' In March they made their official debut in Manchester, and the *NME*'s headline read: QUEUES, CHEERS GREET RONNIE SCOTT BAND MANCHESTER DEBUT. This was the first of many gigs to be greeted in the same way. The band was immensely popular and, as the *NME* reported, 'every solo was wildly cheered, and prolonged applause after each tune often delayed the start of the next'. The crowd screamed for their favourite numbers, such as Jimmy Deuchar's arrangement of 'Seven Eleven' and Tony Crombie's score of 'Just One of Those Things'.

By Easter the band made their debut in London, playing opposite Ronnie's prestigious old employer, Ted Heath, at the Palladium to an audience of three thousand. The *NME* was there and reported: 'In twenty brief minutes the new Ronnie Scott Orchestra established itself beyond any doubt as one of the most formidable and impressive musical combinations anywhere in Europe today. The high spot of the show, judging from the audience reaction, were the two outstanding scores of "Chef Crombie". His "Just One of Those Things" and "Lover Come Back to Me" are typical examples of the inspired demagogy which characterises his writing.' The musicians fed off each other on and off the bandstand, constantly striving for the pure essence of excellence. Their inspiration came from each other but, as was often said by many different people, my father was a special kind of leader who was able to get the best performance on and off the bandstand, in all areas of life, from the people who worked for and with him. No matter what their job was, he had that wonderful quality of making people *want* to stretch themselves to their fullest capacity, making them *want* to please him. Tony recalled: 'When you came off the bandstand with Ronnie, you never knew what the guy was thinking. He was very uncritical; he never made an appraisal of the music. Even when the audience was yelling and jumping up and down with approval, begging for more, Ronnie never made any comments about how the band sounded. The truth lay in the playing. I *always* got the impression that he didn't know how *exceptionally* good he was. It was as though an element of reassurance was always needed. He would never show his hand about anything. Even when he appeared pleased he wouldn't venture an opinion. He exercised a lot of caution. He was a very secretive man.'

Shortly after this, Harold Davidson, a British impresario who always had a soft spot for jazz, became the manager of the band, Pete still handling the day-to-day business. This was the beginning of another lifelong relationship. By the end of the next decade Harold was to play a very important role in Ronnie's and Pete's most important venture ever.

By now my father's motorcycle was long gone, in its place a dream come true. Ronnie's love affair with sports cars, coupled with the fact that he was making a good living, had produced his first partner, an immaculate Jaguar XK 20, the revolutionary British sports car of the early 1950s.

There was an opportunity just waiting around the corner for my father. Norman Grantz, the well-known American impresario, offered his road show Jazz at the Philharmonic to Britain as a fundraiser for the recovery from massive floods that had engulfed Britain during the previous winter. The widespread damage was devastating, particularly coming on the heels of postwar repairs. Because the event was a fundraiser, the Musicians' Union and the Ministry of Labour issued entry notes to the American artists on the strict understanding that they were not to perform at any other venue during their stay, and that the ban was waived in this instance only because of the nature of the event. Two concerts were held on 8 March 1953 at the Gaumont, Kilburn. The American stars were none other than Lester Young, Oscar Peterson and Ella Fitzgerald.

Ronnie was invited to play on the same programme, and for this gig he used a sextet to open each concert for the American musicians. Fans queued for many long hours for tickets, and both concerts completely sold out. There were hundreds of disappointed fans who could not get in to see the shows. London had never seen anything like it, and the press, interviewing fans in the queues, reported that the general feeling was one of anger and frustration towards the Ministry of Labour for banning the Americans from performing in England. For those who were fortunate enough to get tickets, the performances were something they would remember for the rest of their lives. The poignant effect of seeing and hearing their idols perform on stage, far from quenching their thirst for the experience, only whetted their appetites for more and brought home to everybody how much they were missing. Their sensibilities were restricted and limited by being deprived of the 'whole' musical experience. For those musicians who were not among the privileged few who had sampled the fruits of 52nd Street, the reality of their limited knowledge of the music was a form of culture shock. They realised how much *more* there was to learn before they could ever understand the complex whole of this music.

This realisation was depressing: *how* could they seek the knowledge they ached for when the Musicians' Union and the Ministry of Labour were so adamant about maintaining their restrictions?

For my father and Tony Crombie, sitting with Lester Young in his dressing room, asking him questions and listening to him talk, was a golden period that they would cherish for the rest of their lives. Lester Young was unique in every way, as though he were a visitor from another planet. He spoke in a language that was all his own, having his own special names for people. Billie Holiday was Lady Day: she returned the compliment by calling him 'the President' — hence the abbreviation to 'Prez'. Oscar Peterson was Lady Pete, Harry Edison was 'Sweets' and Norman Grantz was known as Lady Norman. Prez always carried a bottle of scotch in a red plaid bag, which he called Red Boy; his joints, which were kept in a pewter pot, to him were Bells. He was creative with language and profanity. When talking to his pianist, Prez would say: 'Have another helping but tone down your left people', meaning 'Take another chorus but play more softly with your left hand'. Stan Getz, who loved Young's music, said: 'He was the first tenor saxophone player I heard play melodically, to make beautiful melodies.' You have only to listen to Stan, Zoot Sims, Art Pepper and Paul Desmond to hear that Young's music lived on in the music of the next generation.

My father described Prez as: 'A beautiful man, and one of the most poetic and innovative saxophonists in the world of music.' But in the reviews that followed the concert the critics dwelled on the fact that Lester Young had slowed down and said he sounded over the hill and how sad it was. My father's response was quite the opposite; his recollection of Prez's performance was: 'Lester just sidled out on to the bandstand and played something like "I Cover the Waterfront" — and that was really the only music of value in the whole concert. To me his was the only worthwhile contribution.' Dad went to Lester's dressing room several times during the day, but one time they were alone together, Prez picked up his horn and proceeded to show my father the secrets of 'false fingering', demonstrating how the same note could be created at different positions on the horn with subtle variations of tone colours. Their time together was exquisite, with the passing on of knowledge from the man who was the creator of a style, and from one culture and generation to another. Although Prez was only in his mid-forties he was not well, and, suffering mental distress, knew he would not be back to play again in England. Six years later Prez was working in Paris but cut the engagement short to return to New York for the final weeks of his life. But he gave Ronnie a legacy that day. There was a special intimacy in the time they spent together, and the way he passed his knowledge on left its mark on my father.

The night before I arrived in London, just eight days before my father died, a young man, whom Dad barely knew, Jim Hunt, a saxophonist who had played the club that night and was about the same age as my father had been when he had sat in Lester Young's dressing room, walked into the back office after his last set. My father was sitting there with his legs in a supportive position, his horn nestled into his left hip, just as it always had for the past fifty-four years when he was relaxed and practising his fingering. Jim and his band leader, Duncan McKay, who was with him, found themselves listening to my father's memories of experiences with the pioneers of jazz, and they watched as my father, unable to blow, fingered the keys of his horn. Dad started reminiscing and, just as Prez had done for him, he demonstrated the same 'false fingering' effects to Jim. The time shared between them in the early hours of that morning was as intimate and precious as Ronnie's own time with Prez had been forty-three years earlier. He had passed the legacy on, maybe sensing, as Prez had done, that time was running out.

That summer Sol and Cissie were planning on taking a break in Brighton. They were going to drive down, and in preparation for their trip Sol had some repairs done to the exhaust of his car. Something went dreadfully wrong, and while they were driving on the road to Brighton they both passed out from fumes that had slowly seeped into the car from the exhaust. The car veered off the road and smashed into a tree, bursting into flames. Fortunately, a bus driver saw the accident, pulled up and rushed to the blazing car, dousing the flames with his fire-extinguisher. His quick action saved their lives. An ambulance arrived and took Sol and Cissie to the Royal Sussex County Hospital. Both were critically injured and were on the danger list for ten days. My father and Auntie Marlene were devastated and rushed to the hospital to discover that Grandma Cissie had been badly crushed and was in a state of shock. Sol had a double fracture of the jaw and a broken pelvis. Once Sol was taken off the critical list, the decision was made to transfer him to the Royal Victoria Hospital in East Grinstead. The hospital was famous for plastic surgery and a lot of research had been done there in treating servicemen who had received bad facial injuries during the war. It was a very difficult time for Ronnie: because of his commitment to the band he was not able to visit his mother and stepfather as often as he would have liked. Auntie Marlene constantly visited them both during their six-week stay in hospital. Even with expert plastic surgery, Sol's face was permanently disfigured by the accident.

Although Ronnie's new cooperative band was always referred to as the nine-piece band, it also had a singer, Johnny Grant. During the course of its three-year life there were a few personnel changes. Johnny Grant was replaced by Art Baxter, a bit of an eccentric character who, when the band's bus was passing through a small English village, dropped his trousers and 'mooned' the villagers. He pressed his bum against the bus window, which was duly framed by the expressionless faces of Ronnie, Tony, Lennie, and so on. Victor Feldman replaced Norman Stenfalt on piano but was also featured with Tony in a drum duet that always brought the house down. Then Tony left, to be succeeded by Phil Seamen, and ultimately Hank Shaw took over from Jimmy Deuchar.

While Tony Crombie was still with the band they decided that they needed a slightly more commercial angle – the band had to make money – so in August 1953 Barbara Jay, a blonde, beautiful and vivacious young woman, was brought on board to share the vocal side of the programme with Art Baxter, just ten days before they were expecting to do a tour of Iceland. This time it was the Icelandic Musicians' Union that stepped in and stopped the tour. This was particularly confusing to my father, who had played Reykjavik the previous year and received a tremendous welcome from critics, musicians and fans alike. As the *Melody Maker* recalled, the unanimous opinion was 'He is the greatest thing that has ever come to Iceland'.

Life on the road with the band during the winter months was a freezing experience most of the time. The old BOAC bus that Ronnie and Pete had purchased at an auction had no heating system, and they improvised with an equally old oil heater that would work only at the magic touch of Lennie Bush, so if he was late, everybody froze. Barbara Jay always carried a hot-water bottle, and she and Victor Feldman bore the brunt of everyone else's humour because they each had a blanket. When en route early in the morning, they would stop at a roadside café and have a good hot breakfast. Barbara would get the waitress to refill her hot-water bottle before she got back on the bus. Once, Tony snatched the hot-water bottle from Barbara and threw it out of the window. Cursing profusely, Les Bristow, the bus driver, brought the bus to a screeching halt as Barbara leaped off and ran back down the road to retrieve her only source of warmth. Totally furious with Tony, she jumped back on the bus, ran down the aisle and pummelled Tony's chest with both her fists while he just stood there, solid as a rock, barely feeling her flying fists and laughing throughout. Life on the bus was filled with teasing and constant pranks, card games were played, risqué limericks were composed, animal noises were made – some imitated, others natural! Tony Crombie described it as 'a madhouse on wheels'! Whenever they went through a town with a bookies, my father would make Les pull over so he could run in and place a bet.

The band drew large audiences wherever they went, they received rave reviews, and night after night the bandstand was surrounded by girls. Ronnie had become so popular he was like a pop star, and girls collected his pictures, wanted them signed, collected memorabilia, saved their ticket stubs, and had a crush on him. There was always a surplus of female company available for all the guys in the band wherever they went. They were the idols of the day.

Josie, now seventeen, who at the age of twelve had been brought to London to live with her mother and Uncle Markie, had spent many weekends at her auntie Cissie's house. Fitting in easily, she soon became a member of the family. She was often visiting when the coach pulled up outside the little house in Edgwarebury Gardens. All the members of the band would pile out into the welcoming warmth of Nanna Beckie's greeting of: 'Come in, boys, come on in. Make yourselves at home. I've just finished baking. Sit down and help yourselves.' Grandma Cissie would put the kettle on. Marlene by now was attending the Guildhall School of Music and Drama, where Ronnie had previously studied harmony. She had decided to embark on a career of acting and was not always home when the bus arrived but often walked in on the crowd in the living room. She recalled: 'They were a group of really very nice young men who were always very sweet to me. I enjoyed their visits a lot.' Not long after, in pursuit of her own profession, Marlene changed her name to Ella Laine. Auntie Ella remembered: 'One of Ronnie's favourite authors was Norman Mailer, and he particularly liked the collections of his journalistic writing. Ronnie knew I enjoyed reading those, too, so he passed the books on to me. I actually still have them to this day.'

Shortly after, Nanna Beckie, at the age of seventy-five, decided to marry

Joseph Martin, a widower. They had been teenage sweethearts and she had not seen him since she was seventeen. Shortly after his wife's death Joseph moved into the neighbourhood and they ran into each other, quickly renewing the relationship of their youth. Nanna decided she wanted a place of her own again and nothing anybody said could dissuade her. Auntie Ella said: 'Nanna never listened to anybody and always did what she wanted, no matter what.' So they were married and Sol paid for the wedding reception, which was held at the Cumberland Hotel. Grandma Cissie now had the kitchen all to herself, which was something she had dreamed about for quite some time. Nanna and Joseph were together for a couple of years and then Joseph died and Nanna Beckie returned to Edgwarebury Gardens.

The beginning of 1954 saw a celebration — the band's first birthday. There was a cake, and they played Manchester on the same stage on which the band had made its debut a year before, but this time they had just been voted Best Modern Small Group of the Year in the *Melody Maker* polls. A mark in the history of jazz, because this was the first cooperative group ever formed, and in the face of all their critics — and there were many — they had pulled it off. The band was an unmitigated success. Pete King told *Melody Maker* when questioned: 'The cooperative angle? Works like a charm. People ask how can we have discipline without a leader. There *is* a leader — his name is Ronnie Scott. The coop basis ceases by mutual consent directly we get on the stand. When we get off, it comes back.' In the necessary musical discussions that ensued offstage, if a last word was needed Ronnie had it. That same month, six years before Dad opened his jazz club, Carlo Krahmer of Esquire Records released the second volume of 'The Ronnie Scott Jazz Club'.

Jock Scott was by now completely delighted with his son's achievements. Ronnie took first place in the *Melody Maker* tenor sax polls and held it for several years. The dynamic quality of the new band, and its obvious popularity, and the steady release of a string of albums from the Esquire Record label were clear indications of Ronnie's musical maturation. Ronnie's Uncle Phil and cousins in New York, Alex among them (who had married Thea), and the cousins in California (Ziggy and Blanche now living in LA) all followed his career with avid interest as Jock spread the news, adding his own personal words of praise for his son's achievements. But, somehow, in spite of the hopes of Jock's family, the relationship that each man wanted to share with the other as father and son was as elusive now as it had ever been.

On 26 June 1954 a *Melody Maker* headline ran: SCOTT DENIED CHANCE TO

PLAY WITH US STARS. Impresario Harold Davidson was working on a European tour with Sarah Vaughan, tenorist Illinois Jacquet, Charlie Parker and J.J. Johnson. He wanted Ronnie and the orchestra to tour with the Sarah Vaughan package. But the British Musicians' Union was at loggerheads with Belgium and Holland, and there was trouble with France, too. The unions in these countries felt they had not had a square deal from the British MU and were in no way inclined to host a British band. Because Sarah was to bring her own accompanying trio with her, the British MU would not let the musicians in, so there was no chance of them playing in Britain. Although Harold Davidson was able to book American artists such as Duke Ellington into Dublin, the MU vetoed their appearance in Britain. So fans and musicians who could not afford to travel abroad were totally deprived of the thrill of seeing the live performances of their American idols.

Uncle Mark was working for the bookmakers at the racetracks. He was one of the top ticktack men, who stand by the side of the track 'talking' to each other in sign language; they were also called 'clerks of the course'. As the odds on a horse change, the ticktack men keep the information current. The flat where he lived with Rosie and Josie was on the second floor and Josie remembers: 'We always knew if Uncle Mark had lost or won by the way he came up the stairs. When he had won he would be as miserable as hell. But if we heard him whistling as he came up the stairs in a good mood we knew he had lost!' Uncle Mark made it clear that he was not the marrying kind, but having no children of his own he doted on Ronnie, and Josie was like his own daughter. At eighteen Josie auditioned as a singer for the Ronnie Scott Orchestra, because she wanted to go out on the road with them. Uncle Mark was very protective of her and did not want her to go, so Josie said: 'I'm going to be all right because I'm going to be with Ronnie. You don't have to worry. He'll look after me!' Mark replied: 'Oh, yeah! Him and all that bloody bebop! I don't think so!' But in the end Josie got her way and went on some of the out-of-town gigs with the band, later becoming engaged to Phil Seamen.

The band was on its way to a five-day gig in Ireland. They had all piled into the coach on their way to Holyhead to catch the ferry. The old bus struggled up the side of a hill, spluttering and stuttering, until it came to a complete stop right on the brow of the hill. Les jumped out and he and some of the guys stuck their heads under the bonnet, but after a short time they realised that there was nothing they could do. From the top of the hill they could actually see the ferry loading in the dock. Barbara Jay remembered: 'Ronnie said: "Oh, that's it! We've lost the bloody gig! We've got five days of work in Ireland and not a cat's chance in hell of getting there." ' As he finished speaking they all heard the rumble of an engine and, turning around, they saw a coaltruck headed towards them. Frantically they flagged it down, and as the truck pulled up everyone could see that all the sacks were empty: the man had finished his deliveries for the day. He quickly agreed to drive them down to the ferry. Ronnie and Pete got into the front of the truck with the driver, but the rest of the band had to stand up in the back with all the instruments and baggage, holding on to whatever they could grab. The back of the truck was filthy, everything covered in black coaldust. The truck rolled down the hill, the guys and Barbara in the back bouncing around with every bump in the road. They caught the ferry by the skin of their teeth, looking for all the world as though they had just come up from a day in the coalmines!

Many years later my father recalled that he found that band very satisfying musically and tremendous fun, saying: 'I've never laughed so much in my life as I did with that band.'

For my father, 1955 was to become a year of not only change but endings and closures. In the early spring the world of jazz lost its 'messenger'. Charlie 'Bird' Parker died in New York, while watching television at the home of Baroness Pannonica de Koenigswarter, on 9 March, aged thirty-four. The baroness was a Rothschild, a very wealthy patron of jazz and always a fan and a good friend to Bird. During the last months of Charlie Parker's life, which were racked with illness brought on by alcohol and drugs, the baroness did everything she could to help him through, right to the end. There is a well-loved story that at a concert held at Carnegie Hall in memory of Bird as the curtain rose for the last encore a white feather slowly fluttered down in the centre of the stage for all to see. Everyone there declared that Bird still lived.

In that summer the Ronnie Scott Orchestra broke up. Work with the band had kept Ronnie away from home during the past two and a half years. Joan had never been happy with his prolonged absences in Geraldo's navy, or when he was on tour with any band, and this last long episode of touring with the cooperative band had taken its toll. Joan had become seriously dependent on heroin and had developed friendships with others who used it and knew of suppliers. Joan had met a young American saxophonist who played with the Stan Kenton Orchestra. His name was Spencer Sinatra and he was also an addict. While Ronnie was on tour with the band they started an affair.

Ronnie was beside himself. He did everything he could think of at the time to break up the new romance, even reporting to Stan Kenton that Spencer was a junkie. In an absolute rage, he confronted Joan and Spencer and a struggle ensued. But it was all to no avail. Joan had completely given up hope of Ronnie ever marrying her. Spencer Sinatra returned to New York, and shortly after Joan followed him. Within a week she and Sinatra were married. Ronnie was devastated, unable to come to grips with life without Joan. Frantic, he sold everything he had to sell and raised the fare to New York. When he got there, he traced Spencer through his gig and followed him afterwards when he went to meet Joan in an all-night restaurant. Even as Ronnie had been gathering up the fare to New York he had no idea what he would do when he finally found Joan and Spencer. When he actually saw them sitting there together in the restaurant, he unexpectedly felt himself become calm. He recognised that they seemed to belong together, and in the end the exchange between them was very brief. He said simply, 'I hope you'll be very happy together', and left.

Ronnie's boyhood friend Victor Feldman was playing with the Woody Herman band in Lake Tahoe, Nevada. Rather than return immediately to London alone, Ronnie decided to meet up with his old friend and hang out with the guys in Woody's band, so he travelled across the country by bus. Seeing his old friend, being surrounded by musicians and playing his horn, all helped to get him back on track, and he flew back to London ready to begin again.

Joan and Spencer had two children. Her family moved from Caledonian Road to New York to be near her. Several years later Sinatra died suddenly, and her family were there to help her bring up the two children. After Sinatra's death, Joan wrote to Ronnie over the years, and they remained good friends, but too much had happened for them ever to come together again as a couple.

Back in London, Ronnie decided to form a big band. Although there were some fine musicians in the band, by my father's own admission the project was a disaster, but it took almost a year before he finally folded the band. For the next six months Ronnie co-led a band with Tony Crombie, and during the same period Ronnie and Pete put on a couple of evenings of jazz at a place called Fordham's at 39 Gerrard Street, a prelude maybe of what was to come.

By the end of the summer the itch to be in the US had returned with a vengeance, and my father decided to take a holiday. As always, his saxophone was the 'first lady' in his life, and he made the decision to sell his first sports car, the Jaguar, to finance the trip. Ronnie headed for New York, where he met up with clarinettist Dave Shepherd, a British musician in the process of emigrating to the US who was working at the New York Stock Exchange while establishing his residency. Dave shared an apartment with a fellow Brit, drummer Kenny Harris, whose legitimate employment was working in one of the large department stores. Each of the musicians was waiting out a period of six months before he could join the local musicians' union. In the meantime they played at small clubs, such as the Casa Lou in a small village on Long Island about thirty miles from New York, and they invited Ronnie to join them.

With them on bass was Mike Collier, who was also the British correspondent in the US for the *Record Mirror*. Needless to say, the British musicians were delighted to be with Ronnie again after so many months away from the London jazz scene. By now the band consisted of two tenors, one alto, guitar, piano, bass, and drums. Mike Collier wrote that they 'swung into an up-tempo supersonic rendition of "Jumpin' at the Woodside" which had this writer gushing with sweat in an attempt to hold the frantic tempo on bass'. At the end of my father's final chorus the applause was thunderous from musicians and audience alike. Mike Collier wrote of my father's playing: 'For the first time in my memory, at least, I could not say Ronnie was showing the influence of Getz, Lester, Sims or anyone else except Ronnie. With no commercial audience to please, he didn't have to worry about throwing in a crowd-pleasing "honk", and the benefit he derived from this was shown in his inventive lines.' Gone for ever were the days when as a young teenager my father had mesmerised his friends with his extraordinary powers of mimicry, playing Coleman Hawkins' solos note for note. My father had learned how to listen to the tenor greats and integrate their message into his soul, emerging with his own distinctive gutsy, driving, full-blown sound that was uniquely 'Great Scott' or 'the Guv'nor' as he was fondly referred to.

This was one of the first Anglo-American exchanges. Eddie Condon's All Stars were to perform in England, and Ronnie's sextet was the British exchange. He put together the group with Stan Tracey on piano (now also a highly respected composer), Lennie Bush, Phil Seamen, Jimmy Deuchar, Derek Humble and himself. Ronnie, all too familiar with Phil's addiction, warned him not to take any drugs on the trip; in fact he begged him not to. Phil acquiesced, promising he would not blow this gig by getting caught with drugs. Ronnie arrived at Southampton, and as he was boarding the *Queen Elizabeth* he was greeted by an officer, who led him to two Customs men and a very sheepish-looking Phil. The Customs men informed Ronnie that they had found narcotics in Phil's drum kit. My father was already very nervous about doing a tour of the US with his British band, feeling that if ever there was a case of taking coals to Newcastle this was it, and now to lose Phil, one of England's finest drummers, at the eleventh hour was too much. No amount of persuasion or begging on his part could soften the immigration men into letting Phil go. This was to be Phil's first and last chance to travel to America. Because of his addiction, he became a prisoner of the authorities and was permanently deprived of the American experience. As he was a registered addict, Phil was never allowed to enter the US. For a musician of his calibre to be so enslaved was always a cause of great sadness to my father.

Ronnie telephoned Harold Davidson and asked him to get hold of Allan Ganley, an up-and-coming young drummer whose bop-orientated style impressed Ronnie. In February 1957, therefore, Allan arrived, surprised and thrilled to be presented with such an opportunity out of the blue. He arrived before the rest of the group, who because of a dock strike in New York had been diverted to Halifax, Nova Scotia, and had to fly from there to New York. To add insult to several injuries, they were not able to bring their luggage on the plane because of weight limitations, so each of the musicians wore as many layers of clothing as humanly possible, which made them look and feel like overstuffed penguins. Allan was at the airport to meet them.

They were booked to play the opening number for an all-black rock 'n' roll show. With Fats Domino, Chuck Berry, Bill Doggett (an organist who had crossed over to jazz) and Laverne Baker, it was a top-class rhythm and blues package. The only reason the British band was there was to honour the new exchange policy, and they were keenly aware of the fact. Kenny Napper, who was on bass, remembered: 'Ronnie went looking for the stage manager to see what time we should go on. He was a very tall, broad-shouldered black man holding a clipboard. Everyone in sight was black, and he looked at Ronnie as if he were mad and said: "There must be some mistake." When Ronnie explained the situation to him, he looked down at his clipboard, groaned, and acknowledged that the band was on his list and grudgingly replied: "OK. Run on and play three minutes and run off." '

No one in the band had ever been exposed to such colossal audiences of never fewer than 20,000 people. Under any circumstance they would have found them formidable. Allan recalls: 'It was ridiculous. Sometimes we had travelled five or six hundred miles to get to the concert. Then we ran on stage and played one number, a Horace Silver tune called

"Room 608", then we came off again, and that was it!'

The black shows had their own transport, but Ronnie's group travelled by Greyhound bus for the whole tour. The long hours in the bus were quite gruelling, but often the rewards that awaited them were glowing like hidden treasure in the soft shadows of small jazz clubs in such places as Buffalo, Indiana and Ohio City. Allan remembered: 'I got closer to Ronnie on that tour than at any time in my life, really. I was still very green, and we used to room together. He took me under his wing. He was fantastic.' After the show in Buffalo Ronnie and Allan went to a jazz club where Sonny Stitt (tenor) was playing with his own group. It was an all-black club and they were the only white guys in there. Slipping themselves into seats, they were instantly swept up in the music. Allan recalled: 'All around us guys were saying: "Hey, man! He's bad! He's *real bad*! He's a *bad* motherfucker." And we looked at each other and said: "What? He sounds absolutely *great* to us." Never having heard the expression before, it took us a while to realise that bad meant really great! Of course, Ronnie picked up on that expression and for the rest of the tour, in an exact replica of their intonations, he would say: "Hey, man! He's bad, man! This guy's *real bad*!" '

In Indiana, when the show was over, Ronnie and the guys could hardly wait to get to a jazz club. This time they discovered Wes Montgomery, an incredible guitar player who had grown up in Indiana. He and his talented brothers formed a band called the Mastersounds. Wes never used a plectrum, always playing with his thumb, and his whole tone was unique. Once you had heard him play, his sound was instantly recognisable. He was a highly sensitive man who embraced all kinds of music and his playing was melodic and lyrical, totally captivating.

It was during this tour that Ronnie saw Stan Getz play for the first time. Having heard all of Stan's recordings, my father was a great admirer of Getz's musicianship. He was a phenomenal musician, the glorious sound that he developed was uniquely his. John Coltrane summed up the mystery and magic of Stan's sound when he once said: 'Let's face it, we'd all like to sound like that – if we could.'

During the 1950s, popular music went through its own revolutionary changes, and American rock 'n' roll was born, springing up as a less sophisticated branch of music from the same blues roots that led to the development of jazz. New dances were created, and new, much younger audiences of teenagers were reached. Rock 'n' roll swept the nation. British stars like Tommy Steele emerged, rising to rapid fame and making more money than anyone in the industry had ever previously done. One of the interesting things about all this was that when the pop artists went into the studios to record, jazz musicians were frequently called on to play, often arriving to find that no arrangements had been written out for them. This happened to my father and his fellow musicians on more than one occasion, their powers of improvisation saving the day. My father's close friend Tony Crombie saw that there was money to be made and, with a family to support, decided to turn his already touring band into a rock 'n' roll group called Tony Crombie's Rockets. Some jazz musicians on both sides of the Atlantic were very successful in making the crossover, temporary or otherwise.

A wonderful young tenor player had emerged in Britain and during the 1950s had established himself as a band leader. His name was Edward Brian 'Tubby' Hayes. The son of a well-known BBC studio musician who had started Tubby off on the violin at the age of eight, a few years later he picked up the tenor and in less than three years was astounding the audiences in West End jazz clubs with his extraordinary expertise, turning pro at sixteen. Tubby had honed his craft in the bands of Ambrose, Vic Lewis and Jack Parnell. He had formed his own octet, with Harry South on piano, but by the end of 1956, for financial reasons, the band had to fold.

Ronnie had special admiration for Tubby, who was a truly multifaceted musician. He was a composer and arranger, and his instruments were tenor and baritone saxophone, flute and vibes, which he played at almost the speed of light with the most incredible dexterity and technique. My father and Tubby got together and formed a band that was to make a mark in the history of British jazz; it was called the Jazz Couriers. Tubby wrote the arrangements, and many of his original tunes were part of the band's repertoire. On 7 April 1957 the Flamingo Club opened its doors to the public for the first time, presenting the first performance of the Jazz Couriers.

Once again, Pete King was at the helm, taking care of all the business and bringing in bookings. In the midst of it all he and his very beautiful young fiancée, Stella Ferguson, were married at a registry office. His partner and best friend, Ronnie, was by his side, as were Benny Green and Harry Morris. It was the beginning of what was to become a very special union that is as strong today as it ever was.

Pete and Harold Davidson worked in tandem, Harold's office sending road manager Dougie Tobutt, a man with a great sense of humour, out on the road with the band when they toured the country with an American blues package. The band's popularity quickly established itself as it repeatedly won readers' polls and the press confirmed that the dynamic performances of the band placed it in the category of most exciting outfit in the history of British modern jazz.

One afternoon my father and Jock had arranged to meet in the Harmony Inn. Ronnie noticed that Jock had lost a lot of weight and looked tired and worn. Concerned, he suggested that maybe Jock should take a holiday. Jock told Ronnie that he had thought about going to Switzerland and said: 'Would you come with me?' Busy with his new partnership and impending work, Ronnie apologised, saying that it wasn't possible right then. This was the beginning of a period that would cause Ronnie pain for the rest of his life.

Jock's sister, Ronnie's Auntie Mary, telephoned shortly after to let Ronnie know that his father had been taken to Hammersmith Hospital. When Ronnie arrived at his father's bedside he was shocked to see how emaciated Jock had become. Ronnie did not know what to say, and Jock was too ill to muster up any show of bravado. The visit was an awkward one, each man's feelings for the other yet again suppressed, with neither able to talk freely even though their concern for each other was deep.

After Ronnie left, Jock asked to be told the seriousness of his illness. Reluctantly, the specialist told him: 'You have cancer of the pancreas.' When Jock asked what his prospects were, the doctor quietly informed him that nothing could be done. Jock could not believe what he had just heard and decided that if this was the case there was no point in staying in the hospital any longer. He telephoned Mary. Jock discharged himself from the hospital and his nephew Sydney came to take him home to his parents' flat. Because he was so ill he could not stay in his own flat alone.

Auntie Mary telephoned Ronnie and he came over to the flat to visit his father on several occasions. In an effort to help everyone relax, Auntie Mary reminisced and told the story of how, when she and Jock were kids, all the family used to gather for Passover. At a point during the meal and service someone has to open the front door and the Prophet Elijah is supposed to come in. It was Auntie Mary's task to open the door, and on this occasion Jock had slipped out of the back of the house, rushed around to the front, and was on his knees at the front door, pretending to be Elijah! Auntie Mary opened the door and got a tremendous shock, jumping out of her skin at the sight of him!

Jock stayed with his family for several weeks. He sometimes went to the track to bet on the greyhounds or to take care of his personal business. One day, Jock telephoned Ronnie and asked him to meet him; Ronnie was busy and said he couldn't, but as the night wore on he wished he had made the time to see his father. When he got up the next day he phoned Auntie Mary and she said that Jock had gone to the Alexandra Park Races. Ronnie felt compelled to find his father and, grabbing his binoculars, headed for the track. Standing at the back of the grandstand, Ronnie spotted his father through the binoculars standing at the edge of the track with a group of people around the bookie. Ronnie ran all the way down the grandstand steps as fast as he could, at the bottom pushing his way through the crowds, but when he reached the bookie's his father had disappeared into the crowd.

The next day Jock announced to his sister that he was going to his flat at Marble Arch because he had some business to take care of. He would be back in a couple of hours. My father's aunt was very upset when Jock went off to his flat, and anxiously awaited his return. When he did not return, handing Sydney her set of keys to Jock's flat, she asked him to drive over and bring Jock back. Sydney remembers: 'When I got to the flat I rang the bell but there was no answer so I let myself in. He wasn't in the living room but his bedroom door was slightly open, so I walked in and saw Jock lying on the bed. I was too late – he was already dead. It was a very traumatic thing for me, the shock of it stays with me to this day. He was my favourite uncle.' Jock had arranged all his financial affairs, putting everything in order. Then he took an overdose of sedatives. Sydney said: 'At the inquest the doctor said he would have been dead in a few weeks anyway. Jock had had enough of all the pain. He saw this as his only way out to save himself and his family from the awful pain and anguish they would have had to endure if the cancer were allowed to reach its dreadful conclusion.'

On 28 May my father learned of Jock's death. Grandma Cissie was so distressed by the news that as she and Ronnie comforted each other she quietly confided to him that she had never stopped loving his father. My grandfather had died at the age of fifty-five. For my father, hindsight was harsh and cruel. For the rest of his life, in moments of melancholy or when the dark veil of depression crept up on him, my father berated himself in many ways for not having nurtured a relationship with his father. 'What if?' was always just below the surface like a serpent waiting to strike when his defences were down.

CHAPTER SEVEN

THE GOLDEN ERA: ACT ONE

He has a way of doing the extraordinary; he does it in the face of odds. I admired that about Ronnie.   SONNY ROLLINS

On Friday 30 October 1959 came the moment which I had been anticipating, off and on, ever since that night on 52nd Street in 1947 when I had seen the Charlie Ventura 'Bop For The People' Band in full cry and marvelled at the electric atmosphere of the Three Deuces.
    If I hadn't been a musician there would have been no Ronnie Scott's club.
                                    RONNIE SCOTT, *Some of My Best Friends Are Blues*

THERE WAS PLENTY OF work for the Jazz Couriers, which was an electrically charged, exciting union. The music was played at breakneck tempos with a concise articulation that never ceased to amaze the listener. They played some high-profile tours, one of which was with the Dave Brubeck Quartet, the American group that was established and popular and would remain so for many years. A highlight of this period was a two-week British tour with Sarah Vaughan, who without doubt was one of my father's favourite singers. He would find a quiet spot and listen to her performance. He felt that her musicianship was in many ways unrivalled.

Since Joan had left, my father had a series of relationships. A pattern was forming in which he developed what he called 'a special relationship' with one particular lady. Ronnie's past experiences with Cynthia and Joan led him to realise that it was only a matter of time before he would be facing the question of marriage again with the 'special' lady in question. Each time he was genuinely in love and decided that if it was the only way to preserve the relationship then maybe he should give marriage a try. A couple of times during the late 1950s and early 1960s, banns were read in church, with his consent, a flat was selected and new furniture purchased, everything was on go – Ronnie was finally getting married. Then at the final moment he backed down. Try as he might, when it came down to the hour of reckoning he *could not* go through with the ceremony. The inevitable break-up was as torturous for him as it was for his partner. He took full responsibility, blaming himself completely for the inevitable pain and misery that ensued, filled with guilt that he had created the situation, making concerted efforts for a reconciliation that was never achieved because the women wanted the one thing that he could give no one. Marriage.

It was inconceivable to Ronnie that you could make a promise to last a lifetime. Grandma Beckie's first husband, Solomon Rosenbloom, had left her with two very small children, and she was ultimately to marry three times. Uncle Markie was convinced he was a confirmed bachelor, although by now Auntie Rosie was considered to be his common-law wife. My father always said that Grandfather Jock should never have married because he was 'not the type'; certainly he never remarried after his divorce from Grandma Cissie. Relating to the three generations of men in his immediate family, who were all well endowed with wanderlust, and being a free spirit himself, he came to the conclusion that for him the state of marriage was a state of bondage.

In later years, when asked about this during an interview for the *Sunday Express*, my father said: 'Being the kind of person I am, the institution of marriage isn't for me. I don't like the idea of signing a piece of paper and being tied to someone. Marriage is like running a band. They are each likely to have an optimum lifespan of three or four years.'

In the summer of 1959 Dad went to Majorca for a holiday. One evening, while exploring Palma, he came across a small jazz club called The Indigo. He met the proprietor, Ramon Farron, who was also a drummer, they chatted briefly and Ronnie asked Ramon if he could sit in with the band. Ramon looked at him doubtfully and asked: 'Can you play well enough to sit in with these guys?' My father responded that he thought he could, so rather reluctantly, not knowing what to expect, Ramon allowed him to sit in. He said: 'As soon as I heard him play I was mortified, so embarrassed, you know. I had no idea that he was Ronnie Scott, *the* Ronnie Scott. Of course, his playing was marvellous! He didn't take offence at all at my mistake, and we became very good friends.'

Ramon was in love with Lucia, Robert Graves's daughter, and one afternoon he took Ronnie to Canellun, a beautiful stone house that Robert had built very close to the foot of a range of mountains in the small rugged picturesque village of Deya. The house looked out across the sea and had a steep craggy descent to an idyllic little bay where you could swim with a mask and be exposed to a world of startling turquoise and a spectrum of hues ranging from green to violet intermingled with the silver flash of fish as they darted to and fro right in front of your eyes. High above the bay was a clifftop. Robert, a very tall man of imposing physique at sixty-four, had an energy level that could daunt a twenty-year-old. Signalling to Ronnie to follow, he sprang nimbly up the steep ascent to the clifftop and dived off the edge, passing the rugged rocks and entering the blue water as straight as an arrow. This was too much for my father, who watched in amazement. As much as he was a thrill-seeker he was never able to handle great heights.

My father and Robert swam together, each enjoying the other's company, afterwards walking and talking. Dad was always a little in awe of Robert, who was a classical scholar, ex-Professor of Poetry at Oxford, a theologian and a prolific writer and poet. My father's education was of a completely different nature, but Robert had a way of making one feel at ease. He had a great love of music and a healthy respect for the artist who translated this language into feelings and emotions for the listener. Back at the house, Robert showed Ronnie his study, the walls lined with books, many of which had been written by him. As they talked, Ronnie ventured: 'I've tried writing, but I find it the hardest thing in the world.' Robert's rather blunt reply was: 'Of course you will. Unless you're God.'

The lifespan of the Jazz Couriers was a little short even by Ronnie's standards, and by the end of August 1959, after two marvellous years of very exciting music, the band folded. Fortunately, the group made several records that will hold their own well into the new millennium and beyond. The last date that they played was in Ireland at the City Hall in Cork.

Thirty-nine Gerrard Street, still owned by Jack Fordham, who also owned a number of other properties around the West End, was a taxi drivers' all-night hang-out and was not making much money for its owner. It had a couple of billiard tables, a few chairs and a counter where you could buy tea and sandwiches; quite a few musicians used to hang out there, too, in between gigs or occasionally to rehearse. Jack knew that Ronnie and Pete had often talked about opening a club and asked them if they would like to rent 39 Gerrard Street. The only question in their minds was how to raise enough money to get it started. Ronnie talked it over with his stepfather, who agreed to help. Even though he had his own business, cash flow at that time was a little slow. Sol went to his old friends Julian and Anne Kovler, who agreed to lend some money to Sol for his stepson's venture. With their help, Sol was able to lend Ronnie and Pete £1,000, and they took a lease on the basement.

The billiard tables were the first to go. They bought some second-hand furniture, friends rallied and helped to paint the place and build a small bandstand, and they bought a baby grand piano. On Friday 30 October 1959 my father's dream of opening a jazz club was realised. Ronnie Scott's Club was born. The club opened with the Tubby Hayes Quartet and the Eddie Thompson Trio. Membership until January 1961 cost ten shillings. Admission for members was one shilling and sixpence, and half a crown for non-members. Opening night showed a good attendance of London's top jazz musicians and a special guest who was Duke Ellington's trumpet player, violinist and vocalist, Ray Nance.

It was a modest beginning. There was no capital to draw on; the membership and entrance fees were the only source of revenue. The rent was in the region of £10 per week, and once that and the running costs of the club were paid whatever was left over was split among the musicians.

My father always dreamed up and wrote the club's advertisements, which were placed in the *Melody Maker*. Famous for their humour, they were written in the hope that they would catch the reader's eye more than a normal ad. This was something that he did for most of his life, including the blackboard that was displayed outside the club, which was written on in a combination of coloured chalks. The fliers of forthcoming events and the cards that were placed on each table were all carefully handwritten by Ronnie before being sent to the printers.

The entrance to Ronnie Scott's Club was flanked on one side by a wrought-iron fence. You stepped off the pavement and entered down a steep, narrow wooden staircase that had a rickety banister on the left-hand side with a wall to the right. Being careful not to crack your head on the base of the steps, you entered an equally narrow, short passage. Facing you was the cloakroom, and immediately to the right was the entrance into the club. It was a long narrow room. To your left was the coffee, tea and sandwich bar, and at the end was the small bandstand faced by rows of wooden chairs. There was no room for dancing. From the very beginning, this was the place for *listening* to jazz. The list of top British bands and musicians who played there was impressive. Ronnie had formed a new sextet, with Stan Tracey on piano, Lennie Bush on bass, Tony Crombie on drums, Jimmy Deuchar on trumpet, Derek Humble on alto sax and Ronnie leading on tenor – another formidable group that played the club frequently and also went on tour. American musicians who were playing concerts in London would visit the club, sometimes sitting in, notably, from the Count Basie band of 1960, Billy Mitchell and Thad Jones, who years later formed his own big band with Mel Lewis which became very well known in its own right. Shelly Manne was also a visitor, and Dad always said that he was pretty certain that Shelly's enthusiasm for the atmosphere of the club is what prompted him to open what became his well-known Manne Hole Club in Hollywood in 1960.

The birth of the new club was followed by the loss of a major influence in my father's life. Nanna Beckie, who had so loved and nurtured Ronnie as a child and was as much a second mother as she was his grandmother, had been unwell and died in a Hendon hospice in 1960. She was eighty-two years old, and up until the time she died had been an indefatigable source of comfort and security for Ronnie. Somehow, the fact that a person has reached a great age is meaningless at a time like this and does little or nothing to ease the sense of loss.

My father often said that one of the reasons he opened a jazz club was so that he would have a place to play at. In the beginning Ronnie Scott's Club was a showcase for the best of British jazz, but as excellent as the music was the British jazz fans did not exactly fill the club to capacity. Ronnie and Pete were having a battle making ends meet, so they put their heads together and decided to follow the arduous course of securing a liquor licence and transforming the place into something along the lines of the Three Deuces.

Wally Houser had just arrived in London, a young alto player who became a lawyer and first met Ronnie in 1953 when the nine-piece band played in Manchester. The two frequently met when Ronnie was in Manchester, the last time five months earlier, when Ronnie told him he was thinking about opening a club and asked him if he knew anything about leases. Wally headed straight for the club to see if he could be of any help and almost instantly became the club's solicitor. A club committee was formed, which consisted of Ronnie, Pete King, Wally Houser, recently qualified solicitor, and Benny Green, formerly baritone sax player in Ronnie's nine-piece orchestra, who by now was already a broadcaster on the BBC's Third Programme (later Radio 3) and journalist writing columns in the music papers. They held meetings, which turned into hilarious interludes when Ronnie would resolve that 'beer should cost tuppence more a pint and there should be unilateral nuclear disarmament'. They took minutes, which must have made great reading. It was all bona fide, membership cards were made up for the customers, applications submitted, and on 14 April 1961 they received a licence permitting them to sell drinks until 11 p.m. The thing that was incredible was the way they got around the problem of having to create an emergency exit. As my father said: 'There *wasn't* one. You came in and if there was a fire you burned to death! That was it. We rigged up a kind of Heath Robinson emergency exit that led into a firm that was on the ground floor. Amazingly enough, the licensing people okayed it.'

Once again, family and friends rallied to help get the club in shape. Pete's father-in-law, a carpenter by trade, came down from Manchester and helped with the extensive woodwork that was to mould the interior of the club. By the end of the summer, major changes had taken place. As you walked down Gerrard Street towards number 39, the strains of a saxophone solo or the rich, full sound of Stan Tracey at the piano poured through a loudspeaker on the stairs, enveloping passers-by and enticing them inside. In the club, the bandstand was now on the left. Built-in upholstered seating ran around the end and back wall, with fixed tables covered with red tablecloths on a tiered platform. On the floor were more tables and hard-backed wooden chairs coming all the way to the edge of the front of the bandstand. Each table had a small shaded, fringed dimly lit lamp and an ashtray on it. Every inch of space was used to its maximum capacity, leaving very narrow passageways, barely the width of an average person, as access to the seats. The walls were hung with pictures of jazz legends. To the right of the entrance was the bar and a small kitchen. The cashier used to sit at a small table at the end of the bar, keeping a running record of every order that went out. Directly behind the cashier, flush with the wall, was a long black-upholstered seat beside which stood a large plant. Opposite, a small hallway led to the office and band room that was shaped like a cave with a ceiling so low that most people had to stoop when standing inside. With the addition of the kitchen, they applied for and received a supper licence which extended the sale of liquor to 1 a.m.

Still struggling, Ronnie and Pete decided to find a way to present some of their American idols to perform in the club. Even though, in 1956, the

Musicians' Union had lifted its ban on public performances in Britain by foreign jazz musicians provided that an exchange deal was arranged, so far this had applied only to concert dates. No one had pursued the possibility of booking the American artists into club engagements. Consequently, it was a major challenge to persuade the union to make the necessary amendments to its rules and regulations. Pete King shouldered what turned out to be a long and tedious undertaking that he initiated by speaking to the British Musicians' Union. Then he travelled to New York and negotiated with the American Federation of Musicians. The outcome was that the exchange policy was extended to allow the American musicians to play at the club in England, then in return a British musician had to play a club in America. This was a major turning point for Uncle Pete, and he made the decision to give up playing and focus on running the club, except for occasions when the nine-piece band was resurrected and he took his place next to Ronnie on the bandstand.

For Pete, the negotiations with the musicians' unions lasted a few years. It took great tenacity and patience to overcome all the obstacles and persuade the unions to further modify their rules and regulations, opening the way for American groups to work at the club. Uncle Pete was very successful in all his negotiations, so much so that he is indirectly responsible for American musicians being able to work in British jazz clubs.

Ronnie and Pete decided to branch out even further, expanding on their practice of years before, when to make some extra money they would rent a space in a hotel, put Ronnie's band on and take money at the door. This time they set up a tour, renting halls in hotels in Coventry, Birmingham, Wolverhampton, Leicester, Nottingham, Leeds, Newcastle, Glasgow and Edinburgh. In May 1961 the *Melody Maker* ran a piece: RONNIE SCOTT WILL TOUR OWN CLUBS, going on to say: 'The Ronnie Scott Quintet makes its first tour of the Scott Club's Provincial branches.' They opened at the Hotel Leofric, in Coventry, on Sunday 14 May.

By September 1961, Pete's tenacity with the musicians' unions bore its first rewards. Tubby Hayes, musician par excellence, was booked to play the Half Note Club, owned by the Canterino family, on 54th Street in New York, thus making it possible for Ronnie and Pete to advertise that the great tenor saxophonist, John Haley 'Zoot' Sims, would be making a month-long appearance at Ronnie Scott's in November.

British jazz fans, who up until now had considered themselves blessed if they were successful in purchasing the highly coveted concert tickets and hearing their idols play for a couple of hours once every few years, for the first time in their lives were able to see an American jazz artist perform three sets a night, six nights a week for a whole month. It was a bonanza! For my father it was a wonder with an added dimension, as he recalled years later: 'That very first engagement of Zoot Sims was fantastic. He's always been one of my all-time favourite musicians, and to have him there for a full month was just marvellous. It was a thrill actually to see him take the stand in my own club.'

Zoot had sandy hair in a crew cut, and blue eyes filled with merriment set into a rugged good-looking face. His shoulders sloped, and his feet beat out the time, his body sometimes swaying, sometimes of firm stance as, seemingly effortlessly, he brought forth a cascade of wonderfully melodic notes, his marvellous style of freewheeling swing instantly lifting the mood of everyone within earshot and delighting the audience with its soaring spirit. Zoot's ballads were seductive and tender; his was a sound that caressed those listening and brought a smile to their faces. Although Zoot enjoyed a drink, he was a mellow person and never became belligerent, and his drinking never interfered with his musicianship. Accompanying him were Stan Tracey on piano, Kenny Napper on bass, and Scottish drummer Dougie Dougan. The rhythm section was of the highest calibre and could more than hold its own with any of the top American artists.

Stan Tracey, a highly creative and accomplished musician, composer and arranger who has his own very distinctive style of playing, was the leader for years of what became known as 'the house band'. The personnel changed quite frequently, largely depending on who was available out of the stable of very fine British musicians. With the exception of a recording that Ronnie made for Melodisc with American pianist Arnold Ross during a tour of Sweden with Lena Horne, the first postwar British jazz album to be made was recorded by Fontana during Zoot's month at the club, with Stan Tracey's trio, Jimmy Deuchar and Ronnie, featuring Zoot Sims.

The only ventilation in the club was through the door itself. There were no vents or windows, and although the entrance was always kept wide open it was of little benefit to the musicians who had to work under the added heat of the stage spotlights. Stan Tracey and his group often had to 'double up', accompanying the American artist and then playing the next set with the British musicians who were alternating sets with the Americans. It was hard work, and every night they came off the bandstand soaked with perspiration. Kenny Napper says he lost nine pounds when he worked at the Old Place!

The versatility of Stan's rhythm sections was unrivalled. They accompanied vocalists, such as Betty Bennet, who was once married to André Previn (they have two daughters), Babs Gonzales and Joy Marshall, a fine American jazz singer who made her home in London. Also, the music of all the tenor greats, plus Wes Montgomery on guitar, was very diverse, so the rhythm sections had to adapt to all the different styles and personalities. The work was incredibly demanding: for instance, Stan and the trio would finish a month with a giant like Dexter Gordon and be completely exhausted. The weeks were long, with all-nighters on Friday and Saturday, then there was Sunday afternoon as well, and on Monday afternoon they had to go into rehearsals to prepare for the opening that night with someone like Roland Kirk, whose musical approach required Olympian strength to deal with his energetic and complex programme. Stan said: 'I never felt intimidated by the challenge of playing with the Americans. When I took the job I had been playing for fourteen years, and as long as the nights were I actually had to be dragged away every night. It was a heavy commitment, but the rewards were immeasurable.'

Ronnie, already established as 'mine host', extended his well-noted repertoire of humour that he had exercised for years as a band leader as he introduced his musicians to the audiences in British clubs and abroad. Joe Greene, an American composer and lyricist, had written a song called 'All About Ronnie' for Chris Connor to sing with the Stan Kenton band. She made a recording of it in 1953. Although the song wasn't actually written about my father, friends quickly adopted it as his, the lyrics really expressing what many people felt about the hospitality that was uniquely Ronnie:

> All about Ronnie is told in a toast.
> Let me propose it, he's my favourite host.
> We'll drink from dry glasses, there's no need for wine.
> Champagne is Ronnie and Ronnie is nigh!

This was a beautiful ballad that Ronnie himself recorded, although when Barbara Jay wanted to sing it with the nine-piece band Ronnie said: 'No way! You can't sing those lyrics with me on the bandstand. We'll have none of that!'

Business improved during the next few years, although there was only so far for it to go because the seating capacity in the basement was only a hundred people. Wally Houser put his expertise to work once again, first securing a music and dancing licence (although there never was any dancing) so that they could then get the Special Hours Certificate which permitted them to sell alcohol until 3 a.m. Zoot was followed into the club by a series of tenor soloists, such as Lucky Thompson, who was the first black American to play the club, Dexter Gordon, who quickly became a close friend of my father's, Bobby Jasper and Benny Golson.

Grandma Cissie and Sol still lived in the same house in Edgwarebury, where Ronnie was a frequent visitor, relishing the balance, the normality, that the comfort of a secure home brought to his now very public life as a musician and club owner. His room, just as it always had been, was ready and waiting for him. In the postwar years Grandma Cissie, Nanna Beckie and all the Jewish ladies used to get together at her house on Saturday afternoons and play a card game called kaluki; the gathering was known as the 'kaluki school' and wagers were placed in the middle of the table. Sometimes Auntie Ella was there too; she had learned to play as a young girl. On one such Saturday afternoon in April 1962, Grandma Cissie was hosting one of her kaluki games, my father upstairs in his room and Sol reading in the back room, when she collapsed as she was pouring tea for the ladies. Sol and Ronnie came running, the doctor was called and arrived in minutes, quickly followed by an ambulance. My father never forgot the doctor's words to the ambulance men: 'I won't be needing you now.' The reality of what those words really meant slowly sank in. Everything had happened so fast: one minute Cissie was alive and vivacious, joking with her friends, and the next she was gone. Grandma Cissie was just sixty-one years old. It had been her birthday only ten days before. The shock to everyone was traumatic.

As Ella and Ronnie stood by their mother's graveside after the services were over, Ronnie turned to Ella and said: 'First Nanna and now Mummy. It's as though it was all a dream.' The losses left Ronnie feeling very vulnerable, completely exposed. Gone for ever was the oasis that had been his retreat all his life. My father didn't take any time off when Grandma Cissie died. He carried right on playing. It was the only way he knew to get through one day to the next. He flung himself into his music, which was his salvation.

Much to my father's delight, one of his favourite American comedians, Lenny Bruce, was booked to play at the Establishment Club in Greek Street, recently opened by Peter Cook and Nicholas Luard. Lenny Bruce was a jazz fan, making Ronnie Scott's one of his first ports of call. The two men instantly related to each other and were soon immersed in a conversation about jazz and comedy. My father had a great appreciation and admiration of Lenny's craft. Bruce's acts, although offensive to some, were brilliant attacks on issues that he considered to be social ills. His brand of satirical humour particularly appealed to my father's own quick wit and intellect, and he was thrilled when Lenny gave him a pass to the Establishment to watch his act. The British establishment, however, was not quite ready for the coarse language that Bruce used to drive his points home, and consequently he stirred the wrath of the then Home Secretary, Henry Brooke, and was duly banned from future performances in Briton.

Amid the growth of the new club, Ronnie was to suffer another loss. His boyhood friend and 'shadow', the man whom the lads affectionately called 'the little villain', Harry Morris, died. He had suffered a heart attack while driving his car and was found slumped over the steering wheel, and died in hospital shortly afterwards. Harry was the first of the East End group to depart this world. An important link in the chain of events, he had been responsible for bringing many of the musicians together in the early days and, as John Dankworth said: 'If it hadn't been for Harry Morris, there might never have been a Club Eleven.' In memory of his good friend, Ronnie held a benefit for Harry's mother at the club. He decided the best way to handle it was to honour Harry during the course of a business-as-usual evening, donating all the proceeds from that night to Harry's mother. Alf Summers, one of the original 'three musketeers', consisting of Ronnie, Harry and himself, added a special touch to the evening by bringing in a long-forgotten recording which was actually Ronnie's first record. Alf, back in February 1944, had booked Levy's recording studio, which was above Chappell's piano store in Bond Street, for Ronnie's quartet to record. Harry Morris, as always, wanted to be a part of it, and Ronnie and Alf, who was on drums, said he could be the MC and introduce the tunes. So the acetate had been made, with Stan Sinclair on piano, and Bill Ewart on bass (who later called himself William Stewart and became a producer for BBC Television). The two tunes that they had recorded, one on each side of the acetate, were 'My Blue Heaven' and 'Blues in C Sharp Minor', with Harry doing the introductions. That night in the club the record was played over the loudspeakers as a tribute to their very special and unique friend.

Roland Kirk, previously a member of Charlie Mingus's band, made his first appearance at the club in 1963. He came from Columbus, Ohio, a black man who was blind from the age of two, an extraordinary musician who played multiple instruments. His main instruments were the tenor saxophone and flute. He was a formidable player, also playing the clarinet and trumpet. But he was also a marvellous showman and played as many as three reed instruments at the *same time*, not to mention bells, whistles, nose flutes and a conglomeration of percussion instruments through which he expressed his seemingly limitless musical prowess and creativity. The British audiences loved him, his inexhaustible energy manifesting itself throughout the performance: the continuous body gyrations, swaying, dipping, bending rapidly back and forth, stomping his feet, with nose whistles, the manzello, strich and slidescope, hunting horns and Swanee whistles all swinging in different directions around his neck on strings, while he furiously played his tenor sax or flute. Roland was a wonderful entertainer who could fill a room with fun and nonsense, on one occasion handing out penny whistles to the members of the audience. The cacophony that followed was unparalleled! But by the same token he was also a virtuoso when he chose to be, and it was during one of these moments that Ronnie described him as 'a highly intelligent, post-Charlie Parker modernist with a fine technique and a lively imagination'.

The unique performer appealed to a wide range of people, not least of which were the Beatles. Paul McCartney recalled: 'I first went to Ronnie Scott's Club in the 1960s. It was perfect for me – I was never bothered there and I could always hear some brilliant live music. I would often drop in after working on one of the Beatles albums and spend an hour or two unwinding at the club. One of the highlights for me was a spectacular performance by Rasan Roland Kirk, and of course it was always great to hear Ronnie at the microphone! He had great style and was never phased by telling jokes to what was often a very tough audience.'

As unorthodox as Roland's performance on the bandstand was, so was his method of coping with club owners off the stand. He had developed his own survival technique, and for the first three nights he insisted on being paid in cash after each performance. After that he trusted Ronnie and Pete implicitly. Dad always said that he was convinced that the fact that he and Uncle Pete were musicians first and the business was secondary is what fostered Roland's ultimate trust in them.

Roland played the club for several years, and even later on, when he had his own group, one thing never changed: when it came time to give Roland his pay, he always checked it to make sure it was correct. Pete paid the American artists in dollars, and, as was his custom, at the end of the week he counted out the money in front of Roland, handing him the wad of bills, a combination of twenties, tens, fives and singles. Unlike British notes, the dollar bills were all the same size and printed on the same quality paper. Pete was fascinated to watch as Roland counted his money, quickly able to distinguish the denomination of each bill. No one ever worked out exactly what the subtle difference was between the bills which Roland's extremely sensitive and well-practised fingers were able to detect.

In June of the same year Ronnie and his sextet, which featured Jimmy Deuchar and Ronnie Ross, was booked to play the Half Note Club in New York to fulfil the exchange quota. The atmosphere at the Half Note was very much to Dad's liking but, although he thoroughly enjoyed the experience of playing there, he still felt uncomfortable, finding it very difficult to play for an audience of musicians whom he had known and admired for years. However, Dad formed a long-lasting friendship with the Canterino family, who owned the club.

The Beatles were the first of several British bands to take America by storm, their popularity boundless. This new export of British music had a great impact on the exchange policy that the musicians' unions had set in place, quickly rendering the rulings insignificant. It was a godsend for Ronnie and Pete, firing their enthusiasm to bring more American artists to the club and opening the way for them to bring in groups as well as solo performers.

By now Ronnie was having an affair with a German girl named Ilsa Fox. Although they never lived together, Ilsa became pregnant and was the mother of Ronnie's son, who was born the following summer on 21 June 1964. She named him Nicholas. Ronnie was no more ready to start a family then than he had been when he was with Joan Crewe but considered it his responsibility to contribute to the baby's maintenance. He and Ilsa maintained their friendship and he visited Nicholas quite frequently.

In March 1964 the great Stan Getz was to play the club for the first time, and it was during his month there that my mother and father were to meet. It was a meeting that I always felt was on the cards because it almost never happened. My mother, Mary Hulin, just twenty-one at the time, had been a nurse in the Midlands and had come to London in the hope of finishing her training at one of London's great hospitals, such as Guy's. While sending in her applications, she took a job in a French restaurant called Le Rêve on the King's Road. Knowing that Mum was a jazz fan, Monique, also a waitress at Le Rêve said: 'Mary, guess who's playing at Ronnie Scott's this month? Stan Getz. We've simply got to go!' The two girls planned their evening and went to the club, but after the first two sets were over they decided to leave. They were actually stepping into a cab outside when another cab pulled up behind them and a young man sprang out shouting: 'Monique! Mon-*ique*! Wait!' He turned out to be a young Frenchman Monique had gone to school with and had not seen for two years. Happy to see her old friend again, Monique sent the cab on its way and they went back downstairs into the club to hear Stan Getz's final set. They had lost their seats and all sat on the long upholstered seat behind the cashier. Monique and her friend were deep in conversation in French, my mother sitting quietly. Ronnie came up to her and started chatting. She did not realise who he was right away. He offered to buy her a drink, she accepted and they carried on talking. The story goes that my father kept refilling Mum's glass. She was drinking scotch, but not wanting to be rude and not wanting to get drunk she dumped the whisky into the pot of one of the huge plants that stood at each end of the seat. My father couldn't get over it, he told me: 'It was remarkable, really, Rebecca. I thought your mother had hollow legs! She'd consumed at least half a bottle of whisky! It wasn't until about six months later that I found out the truth!'

One of the most memorable evenings in the history of Ronnie Scott's Club was to take place in May 1964. Tenor man Sonny Stitt, an aggressive, highly competitive player whose musicianship and technique had left an indelible impression on Ronnie the first time he had heard him in the States, was performing at the club. It was unusual for my father to take the stand with his American mentors, but Stitt had made a remark before going onstage that had somewhat rankled with Dad, whose inhibitions dissolved in a resolution to play. On the bandstand that night were Jamaican guitarist Ernest Ranglin, Gene Wright, bass player with Brubeck, and, from the Ray Charles Band, trumpeters Oliver Beener and Roy Burroughs. They jammed, and it quickly turned into a 'cutting contest' between Sonny Stitt and Ronnie, no less electrifying than the legendary Kansas City cutting contests played out in the late 1930s by the innovators who had ignited the flame that burned so brightly in each of these musicians this night. Stitt tried every which way to throw Ronnie, and on a fast blues changed the key on each chorus. But Ronnie, who was constantly searching for new ideas, had been practising the same technique. Stitt could not shake him. This was a first for a London audience. People were riveted to their seats in rapt attention. The level of exhilaration in the little room was intense, even though the only sound to be heard was the music, rapidly ascending one crescendo after another, and when it finally came to an end there was a split second of silence before the room erupted into an explosion of bravoes and whoops of joy accompanied by thunderous applause. It was a night of

1. Jock and Cissie shortly after they were married

2. Cissie and Uncle Markie

3. Jock and Uncle Harry

4. A very young
Ronnie Scott

5. Sol Berger, Ronnie's stepfather, 1944-5

6. Ronnie's half-sister, Marlene, now
known as Ella, aged 18 years

7. Ronnie aged 16 (*left*) with his first serious girlfriend, Cynthia Gordon, and great friend Harry Morris

8. Ronnie and the lads in Hyde Park, 1948: (*left to right*) Ronnie, Alf Summers, Harry Morris, Nat Cohen, Arnie Price

9. Ronnie's early musical
heroes: Lester Young

10. Coleman Hawkins

11. Dizzy Gillespie

12. Charlie 'Bird' Parker

13. An early gig: Ronnie aged 16 (*far left*) at the Stepney Jewish Boys' Club

14. Ronnie when he was in the Ted Heath Band, aged around 19

15. Ronnie captivates his young audience, 1951

16. Ronnie, Lennie Metcalfe and Solly

18. Ronnie and Barbara Jay, vocalist with the nine-piece band

17. Ronnie and the famous coalition nine-piece band, which he led in 1953

19. On the road in Stockholm with the Clarke-Boland Band, 1969: (*left to right*) Åke Persson, Ronnie and Nat Peck

20. Ronnie with a furry friend in Brisbane, 1974, on tour with Bobby Gien (*left*) and Mike Carr (*right*)

music that is still cherished and talked about today by those who were lucky enough to be there.

My parents' relationship blossomed quite fast. My mother was sharing a flat with four other girls at the time she met my father. They actually lived in George Bernard Shaw's house in Chelsea, which his widow was renting out. Mum always said one of the things she loved about my father right from the beginning was that if he said he was going to telephone at 3 p.m. he would call at exactly that time, you could set your watch by it; he was very punctual and never left you waiting. At the beginning of their relationship they saw each other three or four times a week, Mum often staying over at his flat. One night he made her wait outside the door, saying: 'I'll only be a minute, but there's something I want to show you . . . OK, you can come in now!' Dad, who had a bank of large wooden drawers built in on one wall, was standing by the top drawer, which was open. My mother peeked in and there, snuggled into a pile of his old sweaters, was a family of newborn kittens. Of course, Mum wanted one! They talked very seriously that night. Dad wanted Mum to work in the club, saying: 'You're doing that kind of work now. Why not do it at the club? That way we'll be together.' My mother was reluctant at first. After all, she had come to London with an agenda and was serious about her nursing career. But by now she had fallen in love with Ronnie and deep inside knew that a nurse's schedule would not fit in with that of a musician, so she agreed to work a couple of nights a week at his club. Needless to say, it was only a few short weeks later that she was working there full-time, having made the decision that life with Ronnie took precedence over her nursing. By the end of spring 1964 Mum moved to her own flat at number 2 Chesham Street, in Knightsbridge, the event celebrated by my father bringing her the cherished kitten she had chosen from his litter.

The way Ronnie moved in with Mary could almost be described as surreptitious. Every time he came home from an out-of-town gig he would bring his luggage to the club, then they would both go to Chesham Street and my father would say: 'You don't mind if I leave this here, do you? It just makes things so much easier, you know.' During all of this he moved out of his flat into the White House Hotel. My mother questioned his reasons for doing this, and he told her that a close friend of his who was not married and had recently had a baby had problems with her landlord so he had lent her his apartment while she got back on her feet. Little did my mother know that he was referring to Ilsa and Nicholas. At this time my mother knew nothing of this situation.

About three weeks later, after work was over, Mary and Ronnie, as was their custom, were sitting in the living room drinking a cup of tea when Ronnie turned to Mary and said: 'Maybe we shouldn't see each other any more, Mary. It's not fair to you. I'll never be able to ask you to marry me.' At the time, at a complete loss to understand what had brought this on, having no knowledge of Ronnie's previous track record of almost arriving at the altar before he said no, Mary was caught by surprise, particularly since he appeared to be gradually moving into her flat. Her response was: 'Why should we split up? Who said anything about marriage? I don't really understand where this is coming from.' They talked well into the morning, Ronnie explaining some of the situations he had found himself in as his relationships progressed, how he did not want to repeat the scenario again, by now absolutely convinced that marriage and he were completely incompatible. My mother responded that the institution of marriage was not important to her. What *was* important was to be with the man she loved, and if that required forgoing the formality of marriage then that was all right with her. My father was at once highly relieved that Mum understood how he felt, and far from leaving her that morning Dad owned up that he was actually fed up with living at the White House and was missing the comforts of home. The next day my father completed his move into number 2 Chesham Street, and they were to remain living together until 1974.

Ronnie was thrilled when the great tenor saxophonist Ben Webster played his first engagement, the gentle giant of a man now so renowned for the unique way he blended his breath with the notes, creating sometimes a musical whisper, at other times the fullest, most rounded, whole sound you ever heard. As Dad himself said: 'Ben was incomparable, and universally regarded as having one of the richest and most ravishing saxophone sounds in jazz, particularly on ballads.' Dad clearly felt that he was in a privileged position having musicians of this calibre playing at his club, listening to the guys he considered to be his mentors, night after night, although they would refer to him as their contemporary, and having lengthy, informal discourse with them about every conceivable aspect of music, not to mention the endless stories about their experiences in America and on the road. Via their reminiscences, Dad and Mum were privy to a first-hand account of the history of many different arenas of jazz. A classic example of this is the story told by Ben to my mother, which to this day sends a chill down my spine.

Ben, as did Billie Holiday and many other of his contemporaries as a young man, played clubs in the south of America, which was rampant with rednecks and the Klu Klux Klan. The performing artists, in this case Ben, were not allowed to enter or leave the club by the front door but had instead to use the tradesmen's entrance. This particular night a couple of characters of the KKK persuasion took a particular dislike to Ben, for reasons unknown to him. They made their feelings clear, and when Ben finished playing his first set he quickly packed up his horn and attempted to slip out through the back of the club. Still having one more set to play, he thought that the two men who were gunning for him would not try to make a move until the evening's music was complete. Unfortunately for him, they had other ideas, and as he was about to make his break across what he described as an 'open field' behind the club, the two men appeared at the top of the steps of the tradesmen's entrance in hot pursuit. Ben dropped his horn and with a tremendous rush of adrenalin, fled across the field, leaping over a fence that separated it from woodlands. He zigzagged through the woods, gradually putting distance between himself and his pursuers, who, he later figured out, must have drunk enough alcohol to slow them down. The outcome was that, although he reached safety, he was never able to retrieve his horn. The terror of that night, along with the loss of his horn, made him resolve never again to leave himself exposed and defenceless to the likes of those men. Consequently, he bought a gun, and for the rest of his life was never able to go to sleep without the gun under his pillow.

One evening, Mary and the rest of the staff at the club were preparing the room, setting up for the night ahead, when an attractive young woman with shoulder-length auburn hair, who spoke with a strong accent, came into the club carrying in her arms a baby who was a few months old. She sat at a table with the baby, and Ronnie's secretary, who had greeted her when she came in, went to look for Ronnie. He came out and spoke to the young woman and played with the baby for a while, then shortly afterwards the mother and child left. Mary asked the secretary who she was, and the response was: 'You must know who that is.' After talking for a few more minutes, Ronnie's secretary realised that Mary really had no idea who it was. The secretary told her that she could not talk about it now but that they would discuss it later and disappeared into the office. Mary was feeling distinctly uneasy and knew by now that something serious was transpiring. Finally Ronnie came out of the office and sat Mary down, saying: 'There's something I have to tell you. I'm sorry. I know I should have told you before, but I just didn't know how to handle it.' He proceeded to explain that the young woman was Ilsa and that Nicholas was his son. It took a couple of weeks for Mary to accept the situation and believe everything that Ronnie had told her. There was great concern because Nicholas had two holes in his heart and needed very special care. Ronnie would have to be there for both mother and son, it went without saying. Ronnie and Mary talked things through, Mary eventually accepting the situation and Ronnie continuing to live with her in Chesham Street.

Pete and Ronnie were still juggling with the financial end of things, and, when it came time to give the club a face-lift, all the staff, waitresses included, went to work with a paintbrush and did whatever was necessary to keep things shipshape. There was a great sense of teamwork, a camaraderie between everyone, staff and musicians alike. One of the prerequisites of working at Ronnie's was that first and foremost you had to be a jazz fan. My father had a rule that every employee had to honour. He said: 'Never forget that it is the musicians who are putting the food on your table. Always treat them with the greatest respect. If I ever hear anything to the contrary, you will be fired.' Life at the club was thrilling, my mother often told me. 'Although I was brought up on classical music I had been listening to jazz since I was about twelve. Working in the club was tantamount to me attending jazz studies at the finest university in the world, only better!' To not only hear the music night after night for a whole month but to have the privilege of getting to know the founders of the music themselves was awesome.

By now Ronnie Scott's Club was becoming increasingly popular. Indeed, at times the members of the audience were as well known, if not more well known, as the artists they had come to see. Ronnie was always chuffed when this happened. Mum and Dad loved to tell the story of when Peter O'Toole first came into the club. It was a standing-room only situation, with people packed together like sardines in a tin, and Peter O'Toole was right in the middle of the throng. Ronnie called Mary over and whispered. 'Look! That's Peter O'Toole standing over there.' Quite excited, my mother said: 'Where? I can't see him. Are you *sure* that's him?' Ronnie insisted that it was, but Mary, not being quite so sure herself, wanted to get a closer look, so she wriggled her way through the crowd, and, jostled a bit by the punters, ended up face to chest with Peter O'Toole! Managing to tilt her head back she found herself looking straight into the very bemused, very blue eyes of the man himself. Blushing furiously, feeling that an explanation of her sudden appearance was essential, Mary stammered out that she did not believe Ronnie when he told her that Peter was there and wanted to see for herself. Peter could contain himself no longer and by now was openly laughing as she tried to untangle herself from him and the people milling around them, and beat a very hasty, very embarrassed retreat back to Ronnie.

It was becoming clear to Ronnie and Pete that if they were to make a go of the club they really needed larger premises. The cost of the airfares, combined with the hotel accommodation, the fee for the visiting American artists, and the expenses of running the club, left, to use Ronnie's own words, 'an extremely meagre' margin of profit. So they put the word out and started looking for a space that could accommodate a much larger audience. Although their only contact with the underworld was Ronnie's card-playing buddies, Pete King remembered: 'One night a couple of heavies came in and said they would pass the word on. Lo and behold, a couple of nights later we got a call and one of the Kray twins walked in and took us off to have a look at club premises in Knightsbridge, Esmeralda's Barn. But it wasn't suitable.' And so the search continued.

In March 1965 the Bill Evans Trio, with Chuck Israels on bass and Larry Bunker on drums, played at the club. Bill Evans was a softly spoken, quiet, bespectacled, tall and lanky man with sinuous hands and very long, slender fingers. With the piano stool pushed back from the piano to accommodate his long legs and his use of the pedals, when he played he was bent double, scissor-fashion, with his chin in his chest and his head bent so low that his forehead almost touched the edge of the keyboard, only his hands and those long fingers clearly visible. He had a deeply reflective and sometimes melancholy style of playing with an unbelievable lightness of touch that pervaded every performance. Every night the place was packed, every single person immersed in rapt attention, the only sound that of the euphoric music coaxed out of the piano by Bill. If ever there was an example of Ronnie's dream of presenting marvellous music in an intimate atmosphere, where people just sat or stood and listened with no interruptions, totally absorbed by the music, being fulfilled, then it was surely this engagement.

Since Grandma Cissie's death in 1962 Sol had met and married Rachel, known as Ray. His health not what it was and the loss of Cissie after twenty-five years of marriage left Sol feeling lonely and isolated, and when he met Ray he was instantly taken with her spirit and kind nature and actively pursued her. Ray, an exuberant person who was divorced, sensed his loneliness but was charmed by his attentions. They got married in

January 1963 and Ray moved into the little house in Edgware. Even though Ronnie understood Sol's loneliness, he felt uncomfortable with the fact that he had married so soon after Grandma Cissie's death. But Ray was a very warm-natured person and Ronnie quickly took to her. Sol was suffering from thrombosis, which slowed him down considerably, but he still managed to fulfil his duties to the local British Legion, which he had loyally kept up from the time he was demobbed in 1946. But, in 1965, just eighteen months after marrying Ray, Sol died. Ronnie felt his loss keenly. Sol had been as proud of Ronnie as Nanna Beckie and his mother had been. There was a bond between them. Sol had always been there for Ronnie, and Ronnie had reciprocated in kind when Sol was trying to set up his business after the war and when he started his special fundraising concerts for the British Legion Ronnie was there to help out. Then Sol came to Ronnie's aid, providing the suits for his first real band and scraping together the loan so that Ronnie and Pete could secure the lease on 39 Gerrard Street. Theirs was a good relationship of give and take, respect and love, that had matured as they had. When Sol died, the family observed the traditional mourning period of shivah. Although Ronnie worked every night at the club, he left before midnight and went straight to Edgwarebury Gardens to participate in the seven-day vigil. Ray found great comfort in his presence, and was thankful for his help, saying 'there was nothing he wouldn't do'. Ray remained living at Edgwarebury Gardens until her own death in the 1990s.

S pike Milligan had become quite a regular customer at the club and was a good friend of Dad's. By now he had met my mother, too, and they had also become friends. In the spring of 1965 Spike had started a project to save the Elfin Oak in Kensington Gardens, a project that became a passion. Dougie Rouse, who was a fine carpenter and who used to work the door at the club, helped Spike with the tree. The work took several years to complete.

In summer 1965 Ronnie's and Pete's search for new premises came to an end. They found what they felt was the ideal size and location for the new club at 47 Frith Street, which is still the home of the club today. This was a big move financially and one that placed them in the arena of real business. The business relationship and friendship between Ronnie and Pete and Harold Davison provided the financial vehicle that was a necessity to get the new club up and running. Harold Davison's business had significantly grown, and he was now a part of the major MAM agency.

He booked some of the most prestigious concerts and tours, featuring internationally renowned artists, and had always admired and been supportive of Ronnie's and Pete's ambitions to build Ronnie Scott's Club. The amount needed to launch and build the interior of the new club was £35,000, and Harold lent them the money.

CHAPTER EIGHT

THE GOLDEN ERA: ACT TWO

The best player I've heard here is Ronnie Scott.

ROLAND KIRK, quoted in *Let's Join Hands and Contact the Living* by John Fordham

Ronnie's is a very special place. He believed, as I do, that music should be placed very high, above everything else. It is a beautiful way of bringing people together, a little bit of an oasis in this messed-up world. He achieved that with his playing and his club. SONNY ROLLINS

THE OLD PLACE CLOSED on 27 November 1965. The last American musician to play there was tenor saxophonist Benny Golson. But Ronnie and Pete decided to reopen the old club to present the best in British jazz, just as they had done in 1959. They planned on showcasing some of the excellent younger musicians who had entered the jazz scene and reopened the Old Place in 1966 with West Indian Harold McNair, a tenor saxophonist who doubled on flute. Ronnie and Pete subsidised the club to keep it going for as long as they could afford to, which turned out to be about two years.

The three-week period between the Old Place closing and the opening night at Frith Street was the most hectic time imaginable. All the staff pitched in amid the flurry of carpenters and electricians, and in a frantic effort to get the carpenters to finish Ronnie went down to the East End and got a supply of what were then called black bombers – quite powerful uppers – and fed them to the crew! Ronnie's own description of this episode was: 'The result was fantastic. It was like watching a speeded-up film. Pete and I went home early on Friday morning to get a few hours' sleep, leaving the place looking like the aftermath of a minor earthquake. We came back the next day and the Irish guys were still in a boisterous frenzy of drilling, hammering, sawing, planing, accompanied by a fervour of babbling conversation prodigiously laced with expletives.'

The club opened on Friday 17 December 1965. The featured artist was Yusef Lateef, a marvellous tenor saxophonist who also played oboe and flute, opposite whom was American singer Ernestine Anderson, who became a favourite of everyone who worked at the club. There were no electric lights on the tables, only candles, and there was no front door. The first drink was on the house, and the punters poured into the club while the staff tried to make sense out of chaos. Finally, people were seated and the waitresses set about trying to serve them, avoiding the cables and wires all over the floor. My mother remembered: 'I set out with a tray of about forty drinks. First stop was Bill Eyden, who was the drummer and already on stage. He always had a glass of milk with a shot of scotch in it. I then tried to make my way from the stage to the tables, but my feet got entangled with the cables and with the tray held high above my head on the palm of my hand I teetered back and forth, my only thought not to drop the drinks. I was headed full tilt towards a table in the front row as I staggered to a halt, drinks intact. I was looking straight into the faces of Dudley Moore and Peter Cook, both laughing hysterically at my antics. Regaining my sense of humour, I said: "If you use this in one of your sketches, remember I want ten per cent!" It was such a marvellous opening night. Everybody had *so* much fun – the musicians, the punters, the staff – it was like one great big party.'

The new club quickly took shape, most of the staff from the Old Place transferring to Frith Street. Ronnie's very close friend from the days of the Club Eleven, Jeff Ellison, a drummer, manned the door. Jeff was a handsome man with a thick shock of wavy black hair, mild mannered with a ready smile, and Ronnie's chess partner practically every night. They played for small wagers and constantly pulled each other's leg, Jeff often proclaiming that Ronnie won only when he let him. Then there was George, who hailed from Glasgow, an enthusiastic, hard-working young man who worked for Ronnie and Pete for years. George cleaned the club and did everything that a roadie does and more. He set up the bandstand for every performance, and when the visiting band failed to bring all the equipment with them George would hire amplifiers, and whatever was necessary. He built up trust between himself and the suppliers in the West End. He said: 'In those days your word was your bond, and I was able to borrow equipment for the guys to try out. If they didn't like something it was returned – no charge – until I found something they did like, and then, of course, we paid for it.'

Ronnie used to come into the club at about six in the evening and check that the spelling was correct on the new plush billboard housed in a glass case – gone was the blackboard and coloured chalk of the early days. He and George would set up the sound system and lights for Martin Lyder, who worked them for the rest of the evening. Martin was an actor whom Ronnie had known since the days of Archer Street; he had been in a couple of movies, was charming and elegant, and was also the maître d'. Gypsy Larry was a wonderful character who swept up and did whatever needed doing at the time in the club. He used to play skiffle bass and had worked as road manager for a couple of skiffle groups; he had a weather-beaten face with deeply etched lines, capped by a full head of white hair, and always wore black – a photographer's dream for a portrait study. The staff often irreverently referred to Gypsy Larry as 'Ronnie's Father'! There was a lot of friendly banter and clowning between the staff and constantly with Ronnie. If you were going to work at Ronnie Scott's, a good sense of humour was a necessity.

In 1966 Horace Silver's group was the first American group to play the club. The group made several return visits over the years, and Horace was a great fan of Ronnie's particular brand of comedy and always went out front to see him do his jokes. Even though he had heard some of the jokes several times, he marvelled at Ronnie's delivery, which *never* failed to make him laugh. On one occasion when he was playing the club, Ronnie's group was playing opposite him and it was the first time that Horace had had an opportunity to hear Ronnie play. Horace said: 'During my stay I made a point of sitting out front for all of Ronnie's sets. He was a marvellous player. I was most impressed with his musicianship.' One night as Horace was about to come offstage, he looked out into the audience and saw Clint Eastwood sitting there with a friend. It was shortly after the movie *Bird*, the life story of Charlie Parker, which starred Clint Eastwood, had been released. Horace had seen the movie but was too shy to approach Clint himself, so he went over to Martin Lyder and they started talking about the movie and Clint. Martin, realising that Horace would never do it on his own, ushered Horace over to Clint's table and introduced them. Clint was a real fan of Horace's music and addressed him, much to Horace's delight, as 'maestro'.

Sonny Rollins, who had made his debut in the Old Place in 1965, paid a return visit to Ronnie Scott's the following year. One of my parents' favourite memories was of listening to Sonny for three and, if he felt like it, sometimes four sets a night, every night for a whole month, particularly during his first visit to Frith Street. When the club closed at 3 a.m. and the punters had all gone home, Sonny would get back on the bandstand, with no rhythm section, and would play straight through until 5.30 a.m., or even later, never taking the saxophone from his mouth. My mother remembered: 'His was a majestic figure, smoothly swaying, bending and sometimes pointing the bell of his saxophone way up above his head, his whole being seemingly playing to some higher force, one long ever-changing, multifaceted kaleidoscope of intrinsically woven and connected tunes. And we were all transported with him to that holiest of places. All of us were in awe, and Ronnie had for a long time considered Sonny a major idol. It was like attending a private concert just for the staff.' Sonny reminisced about his visits to the club and his friendship with my father and told me: 'Ronnie was a great player. We used to spend a lot of time together, talking about music, you know, his humour . . . I think he was probably one of the funniest people I ever met. Ronnie's was the only club I ever played where I made friends with the staff and when the gig was over people bought me gifts and I gave them gifts in return.'

Sonny Rollins and Ronnie had Coleman Hawkins in common. He was Sonny's idol, too, and his reason for playing tenor, because as a young man he'd had the chance to play with him. My father and Sonny talked about many things together, and although now Sonny was going through a very healthy period in his life – he had become a vegetarian and practised yoga – he had wrestled with drugs in the past. Sonny credited his desire to get himself straightened out to Charlie Parker. Even though Bird was dealing with a drug habit himself, he was able to be the influence in Sonny's life that helped him to get off drugs while he was still very young. Sonny had just made an album, 'Collectors' Items' with Miles Davis, and Bird found out that he was indulging and got him to understand that it was the wrong way to go. Now in prime condition, Sonny made my father laugh when he told him the story about his daily yoga practice at the hotel. Every day, Sonny removed the sheets from his bed, folded them and put them on the floor for his yoga exercises, completely confounding the maid who made up his bed with fresh sheets and cleaned his room. She could *not* understand why when she came back the next day the sheets were on the floor, and all she ever saw him eat was green apples!

By now my parents had moved from Chesham Street to a small flat on Ebury Street. Before the year was out, trouble was in the air. My father was very sensitive about two things: light and noise. Wherever they lived had to be as far away from heavy traffic as the limitations of the city would allow, the curtains had to be lined with blackout material. The house on Ebury Street was in a terrace, most of which was owned by the same person, who had split the houses into flats and rented them out. The landlord hired a contractor to repoint the bricks on all the houses. With the scaffolding set in place every morning at exactly 9 a.m., about half a dozen men would chip away at the bricks, their hammers ringing against their chisels. It would send my father into a frenzy. His first reaction was to stick his head out of the window and hurl a stream of expletives at the offending workmen. Having let off steam he realised that the landlord was at fault for not giving the tenants any warning of the impending work. It was intolerable for him, so he and my mother immediately applied themselves to finding another place to live.

Since they were forced to move, they decided to look for a bigger place in a quiet mews. Ronnie had always liked Chelsea, which was where Mary was living when they first met, so they decided to focus their search on that area. Right on cue, a two-bedroom flat became available in Elm Park Mansions, Park Walk. Their apartment, number 108, was at the back of the mansions in a very quiet corner, the perfect location for Ronnie. It was a positive time for both of them. My father had the place freshly painted from top to bottom and carpeted throughout; they furnished the bedroom and hung the blackout curtains, but at that point their money ran out, and the first furniture they ever had in the living room were blow-up chairs and an ottoman and, of course, one other essential – the TV, which was vital for the Saturday ritual of betting on the horses.

In preparation for a Saturday afternoon of racing, Ronnie would leave about £100 for George underneath a sculptured bust of himself which sat high on a shelf above the TV next to a stack of records in the office at the club, topped, gangster-style, with a trilby tilted over one eye. A typical Saturday afternoon at home consisted of my father sitting in his dressing gown in his chair in front of the TV sipping a cup of tea my mother had made, with the newspapers spread about him, his hair still ruffled from sleep, one hand on the telephone ready to call George at the club to place his bets. George, of course, was working and had to stop whatever he was doing and run across the street to the bookie's, place the bet and retrieve the betting slips. Ronnie often left it to the last minute to place his bet and there would be a flurry of intense anxiety if George took a long time to answer the phone. George would be greeted with: 'Where the fuck have you been? For Christ's sake! OK . . . quick . . . put £10 to win on—. . . and £10 each way double on— . . . and for God's sake hurry!'

By now my mother would have brought his breakfast in. Inevitably it sat untouched if the first race was about to begin. And as the horses rounded the bend, if Dad's horse was upfront and in the running, he would leap from his chair, legs slightly spread and knees bent, taking on the in-saddle position, his right hand flailing as though clutching a whip, riding his horse in, yelling: 'Come on, my beauty! *Yes!* That's *it! Come on, my beauty . . . Come on! . . .* Oh, shit! Well, maybe the next one . . .' My mother enjoyed my father's antics immensely. Saturday afternoons were thrilling and full of fun. There were more losses than wins, but all were accepted with good humour and it was on to the next race. Sometimes Dad did win, and because he bet on the nose, the winnings could be substantial. On one occasion when this happened he bought new outfits for all the waitresses and new tablecloths for the club.

For Ronnie, 1966 was a year of coming to terms with being a full-time club owner and a practising musician. During an interview with Valerie Wilmer, he said: 'Playing really is a full-time thing, or it should be, and it's very difficult for me to concentrate on it as much as I would like to. But then again, what's the choice? What can I possibly do? Can I just drop the whole idea and concentrate on playing? In the first place there are very few places to play, and in the second place there are certain things about running the club that I like and that I don't think I could now do without. I'm not just talking about financial things; it's just that there's a certain amount of satisfaction to be got out of running a place the way I think it should be run and the times when it's successful and people come who enjoy what's going on.' Pete King, well endowed with an organisational knack, lightened the load to a certain extent by adding to his duties many of the mundane matters involved with the running of the club. Dad said: 'I honestly couldn't do it without him. But one always has things on one's mind about the running of the club, which doesn't help playing.'

Ronnie's and Pete's plans to present a wide variety of stylists with the intention of appealing to a broader and more diverse audience than the die-hard jazz fans that had filled the earlier club required a lot of careful thought and planning. As my father said: 'I want to present as much jazz and as varied a programme as possible.' Doing so was a formidable task, not least because the overheads were substantially higher than they had ever dealt with before, which narrowed their choice of performers to names that would draw a full house. They were walking a tightrope in that they could not afford to lose money; they *had* to at the very least break even every week. But Ronnie never lost sight of the fact that the future of the music was rooted in younger musicians, and the last thing he wanted to do was to have a club that featured nothing but foreign musicians.

That year the club went on to present Jimmy Witherspoon, one of Dad's favourite jazz singers. Ronnie's band had accompanied him during his original engagement in Gerrard Street. He was a giant of a man known as 'Spoon', the kind of performer who had the gift of wooing his audience; at the sound of his voice singing the blues, they melted and became like putty in his hands, absolutely adoring him, always begging for more. In complete contrast Ornette Coleman's quartet played avant-garde music. Then there was Blossom Dearie, who must have had (even to this day) the youngest-sounding, softest, most gentle voice, pretty and blonde, and who accompanied herself on piano as she sang a wonderful repertoire of songs such as 'Peel Me a Grape' and 'I'm Glad There Is You', the latter a favourite song of my parents. If feelings were still hurt after an argument and neither of them could find the words to put it right, it was always settled by one or the other of them getting up and playing a recording of any one of the several versions they had of this tune. Blossom was very particular about the position of the spotlights, and my father was endlessly patient, setting them himself, pandering to her every whim. Later in the year Freddie Hubbard appeared, a young trumpet player who was a bit of a showman and liked to walk around the club in between sets in a red silk robe (rather like the ones boxers wear when walking to the ring) with FH embroidered in white on the top pocket. Roland Kirk and 'Little Giant' Johnny Griffin, marvellous tenor players, also performed during the first year at Frith Street, the soloists of course accompanied by the Stan Tracey Trio. Mission accomplished. Diversity achieved.

Dad was still driving his pale blue convertible MGB sports car that he had when he and Mum first met. In the summer of 1966 they made their second trip to Majorca for their annual month's holiday. Dad became carefree when they went on holiday, completely different from when they were working in the club together. My father hated to fly. It had become an agony for him since 1963 when he was returning from a gig at the Half Note in New York and the aeroplane had burst into flames during takeoff.

All the passengers had to disembark down the emergency chutes while fire engines and ambulances, sirens screeching, rushed to the scene, firemen running in all directions. The experience left him with a terrible dread of flying for many years. Dad and Mum always drove to Dover (except in 1965 when Dad left a week before Mum and she flew down and joined him in Palma). They then took the car ferry to Calais and drove through France and Germany to Barcelona, again taking the ferry to Palma.

They both looked forward to driving on the autobahn through Germany. It was one of my favourite stories growing up. Dad said: 'We had the top down, of course. I would open up the throttle and gradually the speedometer climbed to 70, then 80, then 90 to 95 miles an hour. Your mother would say, "Come on, then, put your foot down, let's go faster". I would bring it up to 100, and the first time that we drove down together in 1966 she looked at the speedometer and said, "But it goes up to 140 miles per hour! Come on, we can do better than that!" It was amazing, really. We went as fast as 110 miles per hour. Even though the speedometer went up to 140, the car wouldn't go that fast. I'm pretty sure I wouldn't have driven that fast anyway!' The road was long and straight and my mother always said: 'Your father was a wonderful driver. His reflex actions were impeccable. He was the safest driver I ever knew. No matter how fast we went I always felt very comfortable with him, and that included driving through the narrow, twisting excuses for a road that wound their way along the sides of mountains in Europe with nothing but a sheer drop of several hundred feet on one side.'

One of the things our family has always had immense fun with is what I suppose you could call bathroom humour, something that a drive through Germany is riddled with when you make a wrong turn off the autobahn and start really looking at the names of villages, and so forth. My mother was always the navigator, map in hand – not the easiest thing to do in an unfamiliar language where correct pronunciation was impossible and such names as Ochsenfurt or Orfurt would render them both helpless with laughter, Dad embellishing the sounds with his own nonsense. After they discovered that they were hopelessly lost, Dad would say: 'Oh, God. It's the Wherethefuckarewe tribe again!' When they finally reached the border, and it was time to show their passports, on this occasion the immigration officer was on the passenger side of the car, and my father handed the passports to my mother, who opened Dad's to look at his picture. Hardly surprising that after a few hours of bathroom humour, when she read Dad's passport out loud she found herself saying: 'Mr Ronald Schatt (professionally known as Ronnie Scott). Schatt? That's your real name?' Before she could stop herself she was laughing uncontrollably, my father joining in, also laughing his head off, when he suddenly stopped and said: 'All right! That's enough! It's not *that* fucking funny, you know!'

My father always thoroughly enjoyed springing surprises on people; he got a tremendous kick out of their reaction. He had decided to surprise my mother during this holiday and proceeded to drive out to Deya without telling her where they were going. As they approached Canellun, Robert Graves's house, Dad missed the turning. It was secluded and difficult to spot, so the surprise lost a little of its edge because he had to solicit my mother's help to find the turning. However, in the distance way ahead of them my mother noticed a very tall figure in a straw hat and excitedly proclaimed: 'Look! There's Robert Graves. He's walking towards us.' My father peered through the windscreen of the MGB but could not distinguish who the figure was in the distance. He turned to Mary and said: 'You've never met Robert Graves. How do you know that it's him?' He was amazed to discover that it actually was Robert. My mother always attributed her recognition of him to his enormous stature – not just the physique because there was something about him that separated him from other men. She was thrilled beyond words to meet a man of his calibre, and was fascinated to sit and listen to him speak about theology and mythology. Mum often told me that 'Robert exuded the essence of life itself, from centuries past to the present day'.

E ven though my father was finding it a challenge to juggle running the club with his playing, the jazz critics were in general agreement that Ronnie had settled down to improvising fluidly in a manner that was identifiably his own, his playing described as sinuous, muscular and quirky as well as sensual. By August 1967 Ronnie formed a ten-piece band, including himself, for a tour with Scott Walker. He was also fluctuating between working with his quartet and quintet, taking gigs all over England, Wales and Scotland with innumerable broadcasts for the BBC Radio *Jazz Club* and *Jazz Session*.

It was during these years that Ronnie toured with the Francy Boland–Kenny Clarke Big Band, which was a multinational band that Kenny Clarke and Belgian pianist-composer-arranger Francy Boland co-led between 1962 and 1972. The band was conceived, sustained and inspired by a dynamic Italian-born big band swing enthusiast, Gigi Campi, who financed his hobby from the profits he made from a highly successful café and ice-cream business in Cologne's famous Hohestrasse, which incidentally, my father said, had the best cheesecake in the world! When asked in an interview by Les Tompkins for *Crescendo* how he felt about playing with the Clarke–Boland Band, Ronnie said: 'It's the best big band I have ever played in, or probably will *ever* play in, I should think. There's been times, sitting in that band, where it's been a really terrific kick. Because I like playing in a saxophone section, and that one was one of the best ever, I think.' Ronnie used to sit next to Derek Humble, on alto sax, whose playing held a special magic for Dad. He had a tremendous respect for him. They were great personal friends, and as far as Dad was concerned Derek was really responsible primarily for that 'kick'.

The spring of 1967 was the beginning of what could be called the era of the big bands. The first American big band was to play the club for two nights. The leader of the band was Buddy Rich. Not only was he a drummer of extraordinary dexterity but he was a showman in the fullest sense of the word, dazzling the audience with his unbounded energy during his memorable performances of *West Side Story*. In order to pay the expenses, Dad and Uncle Pete worked out a way to do two shows a night, emptying the club after the first show and starting from scratch for the second. It took a tremendous amount of organising for everything to run smoothly, and there were set menus that included a small selection of wine or champagne. Buddy Rich appealed to a slightly more mature audience than some of the other jazz players, people who tended to be bigger spenders. It was a fantastic two days and paved the way for a whole succession of big bands over the years. The successive bands – the Clarke–Boland Band, Woody Herman, Johnny Dankworth, Maynard Ferguson, Harry James, Tommy Dorsey, Thad Jones–Mel Lewis, Count Basie, Stan Kenton etc. – played for longer periods of one or two weeks at a time.

My parents' annual holiday to Majorca held a special significance this year. It has always been my favourite story of all about my father and mother. Robert was exuberant the day they arrived and took Ronnie and Mary to see his beloved olive trees, so ancient that their gnarled and twisted branches looked like strange works of art. As they were walking back to the house, Mum remembered: 'Robert turned to Ronnie and me and said, "Let's not go in yet. Come. Come. Follow me. I have something very special to show you." We followed Robert to the bottom of his garden. He led us to what looked like a magnificent tree full of hundreds upon hundreds of blossoms.' Robert explained that it was a very rare cactus that flowered once in every twelve years, and legend had it that if a couple stood under the blossoms and the nectar was shaken over them their love would last for ever! Mum reminisced: 'Robert, his eyes twinkling and a roguish grin on his face, put his hand on my shoulder and placed me under the tree. He then proceeded to coax your father into joining me. Ever reluctant to commitment, Ronnie shrank back from the coaxing, but Robert had such a way with him that to my amazement Ronnie got caught up in the magical spell of Robert's tale and joined me under the cactus plant! Laughing, Robert proceeded to shake the tree all over us, and we were showered with sticky nectar, and Robert's eternal blessing!'

By now my mother had become the cashier at the club, and an autumn jazz festival was arranged which received a very supportive reaction from the press. The package was impressive, featuring an American top brass package with Bob Brookmeyer, Bill Evans and his trio and the Gary Burton Quartet. The idea caught on and the event of an autumn jazz festival was repeated for many years.

Dr Sydney Gotlieb had for several years become known as 'the club doctor', a title which was well earned. On innumerable occasions over the years when Ronnie discovered that a musician was in trouble, from the unheard of to the famous, he would call Sydney, asking him for help, which was never refused. Needless to say, Dr Gotlieb had a lifetime membership to the club with a full range of benefits. Sydney was an avid jazz fan from his early years as a schoolboy attending boarding-school in South Africa. He was in the audience one evening during Bill Evans' appearance at the club. In between sets he and Bill, a discreet and sensitive man with a lively sense of humour, were sitting at a table quietly talking when a young man of about sixteen came up to Bill holding his latest LP in his hands and said: 'Excuse me, please. Would you sign my LP?' Bill said he would be delighted to. As he was writing a thoughtful message on the cover, he asked the young man: 'What's your favourite tune on the album?' A brief exchange about music took place between them, the young student thrilled to be talking to the great man in such a comfortable and informal way. Ronnie walked by, and Sydney brought to his attention the exchange between Bill and the young student. Shortly afterwards, when Ronnie got up on the bandstand to bring Bill and his trio back on for their second set, he opened by saying: 'Ladies and gentleman, Mr Bill Evans. Not only is he one of the greatest pianists alive today, but he is also a great inspiration to the up-and-coming younger generation, which is *very* important. It just gave me great pleasure to see him sharing some of his knowledge with a young student this evening. You've made my night, Bill!'

The little flat in Elm Park Mansions had become a home to Ronnie, the days of bed-sits now far behind him. Both he and Mary were earning more money, and between them they had finished furnishing the flat properly. The blow-up furniture, which had had an ill effect on Ronnie's back because he had one leg slightly shorter than the other and it was prone to 'go out', was replaced by a special chair for him, which was supportive and comfortable, and an ample couch. The second bedroom became a dining room and now friends could come for dinner. Because of the long hours at the club, they also hired a cleaning lady and life was much easier all round. My father constantly reminisced about Nanna Beckie's cooking and how much he missed it and how he wished he could have it again. Finally, my mother could stand it no longer and rang Auntie Ella, now married and living in Birmingham, and asked her: 'Ella, do you by *any* chance have any of Nanna Beckie's or your mother's recipes?' Auntie Ella laughed and said: 'Oh dear, Mary, what's Ronnie doing to you?' Mum told her what was going on and Auntie Ella gave her several of the recipes of Ronnie's favourite dishes, most of which had the influence of a Dutch-Jewish heritage, with exact instructions for preparation. The first dish that my mother presented him with was motza ball soup. Nanna Beckie's recipe produced the lightest, fluffiest motza balls, and the chicken soup was made from a whole boiling fowl and her own unique touch of saffron. When presented with the soup, Ronnie's delight was irrepressible. He could not believe that Mary had actually gone to such lengths to please him, and his eyes filled with tears. Dad started to look forward to eating at home from then on. One of his favourite breakfasts was scrambled eggs, and he showed Mum *exactly* how he liked them prepared. From as early as I can remember there was this bond between my parents. My father *loved* my mother's cooking and often referred to it.

A major event of 1967 was the appearance at the club by the inventor of the jazz tenor saxophone – Coleman Hawkins, known as Hawk or Bean. My mother recalled: 'For those of us who had not been fortunate enough to see Charlie Parker or Lester Young perform live, the opportunity of actually meeting and hearing Bean play a couple of sets a night was incredible.' His was a long-awaited visit, and my father said: 'Coleman Hawkins was the biggest influence on tenor ever since I started playing at fourteen.' About his appearance at the club he said: 'It had always been an ambition of mine to have him play the club, and when he did it was such a privilege to have him there. I'll always be thankful for that. He died so soon afterwards.'

It's interesting that the man who was such an influence on my father actually played with Grandfather Jock in Mrs Hylton's band in 1934. Hawk was able to visit England under Jack Hylton's sponsorship, working for both bands. He then went to the Continent, playing with various groups in France, Belgium, Holland, Switzerland and Denmark, becoming a major influence on their jazz.

Although he was only sixty-three years old, Hawk appeared to be a frail old man, old beyond his years, but he had a tremendous inner strength, and his playing was still fantastic. Bean lived on a diet of Rémy Martin, iced water and cigarettes with the occasional bowl of minestrone soup which he rarely finished, but, amazingly, no matter how much he drank he never appeared drunk and it certainly never affected his playing. However, his health was of great concern to Ronnie and Pete. One night at about midnight Ronnie rang Sydney Gotlieb, waking him out of a deep sleep. Ronnie explained that he was very worried about Hawk; he was sure that the great man was ill. Sydney got dressed immediately and came down to the club. He examined Bean, and his diagnosis was pneumonia. Sydney had already been giving Hawk daily vitamin B injections. It was the final night of his run at the club, and Dr Gotlieb tried to persuade him to go to hospital. Hawk would have none of it; he did, however, submit to receiving treatment in his room at the Piccadilly Hotel, which consisted of massive doses of antibiotics. But before he would do that, he insisted on going back on the bandstand, made a little speech to the audience and rounded off the night with an incredible rendition of 'Body and Soul'.

Shortly after Bean's appearance at the club, the club agency, Ronnie Scott Directions, had set up a tour for Ben Webster and thought it would be a great idea for Bean to join him on one of the dates at a university in one of the Home Counties. Unfortunately, Bean was still seriously ill at the time and Ronnie and Pete decided to cancel his appearance. But much against the advice of Sydney, who was still treating him at the hotel, Bean absolutely insisted that he was going to play with 'my man Ben'. He said: 'I'm not going to let the people down.' When he got to the gig he was so ill that a doctor was summoned by Jimmy Parsons, who had accompanied him to the university. The doctor, agreeing with Sydney's diagnosis, administered an injection of antibiotics and adrenalin and recommended that Bean be taken to a hospital. Bean point-blank refused to go anywhere but on the bandstand. Miraculously, he pulled himself together by sheer willpower, and the majestic sound of his horn filled the auditorium. Bean continued to ignore the fervent advice of his doctors to stop touring and playing and, although he by now had also contracted chronic bronchitis, boarded a plane to Stockholm and completed his tour, of course maintaining his diet of abundant quantities of Rémy Martin along the way. The gruelling rigours of his routine and his diet finally got the better of him and even his incredible iron will, grit and spirit finally succumbed, and in May of 1969 jazz lost the originator of the jazz tenor sax.

CHAPTER NINE

THE GOLDEN ERA: ACT THREE

Youth is not an age. Youth is a quality you never lose.   FRANK LLOYD WRIGHT

Ronnie was aware of humanity; he cared about people. Musicians gave willingly and generously of their knowledge. Ronnie took the ideas and made his own unique creation out of the knowledge, always searching for a better sound.   LAURIE MORGAN

I will always remember Ronnie with great fondness as a true 'original' who for decades was an invaluable part of the London music scene.   PAUL MCCARTNEY

FOR SEVERAL WEEKS IN 1967 the press had been covering the increasing friction between Israel and the surrounding Arab countries. As the pressure mounted, a recruiting office was set up in London for volunteers to sign up to go to Israel to fight. Although my father was a secular Jew, he had very strong retaliatory feelings towards anyone or any group who threatened the lives of Jewish people. The old urge from Ronnie's boyhood years to become a bomber pilot returned inasmuch as he was incensed by what was happening in Israel and determined that this time he absolutely had to be a part of it. He was too young to participate in the Second World War and, irony of ironies, this time the army recruiting office turned him away because they said he was too old. When the conflict was over it became known as the Six-Day War. The Israelis had defeated the forces of Egypt, Jordan, Syria and Iraq. Israel captured the Sinai Peninsula and the Gaza Strip from Egypt to the West Bank of the Jordan, east

Jerusalem from Jordan and the Golan Heights from Syria. Ronnie had cheered the Israelis on every step of the way. He made jokes about being rejected because of his age, but deep down inside my father had really wanted to do his bit for Israel and felt he had been somehow cheated out of it.

As for most people, coming to terms with being in his forties proved to be a difficult transition for Ronnie. The rejection from the army made him acutely conscious of his years, and having recently gone through a period where out of the blue he was struck down with Bell's palsy, a condition that involves at least partial facial paralysis, his sense of resolve had been shaken. The palsy was devastating, because, of course, he could not play. The worst part of it all was that the doctors could give him no idea of how long the paralysis would last; the best they could offer was that they thought it would eventually go away. Ronnie was the kind of person who required all the facts, in depth and on the spot, and preferably instant treatment. With this particular malady, none of his questions could be answered; the information was not available at that time and he found himself in limbo. He was left with doing his nightly introductions at the club, followed by his now-well-established fifteen or so minutes of stand-up comedy, to which he added the new finale: 'Thank you very much, ladies and gentlemen. You've made an old man very happy.' Dad was absolutely devastated and became somewhat depressed.

After he and my mother got home from the club in the early hours of the morning, Dad could not go into the flat. He needed to walk, so he and my mother would walk, sometimes for hours, my father becoming increasingly unsure if he could handle the situation for much longer. It was the not knowing how long this thing was going to go on for that constantly gnawed at him. As time passed he became more and more agitated about his embouchure, fearing that he might never get it back. Entering a period of severe self-doubt about what he was doing with his life, he would say to my mother: 'What am I *doing*, Mary? I'm really not that great a player *anyway* . . . and now all I do is get up in the club and tell a bunch of bloody silly jokes. What's *that*, for Christ's sake? I'll tell you what it is: it's *nothing*, that's what it is.' Mum would laugh at this point and remind him about just how much everybody loved his jokes. They had almost become as much a part of Ronnie's public persona as his playing, and it had reached the point where customers actually asked for certain jokes, saying: 'Aw, come on, Ron, tell us the one about the teddy bear.' This was something he had incorporated into a skit when touring rural England,

and it went like this: 'I went into a chemist's shop up there and I said to the guy behind the counter, "Do you have cotton wool balls?" And he said: "What do you think I am, a teddy bear?" ' My mother knew that if she could get him back to the point where he could use his ability to laugh in the face of adversity then he would come through this period intact. Ronnie's anguish was that he felt like a clown, yet he was essentially a musician, and without being able to practise his craft he felt he was losing control.

Fortunately for all concerned, the palsy did fade and gradually, over a period of months, Ronnie regained full muscular control of his face and took to practising daily again. The familiar glass of water in which he used to soak his reeds once more appeared, the reed-cutter and endless lines of reeds spread out on the dining room table, my father trying one after the other in his ceaseless search for the one that held the most magic. In that area, at least, things were back to normal. Once the reed was selected, then it was off to the club, where he would practise the saxophone for most of the afternoon. In a very short time he was playing again and feeling much better about his musicianship.

George's brother Donald had joined the staff and used to work with George in the club, so now, when George was busy, it was Donald who put the bets on for Ronnie. The brothers noticed that although Ronnie always backed the horse to win, on many occasions it came in second, so they decided to back the same horse each way, and before long they were winning quite a bit of money, and every time that Ronnie won he always gave them ten per cent, so it meant they always ended up winners. Albert Dimes, one of the local hoods, often used to stop by the club in the afternoon to watch a race with Ronnie on TV, and George and Donald got a kick out of watching Dad 'ride' his horse to the post, yelling: 'Come *on*, my cocker, come *on*!' Every day he would send one of them out for cigarettes and a cup of tea, always giving them a few pounds and *never* asking for the change. In between the racing, when the club was not being used for rehearsals or press receptions, my father could be found pacing back and forth across the length and breadth of the club practising his saxophone.

Donald told me that Dad was insistent that the club should be scrupulously clean. The front desk had to be polished and the glass doors sparkling. Sometimes he would walk in and blow a fuse if the street outside the front of the club was not clean. The entrance had to be kept immaculate at all times because customers stopped by during the day to make bookings. It was well known among the people who worked at the club and those who knew my father that he had no tolerance for fools and had a very short fuse if he thought that a job was not being done properly. But his bursts of anger were over quickly, and nine times out of ten Ronnie would storm out of the club only to return ten minutes later with a big grin on his face and all was forgiven and forgotten.

Towards the end of the year NDR Radio/TV in Hamburg had organised a week-long workshop programme. The line-up included two Austrian musicians, pianist Fritz Pauer and trombonist Erik Kleinschuster, together with several of the younger British players, including John Surman on baritone, Alan Skidmore on tenor, Mike Osborne and South African bassist Harry Miller, with Ronnie Scott. This was at a time when 'free jazz' was in vogue, and John Surman recalls: 'I suspect that Ronnie might have found some of the music a little avant garde for his taste — but nevertheless he was happy to be fully involved in all the experimentation, and the week produced a great deal of really good music.'

By now another natural phenomenon was taking place, and Ronnie couldn't dodge it any longer: he needed glasses, just one more tangible fact that confirmed he was getting older. Ronnie asked Mary to go with him to help choose the spectacles. It took a couple of hours, but Dad really got into the selection process, trying on some thick dark tortoiseshell frames, turning his black leather jacket collar up, contorting his face and momentarily turning himself into a villain. Then, with a pair of thin wire rounded frames, he slid them down his nose, peering over the top with a smirk on his face, and transformed himself, by hunching his shoulders so they sloped slightly to one side and nervously wringing his hands, into Dickens's Uriah Heep. By the time he'd finished, the optician and shop assistant and all the other customers were helplessly laughing. Eventually, between them they selected a pair of wire-framed glasses that Dad thought he could live with, and in the end Mum had him convinced that he looked great in them. To the day he died my father wore the same style of glasses that they had selected that day, always with a metal frame that had a bar going across the top; he fluctuated between gold and silver. Dad never really lost his dislike of having to wear them, especially when he was playing. In later years, when he needed bifocals, he wore them all the time. When he came to visit us in New York and Mum finally had to wear glasses herself, Dad used to try hers on to see whose were the strongest, and funnily enough Mum's eyesight ended up about the same as his even though Dad was sixteen years older. He loved that and used to gently pull her leg about it in restaurants. Mum would be searching for her glasses in her bag and Dad would nonchalantly say: 'Here, use mine!'

The 1960s and early 1970s were a time of growth for the club and Ronnie. He had been a musician now for nearly thirty years and had been a major influence on the British jazz scene for at least twenty of those years. Ronnie Scott's Club had become one of the great international jazz institutions. Dad formed a new band, taking a fresh approach to his music. The workshop in Hamburg had made a strong impression on him, so he invited some of the younger musicians who had very strong ideas of their own expressed in 'free jazz'. The band included Tony Oxley on drums, who had become a regular accompanist for visiting musicians at the club and is an innovator constantly stretching the traditional limits of 'time' but always bringing his deviations from the norm back to the original pulse of the tune. My father thoroughly enjoyed Tony's originality; he was a challenge to play with. His favourite classical composer was Beethoven. It also included John Surman, who had been a member of the workshop and was influenced by John Coltrane, one of Dad's favourite saxophonists; John is a formidable baritone player; Kenny Wheeler on trumpet, also an accomplished composer and arranger, his playing and writing very original; Ray Warleigh, a very fine alto saxophonist and trombonist; Chris Pyne with Ron Mathewson on bass, the latter a member of the house band as well as Ronnie's own groups for years; and Gordon Beck on piano, also a writer and arranger, a fully accomplished musician. Dad's old friend Tony Crombie played drums alongside Tony Oxley, and when talking to Les Tomkins during an interview for *Crescendo*, Dad said: 'For me he's a great drummer. I'd rather play with Tony than most other drummers I know.'

By 1968 Ronnie was forty-one years of age and commanded so much respect as a leader by his fellow musicians of all ages they had for several years called him the Guv'nor. Most of the guys in the band were considerably younger than he was, in their twenties. It was a powerful ensemble that received rave reviews. John Surman remembered Ronnie as a leader, saying: 'Ronnie never sat back and took it easy. I can honestly say that he was as eager to blow as anyone – and keen to rehearse new material too.' The band made their first album together in March on Realm; it was called 'Live at Ronnie Scott's'. They also did TV and radio appearances, and went on tour. Tony Oxley was replaced with Spike Wells on drums, but ultimately the two-drummer format was abandoned and the group ended up with one drummer, Tony Crombie. Tony was also called on to play with some of the American soloists, such as Dexter Gordon, Ben Webster and Coleman Hawkins. Tony told me: 'It was a very interesting experience to play with these guys and listen to them from the bandstand, which is quite a different perspective from sitting out in the audience. I am deeply grateful to Ronnie for providing me with the opportunity to accompany many of the great jazz stars.'

One day when we were talking about pop groups Dad told me about the day he received a call asking him if he would do a session on 6 February for the Beatles. They were coming out with a new record called 'Lady Madonna'. Ronnie was disappointed that when he and the other musicians arrived at the studio the Beatles were not there. After their part of the recording was complete, Dad listened to the tracks and he was quite pleased with his solo. He said: 'Becky, *that's* my claim to fame. I took a solo on "Lady Madonna" by the Beatles. They broke up shortly after that, I might tell you!'

The club was flourishing. In 1968 one of the groups that brought the year in was the Kenny 'Klook' Clarke Trio, with French organist Eddie Louiss and Jimmy Gourley on guitar. The jazz critic Ralph J. Cleeson wrote of Klook's musicianship: 'I have a suspicion that Kenny Clarke, placed in the rhythm section of almost any group, is the equal to half a dozen poll winners, several thousand volts, and the pocket history of jazz.' The young British drummers of the day flocked to the club and were treated to a drum clinic by Kenny Clarke, who demonstrated his sight-reading method assisted by keen volunteers, and his formidable drum technique. Klook lived in Paris and visited the club during the course of several years as a member of the audience. Others who performed at that time included Phil Woods, alto sax, an absolutely wonderful player and still going strong today. His saxophone is legendary in itself because at one time it belonged to the inimitable Charlie Parker. Then came Hank Mobley, one of my father's favourite players. He always described Hank as being 'a very warm, melodic player with good conception'. Right up until Dad was unable to play the saxophone any more, he had two practice books that he used for years. One of them was by Hank Mobley, the other by John Coltrane.

Ronnie was getting restless. His relationship with my mother had become a little too comfortable. He didn't know what he wanted any more and discussed the situation with Mary. He needed to be alone for a while, so they decided to take a break from each other. My mother made the decision to go to Palma, a place where they had always been able to find peace together. She felt it was important to leave England completely so that Ronnie had total freedom. Ronnie shared the information with his close friend Spike Milligan, explaining that he did not know what he wanted any more and felt he needed about six months alone to sort things out. Spike and my mother talked about the situation and her impending visit to Majorca, and Spike wrote a letter to Robert Graves explaining the situation to him, saying that Mary would very much like to see him during her stay and that he should expect to hear from her. On 25 June Mary was on her way to Majorca, staying in the Hotel Balle, where she and Ronnie usually stayed. Ronnie went to Germany to play with the Clarke–Boland Band. They talked every day on the telephone and cards went back and forth. Ronnie returned to London, and by the end of August he had had enough and asked Mum to come back home from what turned out to be nothing more than an extended holiday. He booked her flight and was at the airport to meet her. The break had served its purpose, and they were glad to be back together again.

Circumstances had changed at the club, and on Mary's return she took over the responsibility of handling the bar and waiting staff. Pete and Ronnie were pursuing the possibility of taking over the building next door, which was shortly to become vacant. Again the main obstacle was financing because major renovation would be necessary to turn the two buildings into one. The original loan from Harold Davidson was still in the process of being paid off, and Harold agreed to extend it to cover the necessary alterations. Ronnie and Pete had had an association with the Harold Davidson office for many years. Harold had been extremely helpful with the musician exchange process that always remained in effect and felt that Ronnie and Pete were doing something that was very worthwhile and consequently gave them his support and assistance in every way he could.

All transactions were completed on 14 September 1968, and the club closed down for renovation work; it was due to reopen on 30 September. Forty-six and forty-seven Frith Street became one building, the adjoining wall knocked down. The idea was to have three floors of entertainment, and the ground floor, which originally held about 200 people, was extended to accommodate 350 people seated. The bandstand, which used to stand against the wall that had been knocked down, was now moved to the adjacent wall to centre the club, with the tables and chairs surrounding it, amphitheatre-style. The red tablecloths and dimly lit lamps with multicoloured shades with a black fringe were all retained. The walls, painted white, became a gallery for large photographs of everybody who ever was and is notable in jazz and for the masks, softly back-lit, that Ronnie used to bring back from his travels abroad. To the left of the bandstand as you come in is a long padded bar. A room was built upstairs which, with sculptured seating and room to dance, held about 150 people.

Dad's original idea was to show old films. He *loved* W.C. Fields and Laurel and Hardy, and on opening night he wanted to show *The Bank Dick*. Much to Dad's great disappointment he and Uncle Pete had trouble trying to secure the right to show the films from the film companies and the idea never came to fruition. Other nights they planned to have a discotheque, or a live group, with some nights left open for British jazz groups to play. Downstairs is a small bar catering to thirty or forty people. Ronnie used to refer to it as 'the chat-up room' and initially installed a football machine in there, he said 'to bring back memories of the Harmony Inn of my youth'. Today, jazz records are played in the bar and there is a TV for anyone who wants to watch; also, a small band room for visiting groups and new Ladies and Gents were built on this level.

Thirty-one years later this is exactly how the club looks today. It has become a hallowed hall of jazz history. The atmosphere that Ronnie was so determined to create for British audiences is the same today as it was back in the early days of the Old Place forty years ago, only now it is a little bit richer because the walls themselves seem to have soaked up the music of the decades, the jokes and the laughter. The essence of those magic nights lingers, welcoming and enhancing the performance of today's great artists.

The deadline of 30 September was not met, and there was still much work in progress as Buddy Rich and his big band arrived to play the opening night of the new Ronnie Scott's. The band was booked to play for three nights. The audience was treated to a combination of extraordinary musical performance and comedy. Ronnie often said that Buddy could have earned a handsome living as a stand-up comedian. His ability to toss out ad-lib comments to the members of the band as they were playing, or to anyone in the audience who was unwise enough to heckle him, with the rapidity of his devastating whiplash response, would give many a professional comedian a moment of envy. Buddy and Ronnie often exchanged a few sharp shots as Buddy was getting on or off the bandstand, much to the delight of the audience. This particular night, after Ronnie had finished announcing the band for their first set, Buddy's response was: 'This is the first time I have ever had to play in the middle of a building site!'

Ronnie often talked to Mary about his relationship with Jock Scott, always with regret that they were never able to establish a closer relationship. Mary was adopted and wanted very much to find out about her heritage, and they had many discussions about her unknown father and about Jock's very long absence during Ronnie's childhood and formative years. Sol had been a wonderfully supportive stepdad, as had Cyril Hulin, the man who had adopted Mary, but even so each of them felt they had missed something very important by not knowing their biological fathers during their formative years.

After Grandfather Jock's death in the 1950s Ronnie's visits to Uncle Phil in New York ceased. In fact, since Grandma Cissie's death and the passing of Sol, Ronnie very rarely had contact with members of his family unless they came to the club to see him, with the exception of Uncle Markie. Their relationship remained very close. Uncle Mark was working for Jack Bimstock at the Victoria Sporting Club and still went through his periods of either being loaded or broke. He could have been one of the wealthiest men in London, but Uncle Mark, as Josie put it, 'didn't believe in bricks and mortar. Every house we ever lived in was rented.' It was the same with Grandma Cissie and Sol, and Nanna Beckie, and Grandfather Jock: none of them ever bought a home. When Uncle Mark was on a winning streak he and Auntie Rosie rented a marvellous place called Hamilton House in Southampton Road. The rent was exorbitant, and as Josie said: 'They furnished it something like Buckingham Palace!' Uncle Markie won fortunes and lost them, money meant nothing to him. When his luck had run out he used to come to the club in Frith Street for his dinner, and Ronnie took care of him until his luck changed again. Some mornings after the club had closed my father would take Mum to the Victoria Sporting Club to see Uncle Mark, and they often breakfasted together on smoked haddock. Ronnie really was not a casino man; he did not get pleasure out of slot machines, although he would play a game of crap and always did the football pools, but cards and the horses were where he got his real thrills.

Since the expansion of the club Dad and Uncle Pete were enthused with fresh ideas about what could be presented at the club now that they had more room, while always keeping in mind that although the club had become well known for the American artists who appeared there, it still remained a mecca for British musicians. Ronnie and Pete always tried to provide as many working opportunities as possible for British jazz men, who were booked to play opposite, or with, visiting Americans. Also, Sunday sessions were started for the British guys, and then later on Ronnie and Pete made the club available without a fee on Sundays to a musicians' cooperative so they could present their own concerts. My father told Max Jones during an interview for the *Melody Maker*: 'Then we are thinking of putting on off-Broadway shows, and perhaps the occasional comedian.

We are on the lookout for talent that has not been over-exploited. We want the place to be more of an environment than simply a jazz club.' Miles Davis had never played the club, and my father wanted very much to present him on the main floor in the jazz room. Miles had visited the club several times as a customer. One such evening he came to see Selena Jones, a wonderful singer. Dave Holland, a British bass player, was a member of the trio accompanying her. Miles was completely knocked out with Dave's playing and asked him to join his band. Of course, Dave accepted – to play with Miles Davis was a coveted opportunity. Dad decided to approach Miles through Dave to see if Miles was interested in making an appearance.

On New Year's Day 1969 the Rangers *v.* Celtic soccer match was held at Ibrox Park in Glasgow. Ronnie knew that Donald, who had gone home for the holiday, was attending the match and was horrified as he watched the game on television and saw the crowd go mad. People were trampled on and crushed, and over seventy spectators were killed that day. Ronnie immediately telephoned Donald's dad to see if he had heard from him and if he was OK. He was terribly worried and it took some time and a couple more phone calls before Donald's safety was confirmed. Donald shared with me: 'That was the great thing about your dad. We knew that he genuinely cared about people, so the arguments didn't matter, and he *never* held it against you when it was all over.'

In February 1969 the Clarke–Boland Band led by co-leaders Kenny Clarke, drums, and Francy Boland, piano, made its debut at the club. The international personnel were American, German, Swedish, Dutch, Belgian, Yugoslavian and British. The line-up with two drummers, Kenny Clarke and Kenny Clare, was: Jimmy Woode or Jean Warland (bass), Dave Pike (vibes), Benny Bailey, Idrees Sulieman, Dusko Gojkovic, Jimmy Deuchar, Derek Watkins, Art Farmer and Rick Keefer (trumpets and flugelhorns), Åke Persson, Nat Peck, Erik van Lier (trombones), Derek Humble (alto sax), Ronnie Scott (tenor sax), Tony Coe (tenor sax and clarinet), Johnny Griffin (tenor sax) and Sahib Shihab (soprano sax and bass sax). Ronnie played with the Clarke–Boland Band from 1962 until the band folded in the 1970s. The calibre of his fellow musicians presented a challenge and he held them in high esteem. The consummate musician, Ronnie experienced some of his finest moments sitting in the sax section next to Derek Humble (he always said that he would play with Derek whenever the opportunity presented itself) and playing alongside Johnny Griffin, Sahib Shihab and Tony Coe.

During his tenure with the band Ronnie also did all the announcing, accompanied as usual by his oblique humour. The band was genuinely unique in jazz history. It was conceived, sustained and inspired by a dynamic Italian-born big band swing enthusiast, Gigi Campi. The members of the band, all major soloists in their own right, thrived on teamwork, and were able to create that delicate balance of structure and freedom which allowed the soloist on each number the support to fly and soar, making for a very powerful, poignant, virile, vigorous, sensual and driving *tour de force*. Amazingly, the band came together for only about two months out of every year, so on occasions they would play a concert with practically no rehearsal. Even so, such was the rapport between the musicians, and the combination of the superb orchestrations of Francy Boland, who did *all* the arrangements for the band, and his gift of writing for the musicians as individuals, which gave them a spirit of looseness, that they created absolute magic.

Although Ronnie thoroughly enjoyed touring with the band, flying was still an agony for him, haunted by his memories of his plane in 1963 bursting into flames as it taxied down the runway in New York. He could not approach the steps of an aeroplane without his 'potion'. The touring took the band all over Europe to such places as Berlin, Mainz, Baden, Prague, Vienna, Lugano, Rome, Brussels, Rotterdam, Cologne, Ostend, Rimini and Saarbrücken. So since Ronnie could not avoid flying, about twenty minutes before he was due to board the plane he would take a large drink of vodka and tonic and a couple of tranquillisers so that by the time he had to board he was oblivious to the daunting prospect. It was on one such occasion in 1968 that my mother met up with Dad in France and went with him and the band to Cologne. They were at Orly Airport with Johnny Griffin and Åke Persson and right on schedule Ronnie took his potion, but about five minutes later an announcement came over the speakers saying that the flight to Cologne was delayed by thirty minutes! Mum was mortified. Dad became dopier and dopier, finally slipping into a deep sleep, then came the announcement that the plane was ready for boarding at gate number thirty something, which was miles of corridor away from where they were sitting. Panic abounded. Ronnie was by this time a dead weight, and no one else was around to help. Mum recalled: 'Åke got a cup of cold water and poured it over Ronnie's head. In the end we got him into a semiconscious state, and fortunately Åke, who was a strapping six feet two, got him to his feet and did most of the supporting, with me holding him up on the other side. Meanwhile Johnny ran hell for leather to the plane to get them to wait until Åke and I arrived with

Ronnie slumping between us. We made that flight by the skin of our teeth, with Ronnie intact for the gig that night!' It took many years, but eventually my father overcame his fear of flying and had no further need of his potion.

April 1969 saw a return visit of Stan Getz and his quartet, with Jack de Johnette on drums. Stan was on top form during this run, as Ronnie said: 'Stan is spellbinding as a musician. He is a master technician, a brilliant melodic improviser and an artist of impeccable taste.' One evening Stan came into the club with his friend Peter Sellers. They had just spent the afternoon together, and Stan went on to do the first set. Jack de Johnette remembered: 'Stan was having a little difficulty blowing. Peter Sellers, who was sitting at a table right in front of the bandstand, was doubled over with laughter. The more trouble Stan had, the more he laughed. All of a sudden Stan realised what had happened, and he leaned forward and said to Peter: "You bastard! You put pot in those brownies!" Everybody cracked up!' The audience cottoned on. Peter was reliving his role from the movie *I Love You, Alice B. Toklas*, which had been released just six months previously in October 1968 and was incredibly popular both in Britain and the USA.

It was also during this run that Judy Garland, booked to play at the London Palladium, came to the club to hear Stan play. Although frail, she was still incredibly beautiful. Stan spotted her in the audience and dedicated a couple of tunes to her, then coaxed her to join him on the bandstand. Judy was wearing an off-the-shoulder red dress with a very full skirt. She sat on a stool that was quickly provided for her, the circular skirt completely surrounding it. Judy's exquisite face, with large, soft, dark brown eyes, framed with prettily coiffed dark hair standing out against her white shoulders and in contrast to the red dress, was absolutely magical. Stan gave Judy centre stage while he stood to one side quietly accompanying her with his gentle melodic phrasing, the haunting tone that was uniquely Getz, as Judy, in fine voice, sang two numbers. It was a rare moment in music, and the audience was enraptured by the performance. This was a memory cherished by both my parents. Tragically, Judy Garland died just two months later, on 22 June 1969, at the age of forty-seven, in her London flat, from an overdose of barbiturates.

Playing opposite Stan Getz was the Scaffold, a comedy group of three. This was by no means the first time that comedy had been presented at the club. My father's love of comedy and his belief that it went hand in hand with good music threaded its way through the 1960s and early 1970s, beginning with the performances in the old club by Cecil 'Flash' Winston, an old friend of Ronnie's from his teenage years. Flash was a drummer and a pianist and did comedy too; he was in pursuit of a career as a stand-up comedian and Ronnie and Pete had booked him into the club. The Scaffold, Mike McGear (Paul McCartney's brother) Roger McGough and John Gorman were hilarious. In one of the routines John for two shows a night every night for a week shoved three cream-filled chocolate eclairs in rapid succession into his mouth to the accompanying taunts of Mike and Roger. Jack de Johnette watched each show every night, never tiring of the routines. He recalled: 'I used to wait for the eclair scene. Each performance was as fresh as the first. I was amazed that he could do that night after night with no ill effects!'

Another comedy group to play the club was Cheech and Chong. They were all the rage and had an album out that was doing very well. Then came Professor Irwin Corey, who during his visit included an involuntary Miles Davis in his act. Miles, an outspoken advocate for black people who quite understandably harboured a strong animosity against their exploitation by whites, was sitting with his entourage of young ladies at a table right in front of the bandstand. Miles was dressed in a white suit and was wearing a white trilby and enormous, very dark sunglasses. In the middle of his act, Professor Corey bent down and deftly snatched Miles's dark glasses off his face. Corey then put the glasses on, looked out at the audience for a moment or two, and then said to Miles, 'Hey! No wonder you're smiling – everybody looks black!' Miles joined in the laughter as Irwin Corey handed him his glasses.

The first musical experiment occurred in 1969, which was the year of Ronnie Scott's tenth anniversary, with a combination of classical and jazz guitar featuring John Williams and Barney Kessel. This held a particular fascination for my mother. My grandmother, Barbara Hulin, was a music teacher, and Mum was brought up with classical music and used to play the violin, although at the same time she loved jazz and would listen in secret to a French radio station to hear Billie Holiday, Lester Young, Charlie Parker and Coleman Hawkins after everybody else had gone to bed. My parents had wonderful memories of this engagement, the musical combination far surpassing their wildest expectations and dreams, and filling them with a sense of adventure. The unswerving integrity of both artists swept the audiences through a week of lyrical, witty, romantic and glittering musical heights. There were no hecklers or talkers during this run; every night was like a concert. The experiment was a resounding success, so much so that John Williams performed at the club on several occasions.

When John Dankworth and Cleo Laine played the club with John's big band, the audiences were incredibly enthusiastic with their applause and shouts for more. Knowing that it was Cleo's practice to do an encore, sometimes two, Ronnie was out front by the door thinking he had another ten minutes or so before he had to get the band off the bandstand. Cleo came to the end of her last song and signalled to John that she was leaving, there was going to be no encore. John remembered: 'She dashed past me, saying, "I can't wait! I *have* to go to the loo *right now*." Ronnie came running up to the bandstand to get us off. He was very concerned and asked me: "What's wrong with Cleo? Did I say something to upset her?" By now I was laughing and said: "No, Ron, but if you want Cleo to do encores you'd better get a loo fixed up in the dressing room. She *had* to go!" ' At that time the only ladies' room was the one all the way downstairs in the basement. The next night when John and Cleo arrived at the club and went into the dressing room, which was equipped with a small washbasin, they found a new addition to the furnishings: a commode sat in one corner. A notice had been taped to the wall above it, handwritten by Ronnie, stating: 'No Number Twos, Please!'

The list of big bands that followed from the 1960s through the 1970s was truly impressive: Woody Herman, Maynard Ferguson, Johnny Dankworth, Harry James, Tommy Dorsey, Thad Jones–Mel Lewis, Count Basie, Stan Kenton and Buck Clayton with his All Stars. An outstanding trumpet soloist, Wilbur 'Buck' Clayton, who made his reputation with the original Count Basie Orchestra, was also a brilliant orchestrator and composer. One night after the band had completed its first set, as was Buck's custom, he sat down to eat a chicken dinner. Somehow he bit into a chicken bone, and his front teeth, which were part of a bridge that had been giving him trouble for some time, completely broke. It was catastrophic for this to happen to a musician whose embouchure is his life. Buck determined to see the night out, glued the bridge back in and somehow managed to play enough to get through the rest of the evening. My mother always made sure that the musicians were taken care of and had served Buck the ill-fated chicken. Knowing the severity of the situation she was highly concerned about Buck's embouchure. This event turned into a seven-year nightmare for Buck. He and my mother were good friends and they corresponded from time to time. When we moved to New York, my mother and I visited Buck and his wife in Jamaica, Queens. He and my mother had many long conversations about the damage that chicken bone did to his mouth. Buck went to innumerable dentists, none of whom was able to restore his embouchure. At times he was very depressed because he could not play, but he kept battling with the problem and eventually found a couple of dentists in Boston who devised and implanted a shield for him. After about six months he got his 'chops' back and was playing again. He told Mum many times that the only thing that kept him going and really saved him through those seven years was the fact that he could lose himself in writing arrangements and orchestrations. In 1996, when Dad started having problems with his teeth and could no longer play, I couldn't help thinking that if he had been able to compose and write arrangements it might have made the world of difference. He would not have had to deal with that overwhelming feeling that everything was over for him.

C rescendo magazine ran a subtitle: WHEN RONNIE SCOTT FINALLY RAISED THE PORTCULLIS. The article, written by Laurie Henshaw, stated: 'For such a jazz-steeped bastion as Ronnie Scott's to open the portcullis to pop might seem as heretical as the Orangemen going over en masse to the Church of Rome. At least, in the blinkered eyes of jazz purists. Nevertheless, in a brave and imaginative gesture that might have aroused a "sell-out to commercialism" chorus from the jazz aficionados, Ronnie Scott and Pete King did initiate a pop policy at the club. And it has proved an unqualified success.'

The groups that Pete and Ronnie booked had an affinity with jazz, and as a testimony to their musicianship they sometimes played the main jazz room. The first group to be booked into the upstairs room was called Affinity, featuring singer Linda Hoyle. Ronnie noted that forward-looking groups like Pink Floyd, Soft Machine and the Cream, to mention just a few, were actually playing jazz of a kind; he was aware of the influence that jazz had on certain pop musicians. Pete, too, had his preferences and admired Affinity, a group called Lace and Humble Pie, saying: 'Peter Frampton is more than just a pretty face. That kid can really play.' It grew into a new era where the pop groups' managers et al. would rent the main floor of the club in the afternoons for such things as press receptions, or promo receptions that would include the record companies, and so business expanded without deviating from the main attraction, which was the jazz itself presented every night in the main room.

More than a year had passed since the Old Place in Gerrard Street had closed. Ronnie and Pete were still trying to find a way to present the new advanced British jazz groups, and they decided to revive the Old Place in the upstairs room at Ronnie Scott's in Frith Street. The plan was to present the best of British jazz from Monday to Thursday from 8 p.m. until 11.30 p.m., with a different group each week. The idea behind this was to provide a home for groups that were not well known enough to play in the main room downstairs, which had to bring in enough money to pay the rent, and to run the music in conjunction with the discotheque. After 11.30 p.m. records were played and people could dance until 3 a.m. Fridays and Saturdays reverted to the normal discotheque — pop groups and all-night dancing. The jazz nights were to open on 4 August with the Mike Westbrook Group.

Disaster struck on the night before the opening when a fire broke out in the upstairs room. Fortunately, no structural damage occurred, but nevertheless new seating had to be built and the place had to be replastered and painted so the opening was rescheduled for 15 August with the Chris McGregor band.

Luckily, the fire did no damage to the jazz room and did not interfere with the BBC taking over the club for six days during the early part of the evening, until about 10.30 p.m., to film a series of programmes of British jazz called 'Jazz Scene'. They filmed two shows a day, which were to be shown some time in the autumn on BBC2, with Ronnie introducing each segment, produced by Terry Henebery. They presented such artists as Tubby Hayes, Johnny Dankworth's Seven, the Mike Westbrook Big Band, the Graham Collier Sextet, the Alex Welsh Band and John Surman. This series was so successful that Terry Henebery booked the club for another BBC2 jazz series, this time with American artists, which took a couple of weeks to complete; each show was produced in front of an invited audience. This was the first and only time that Miles Davis was to perform at the club. Ronnie acted as compere for the sixteen-week series, which consisted of about forty-five separate links to introduce all the different segments. He had to do this in one afternoon as though the whole thing was live.

The line-up of performers was impressive, and indeed made the occasion a memorable one. It included Lionel Hampton, Sarah Vaughan, Cecil Taylor, the Oscar Peterson Trio, and the Clarke–Boland and the Buddy Rich Orchestras. Cleo Laine, Jon Hendricks and Annie Ross were among the audience on the night that the Buddy Rich Orchestra played, and after the cameras stopped rolling Buddy decided to do an encore for the audience, and Jon and Annie took the stage to sing with the band some of the brilliant repertoire from their days in the Lambert, Hendricks and Ross vocal group. Then Cleo went up and joined them. It was one of those rare, spontaneous occasions in jazz when all the performers involved excelled themselves, and the response of the audience was such that an electrifying surge seemed to circulate between the performers and the audience. The level of communication was incredible.

Ronnie Scott Directions expanded their clientele to pop groups, and Affinity was the first to join the roster. Chips Chipperfield, who was later joined by Jimmy Parsons, helped run the agency, which booked tours and concerts of every description. The office was in rooms above the club. Between them, Ronnie and Pete were building the business to encompass as many areas as natural growth led them into – publishing, production, come what may. Wally Houser, in his role as solicitor, was right there throughout, setting up the companies and taking care of the legalities as and when necessary. Wally was also a personal friend of my father's, and on many evenings in the 'inner sanctum' they would do *The Times* crossword together. Wally shared Ronnie's fascination for films, particularly for the old Hollywood bit players whom Ronnie was very adept at taking off, and my father would get Wally to try to guess the name of the actor. Wally remembered: 'We loved all that. In fact I bought him a book called *Who Was That?* which was filled with pictures of the faces of little-known actors you would see in the old films.' Ronnie was already well known when Wally first met him in Manchester as a young saxophonist himself, and Wally recalled: 'I've always said that Ronnie was in fact the leader of my generation. He was what I wanted to be: a charismatic frontrunner who showed the way to all the younger jazz musicians. And it wasn't only the jazz; it was his entire demeanour. He personified "cool" in England before it happened.'

Spike Milligan was a frequent visitor to the club. He liked to sit at a particular table, and in those days enjoyed a bottle of Mateus Rosé which Ronnie often had sent over to his table for him. Like Ronnie, Spike hated it when people in the audience talked through the music. There was an ongoing banter between him and Ronnie because Spike would have liked to have his table hooked up to the sound system so that he could listen in peace to the music through earphones. This arrangement never actually materialised, but Ronnie, when doing his fifteen minutes of stand-up, would rib Spike by telling the audience the story, saying: 'The funny thing is he's often one of the noisiest members of the audience! Look, Spike, wherever we seat you, you're going to be near Milligan!' In all seriousness, although the audiences had changed since the nights at the Old Place when you really could hear a pin drop, my father went to great lengths to try to control the level of chatter in the audience. While the music was on he would often stand by the sound booth at the back to the left of the bandstand and would ask my mother to stand to the right at the back of the club, and together they would 'shush' the offending customers. It would catch on like a forest fire, and within seconds other customers who wanted to listen would join in the 'shushing'. Most of the time this ploy worked very well and a respectful silence was maintained. However, on occasions the offending customers were either too drunk to notice or just plain ignorant. On one such evening my father took the stand to take the band off, and he addressed a particularly raucous table of four, pointing at it from the bandstand and saying: 'Excuse me, madam . . . sir . . . excuse me. I think you must have come to the wrong place. You're obviously not in here to listen to the music, so would you please go to the coffee shop across the street where you can talk to your hearts' content. And on your way out you can collect your admission fee from the front desk.' The rest of the audience applauded and the group left immediately.

It was my father's habit in the early hours of the morning to run down to the all-night newsagent's and pick up the papers as soon as they came out. He would always pick one up for Jeff, who was tending the door, at the same time. One night he had something on his mind and forgot Jeff's newspaper, and this happened twice in one week. Jeff started to rib Ronnie unmercifully about losing his memory, teasing him about his age; they both shared the same birthday and often exchanged friendly banter over the subject. This evening, laughing, Jeff pulled out a piece of paper and wrote out a contract which read: 'I, Ronnie Scott, do hereby declare that I will bring Jeff Ellison his newspaper every night from now on. Signed by Ronnie Scott.' Jeff made Ronnie sign it. After the joking was over Jeff stuffed the 'contract' into his pocket and took it home, but he kept it among his memorabilia, and dog-eared and tatty as it is today, Jeff's widow Marge still has it.

The year ended on a high note for Ronnie musically. He put together a sixteen-piece orchestra for a Granada TV show called *Getting Sentimental Over You*. It was a TV special and the band accompanied the singers Lita Rosa, Marion Montgomery, Cleo Laine, Dickie Valentine and Vince Hill. Maynard Ferguson, the well-known trumpet player and band leader, was featured as a guest artist. In addition to this, Ronnie and his orchestra provided the music for a feature film about the 1969 Cannes Film Festival called *Festival Game*.

The eight-piece band had narrowed down to a sextet with some changes in personnel. The group started off the 1970s by playing at the club in January, they went on to do out-of-town gigs, and in March played the International Jazz Festival in Prague for five days. The governmental restrictions that afflicted the residents of Prague – wages were small and frozen, people could not afford any luxuries – touched my father deeply. He had made friends with a family there and, although he brought home a few keepsakes, he gave them all the money that he had been paid for his performances. Later on that year Dad formed a trio with Mike Carr on organ and Tony Crombie on drums. They played the club, toured Great Britain and Europe, and did several radio broadcasts. The trio was a combination that my father enjoyed immensely. Mike Carr played the Hammond organ and was as active with the foot pedals as he was with the keyboard, producing an exciting sound.

It was during the early 1970s that Ella Fitzgerald came over to do a show at the Grosvenor House Hotel, Park Lane, opposite Oscar Peterson's trio. Ronnie formed a big band especially for the occasion to accompany Ella. Among the musicians he selected to play in the band was Vic Ash, clarinet. Vic had not played with Ronnie since he was a very young man at the Club Eleven and had gone down to hear Ronnie play. In those days the clarinet was not a very predominant instrument in the world of bebop, but Vic was an enthusiast and asked Ronnie if he could sit in. Ronnie said: 'Yes, sure. Come on up.' Vic told me that he would remember that night for the rest of his life. He got up on the bandstand, knocked out that Ronnie had agreed he could sit in, saying: 'He didn't know me. He may have heard me play, but I'm not a hundred per cent sure about that. However, as I got on to the bandstand the drummer turned to me and said, looking at my clarinet: "You're not going to play that fucking thing, are you?" So I looked at Ronnie pleadingly, almost in tears, and Ronnie said: "Don't take any notice of him. You play." That was wonderful of Ronnie; his encouragement was great. I never dreamed that I would be playing with him in one of the bands that he had, and all those years later I was to sit next to him for the week we accompanied Ella. I felt very honoured, it was a wonderful week.' Vic Ash often stopped by the club to listen to the music, and fondly recalled: 'Ronnie used to always call me Victory all through the years right up until the last time I saw him, which was about three months before he died. I was rehearsing in the club for something and he walked in and said: "Hey, Victory." And I always called him Ronaldo.'

The club saw the new decade in with return visits from Roland Kirk and

Stan Getz, who had just recovered from double pneumonia and was suffering from a broken foot. His family was with him during this engagement. They had rented an apartment by the Mediterranean in a small town east of Málaga, and also a flat in Mayfair, London, spending most of their time in Europe for the next couple of years. Stan's daughter Beverly attended an all-girls boarding-school in Oxfordshire. It was during this visit that Stan, who had formed a friendship with my mother, introduced her to his wife Monica and daughters Beverly and Pamela. Soon they all became friends, and unbeknown to my mother at the time this friendship would prove to be her safety net in a time of great need only four years away.

CHAPTER TEN

IS IT ALL POSSIBLE?

Life is a gamble, at terrible odds – if it was a bet, you wouldn't take it.

TOM STOPPARD

Dizzy gave more of himself than any musician I know. He personally taught all the trumpet players who were playing at that time and a lot of drummers too. He's a saint. KENNY 'KLOOK' CLARKE, quoted in *Notes and Tones* by Arthur Taylor

For me the greatest thing I have ever heard has been Sonny Rollins. He's the kind of guy if he works here for a month I'll be out there every set, listening. And after a while it's difficult to do that, you know. But with Rollins, I'd hate to miss a set – because you never know what is going to happen.

RONNIE SCOTT, 'Ronnie Scott's Opinions', *Crescendo*

D uring the Getz run Ben Webster, who lived in Denmark, was visiting London and came to the club. Ben was drinking quite a lot at the time and, with conscious deliberation, was making his way through the tables to the office at the back of the club. Stan was sitting at one of the tables with Sydney Gotlieb, engaged in conversation. Ben, who was a massive man, seeing Stan, leaned across Sydney and asked: 'What the *hell* are you doing here, you white Jew boy?' Needless to say the comment lit Stan's fuse and, rising to his feet, he promptly responded in kind, the two men glowering at each other with Sydney in the middle. Ronnie spotted the situation and arrived at the table in the nick of time. Placing one hand on each man's shoulder he calmly but firmly instructed them both to 'Sit!', which they immediately did, like lambs. Then he proceeded to talk to everyone in general about a completely different subject, and within minutes the two musicians were contentedly conversing with each other and Sydney as though nothing had happened. Dr Gotlieb, who to say the least had felt extremely uncomfortable sandwiched between these two very irate men, marvelled at my father's ability to effortlessly defuse the situation.

Jack de Johnette, Stan's drummer, would often listen to Ronnie play, sometimes on sound checks in the afternoon, at other times when his band was playing opposite the American guest artist, and sometimes when Hank Mobley, who lived in Paris and played at Le Chat Qui Pêche club, was performing at Ronnie's. Jack remembered: 'When Hank was playing at the club, Ronnie picked up some of his stuff, maintaining his own distinct sound but using Hank's loose kind of technique. Whenever I heard him play he would swing and was very melodic. I'll never forget the way he played "What's New?", very warm. He always played with deep feeling; his ballads were always straight from the heart.'

It was during these years that Princess Margaret, often accompanied by Peter Sellers and sometimes Spike Milligan, would come to the club. When she was first introduced to Ronnie she said: 'Ah, yes, you're the club' – an interesting observation. As Uncle Pete said: 'Ronnie had the ability to talk to people and break down barriers, and with his humour he was able to break down the audience. His presentation grew and he enhanced the club, becoming as well known for that as his music.'

Ronnie and Pete had set a very high standard of music at the club which they kept going with a variety of music in the 1970s. Some were return visits, but there were still many first-time sessions to be heard. To name just a few, Charles Mingus, Earl Hines, the Harry James big band and Maynard Ferguson's big band, Herbie Mann and Anita O'Day all appeared between 1970 and 1971. A return visit of the Clarke–Boland Big Band, this time for a three-week engagement, was a distinct highlight, playing to a full house every night. Unbeknown to Dad at the time, this engagement was to become highly significant for him: it was the last time he would sit next to his old friend Derek Humble as he led the saxophone section.

One of the policies at the club ever since the day of its inception was that old friends were always welcome, Alf Summers remembering the old days in Gerrard Street when he would just walk up to the door and say, 'Alf Summers, friend of Ronnie Scott's', and Ronnie would come to the door and usher him in. But later on, through a third party, Alf learned that Ronnie had said he could not make the club pay because he had so many friends and musicians who all walked in without paying; there were hardly any paying customers. Alf said: 'I felt a bit guilty about that, so every time I went to the new club in Frith Street I used to beg to pay. But Ronnie and Pete would say: "We've got enough paying customers now. You don't have to pay any more." That was the only time I argued with him, when he wouldn't let me pay.' Sometimes other friends from the days of the Jewish youth clubs would be quietly sitting at a table and Ronnie would spot them and say: 'You didn't pay to come in, did you?' The answer was often in the affirmative, and as Alf Shaw remembered: 'Ronnie would disappear and come back with a refund off the door.' So many people have told me that all through the years Dad was a very generous man, and a gracious host, often sending drinks over to tables or picking up the entire bill, making sure that friends and musicians were well taken care of.

Much to the amusement of many of Ronnie's friends and the musicians, my father in profile bore an uncanny resemblance to Giovanni B. Montini, Pope Paul VI, and as a result Dad was the butt of many a wisecrack. But Åke Persson, a close friend of Dad's and a fantastic trombone player in the Clarke–Boland Band, during his travels came across a postcard profile portrait of the Pope and mailed it to Ronnie at the club, writing: 'Ronnie, you are really big time. Your picture is out all over the world, and Jew you look beautiful! I think some hip, I mean very very hip shit!' The card was a source of much levity for several weeks among the musicians and friends who wandered in and out of the club.

Dad still played cards across the street with Albert Dimes and his cronies. The only problem was that sometimes he lost and the debt would accrue and the winners would pour into the club for a few evenings of food, wine, good music and merrymaking, often to the discomfort of the regular punters, who would gather up their belongings and leave! This obviously was not good for business and was something that Uncle Pete did not derive too much pleasure out of either. Often Ronnie would start out on a winning streak, but then his luck would change and he would start losing. In an effort to regain his lucky streak he would phone the club and get my mother to come and stand behind his left shoulder as he played, because she brought him luck! Often when his call came through, the club would be quite busy and Uncle Pete was not too pleased with this arrangement because Mary was needed in the club. But when he considered how much money was lost when the mob came into the club he decided that the lesser of the two evils was to go along with the arrangement. My father told me: 'Albert was a very loyal friend to me, and on the rare occasion in the past if anyone created a disturbance – and looked like a villain – I would mention it to Albert and that troublemaker never came to the club again.'

Tragedy struck when Derek Humble, who had for the preceding three years suffered from the traumatic repercussions of a serious head injury, died on 22 February 1971. Dad considered him to be 'the complete lead alto saxophonist and a glorious soloist'. He and my father had been kindred spirits musically from 1950 and played together in many different circumstances over the years, becoming close friends en route. Dad described Derek as 'a friend I cannot afford to lose'. He was deeply distressed by the loss of his friend and penned a full-page tribute to Derek in the *Melody Maker*. Although Dad had over the years contributed articles from time to time to various jazz publications, this particular tribute was such a sensitive and well-written piece that afterwards he received offers from various publications to become at least a part-time journalist. Although he had what it takes to be a great writer, the call from his soul was music and the saxophone his medium. As he said: 'As long as I'm playing my instrument, that's enough really. I'm a jazz musician and this is really my excuse for existence.' Interestingly enough, when it came to writing music, Ronnie had trouble putting it down on paper. He would hum tunes to friends and they would write the melody down for him. The few original compositions that he did leave us with were straight from the heart, such as 'Some of My Best Friends Are Blues', 'I'm Sick and Tired of Waking up Tired and Sick', 'Ronnie's Blues', 'Blues in B and B Flat', 'Treat It Lightly' (inspired by Sonny Rollins), 'Scott's Expedition', 'Double or Nothing' and 'Fast and Loose'.

During these years a fair amount of new music was emerging, some of it called 'Free Jazz' or 'Avant-Garde' or 'New Wave'. Popular music was evolving and some really good bands were appearing. Ronnie was not a musical bigot by any measure; he listened to all kinds of music and respected the different avenues that some of the veteran musicians decided to explore. When the music world lost John Coltrane at the age of forty in July 1967, his full potential still unrealised, it was a tremendous blow to all concerned. John Coltrane was a favourite of my father's, although Dad was quite clear about the fact that he preferred his earlier work, which encompassed expressions of Coltrane's lyricism, melodic outlook and incredible technique, recognising that not everyone was able to go along with his development into the Avant-garde. As he said to the *Melody Maker*: 'When a guy of his stature decides to go a certain way, he must command your respect and attention.' Not all the musicians who chose this particular avenue of music commanded my father's respect. He openly admitted that he could not get much at all from some of their renderings, stating in another interview with the *Melody Maker* that 'if you gave a saxophone to a chimp, it would make some very original noises'.

My parents had been together for seven years now. The little flat in Elm Park Mansions had become a real home, a place where my father could completely relax. Working in the club together only enhanced their relationship, but music was an integral part of their lives – and not only jazz. Dad also liked to listen to the classics. He loved Vivaldi's *The Four Seasons*, and Ravel, Debussy and Chopin were among his favourite classical composers. He was also partial to Italian opera, particularly Puccini.

In March 1971 Dad was to lose another friend. Harold McNair, the Jamaican flautist and sax player, became very ill with lung cancer. He had gone through surgery as a last resort, which brought only temporary relief, so my father arranged a benefit for him at the club and many of Harold's friends played. The immediate object was to assist with the expenses of a long holiday abroad for him and his wife Hilary. They actually went on a world cruise, living every minute to the -nth degree, a time together that they both cherished.

Hilary telephoned Ronnie and Mary on 7 March and asked them to come to visit Harold, who really wanted to see Ronnie. Ill as Harold was, it was an evening of reminiscing and friendship. Earlier, Harold had insisted that Hilary buy four tickets for the Muhammad Ali – Joe Frazier fight that was being broadcast via satellite from Madison Square Gardens, New York, to the Marble Arch Odeon in London the following day. The level of promotion for this fight was unparalleled in the history of boxing. Harold said: 'Ronnie, I'd hoped to be there with you, my treat, but I don't think that I'm going to be here tomorrow. I want you and Mary and Hilary to go to the fight in style. A limo will pick you all up and take you there. All of you must promise me that no matter what happens you will do it! It will make me very happy.' The promise was made, and Ronnie and Harold entered into a debate about who was going to win the fight. Ronnie, of course, had to make a wager. Harold favoured Joe Frazier, and the discussion was animated. Shortly afterwards my parents left and went on to the club. Later that night the call came from Hilary; Harold had indeed died. Everyone agreed to keep their promise and they went to see the fight. The seat that had been purchased for Harold remained vacant, and yet the three of them felt that he was right there cheering Frazier on. It turned out to be one of the greatest heavyweight championship battles ever. In the fifteenth round Joe Frazier landed perhaps the most famous left hook in history, catching Ali on the jaw and dropping the former champ for a four count. At the end of fifteen gruelling rounds, Frazier got the nod from all three judges and left the ring as the undisputed champion. What a night. At age thirty-nine, Harold went out in style, with his friends honouring his memory just the way he wanted them to. I always find myself marvelling at Harold's courage every time I think about this story.

During the same month Ronnie came face to face with the seriousness of his son's ill health. Nicholas, who was now seven years old, had to have an operation to repair the holes in his heart. It was very dangerous, and there was a possibility that Nicholas would not survive. My mother had always been very supportive of Dad being there for Nicholas, and her nursing experience had helped her through Ronnie's constant visits to hospital during his early childhood. Life had not been easy for Ilsa. The night before the operation, as Ronnie paced the flat filled with anxiety and concern for his young son's welfare, he and Mary talked about the possibilities that lay ahead. Mary respected Ilsa as an independent and determined young woman who was clearly completely devoted to Nicholas. If anybody could strengthen Nicholas's will to survive, it was Ilsa. Ronnie agreed.

Fortunately, during the course of the year Nicholas recovered well, resuming many of his activities. It was a tremendous relief all round, and Christmas was extra special in celebration of his recovery.

E arly one evening Ronnie was sitting at the front desk with Mary. As was his custom, using a felt-tipped pen he was writing out the brochures for the following month's coming attractions and working on the layout for the printer. As they were chatting, in walked Roy, who worked the customers' bar in the jazz room. Mary looked up and said: 'What are you doing here? I fired you last night.' Roy said: 'I know, but I thought I'd come in anyway, just to see if you'd change your mind.' Ronnie looked at them both, saying: 'You fired Roy? What happened? You can't fire Roy. He *loves* jazz.' Mary responded: 'Maybe too much. He was so busy listening that the customers couldn't get a drink!' Ronnie chuckled, suggesting that Roy might try serving and listening at the same time, and Roy was duly reinstated with no hard feelings.

In June of this year the Clarke–Boland Big Band was gathered at Cornet Studios, Cologne, to record an album called 'Change of Scenes'. Stan Getz was invited to record with the band, and one of the things that made it a unique album was that Stan was adamant that the session was not to be a 'guest-soloist-with-big-band-backing affair'. Francy Boland wrote six suites specially for the album, a phenomenal example of his ability to write each part specifically for the individual musicians in the band. As Bob Houston so succinctly described at the end of his liner notes for the album: 'Within these six suites is captured the essence of Stan Getz as a major jazz stylist. Not the Stan Getz of "Long Island Sound"; not the Stan Getz of "Four Brothers"; not even the Stan Getz of "Focus", probably his greatest single artistic achievement until now. This is Stan Getz now; a mature and complete musician, reacting to and being inspired by the music of Francy Boland and the CBBB. A mutual musical catalyst. It is safe to predict that none of them may ever be the same again.' Ronnie soloed on one of the miniature saxophone concertos, called 'Touchstone', and Stan was so moved by Ronnie's performance that he congratulated him on his contribution. My father had a great admiration and respect for Stan's musicianship. Stan was recognised internationally as one of the great jazz virtuosos, so his endorsement of Dad's playing meant a tremendous amount to Dad.

Over the years there was a camaraderie between them, with inevitable discussions of reeds and mouthpieces and music. Stan was born on 2 February 1927, just five days after Ronnie. They kidded each other about their birthdays constantly, Stan always teasing Ronnie about being older than him, then Ronnie would pull rank on Stan, and so it would go on. Although there were periods when Stan was drinking and it is a well-known fact that on occasions major disputes took place and heated arguments ensued, as my father said in *Some of My Best Friends Are Blues*: '. . . I guess it did us all good to get the frustration out of our systems because when the dust had settled we stood around looking at each other sheepishly and realised that somehow we didn't have problems any more.'

Stan was among the large number of people who have always said that when Dad was on stage at the club making his jokes, even if you had heard them a thousand times it didn't really matter: it was his impeccable timing, his unique delivery, the deadpan face which made you laugh. Zoot Sims' wife Louise always made sure she sat at a little table to the side of the bandstand during her visits to the club. She told me: 'I watched all your dad's intermission jokes. I just loved him – over and over again I listened to his routines and laughed each time as though I was hearing the jokes for the first time.' All the many musicians, British and American, I have spoken to are in complete agreement with Louise: they all looked forward to the fifteen minutes of banter between each set. Dad's mind was as quick as lightning, and if there was a heckler in the club he would go back and forth with stinging one-liners. Mum often tells the story of when she was working at the club and a very loud, snobby woman heckled Dad while he was telling his jokes. He let her carry on and on, and when she finally stopped, looking her right in the eye with a dead straight face, he said, 'Madam, are you aware that in India you would be considered sacred?' There was a split second of silence and then everyone in the audience roared with laughter and the unfortunate woman left with her escort.

What the audiences didn't hear much of was the everyday one-liners that he would deliver as a response to whatever was happening at the time. One night Allan Ganley, who was home from his residency in Bermuda, walked into the club with a fantastic tan wearing a white suit. Ronnie looked up and said: 'Here he is, Allan Ganley, our man from Havana!' Allan, the first to admit that he is endowed with a large nose, laughingly told me that Ronnie used to tease him, saying: 'You've never been beaten in a photo finish!' Chips Chipperfield told me about a night he was working at the front desk on the door. Some nights were slower than others, and if there was a lengthy lull in business Chips liked to read a book. Pete had a problem with this and told Chips that he could not read while he was attending the door. It was a Wednesday night, which tended for some reason back then to be the slowest night of the week, and Chips was bored to tears. Ronnie was doing his usual thing of pacing up and down the club – he always said it helped him think through whatever was on his mind at the time – and as he walked past the front desk Chips said: 'Ronnie, what's wrong with Pete? He won't let me read a book when it's not busy.' Ronnie made his turn, and as he was approaching the desk, still walking, he said to Chips: 'Pete has a problem with books.' Chips replied: 'Why?' Ronnie looked over his shoulder and responded: 'He read one once.'

Although a voracious reader himself, Ronnie did not have a taste for the classics at all; his preference was with the contemporary, with the exception of philosophy. Authors such as Dickens, Pushkin or Tolstoy, or tales of mythology for example, held no interest for him. On a 1963 visit to Marjorca, when they were at the Indigo Jazz Club, Robert Graves proudly presented Dad with a book, *T.E. Lawrence To His Biographers*, the biographers being Robert himself and B.H. Liddell Hart. The subject matter was information about Lawrence of Arabia in the form of letters, notes and answers to questions, edited with critical commentary – a literary work. Ronnie lent the book to Chips, telling Mary: 'It's not really my cup of tea.' Thirty-odd years later, after Dad's memorial service, Chips returned the book to us. Although I never met Robert Graves, I felt that I knew him through my parents. They both told me many stories about him. He was a part of my growing up, in a way, and we had some of his books in America, mainly poetry and mythology.

In January 1972 my mother became pregnant with me. My father's reaction was one of sheer panic. Eventually, Mary got him to explain his fears. He was terrified that something would go wrong and that the baby would not be healthy. He was still only forty-five so my mother, who was twenty-nine, tried to explain to him that there should be no problem, that it's only when the woman is older that risks are higher. Completely unable to assuage his fears, Mary made an appointment at a well-known clinic so that tests could be run to ascertain that the baby was healthy. Ronnie calmed down considerably, welcoming a medical examination, and together they kept the appointment. The doctor at the clinic quickly assessed the situation and was able to reassure my father that his genes were all healthy and, after examining my mother, assured him that both she and the baby were perfectly healthy and that there was no reason to do any invasive testing. It was as though my father had been given a new lease of life. He was ecstatic that all was well and from that moment on looked forward to the arrival of the new baby. They agreed that if the baby was a girl, Daddy would choose the name, and, if a boy, Mum would choose, the one stipulation being that under *no* circumstances could she call him Ronald, because in the Jewish tradition you must not name a baby after anyone who is still alive, only after those who have passed on.

S tephane Grappelli, who made his name playing with Django Reinhardt, the Belgian gypsy guitarist, made his first appearance at the club. Stephane, an elegant man of immaculate taste, played swinging violin. His playing always seemed full of joy, melodic and romantic; his style was straightforward and clean. Audiences thrilled at his musicianship. Stephane's friend, Yehudi Menuhin, came in to hear him play several times during the run and one night sat in with him for a couple of tunes. It was an extraordinary performance, and afterwards each of the virtuosos expressed his trepidation at being able to make it work musically, but the set was a resounding success and the audience could not believe what they had just heard.

In April that year Ronnie was asked to put together a big band to accompany Jack Jones on a one-month British tour. They were to play

Fairfield Hall in Croydon. Just as George was about to leave the club at 7 p.m., Ronnie phoned and said to Pete: 'Send George here. I need him.' So George caught his second wind, jumped in a cab and went to the hall to help set things up for the band. He said: 'I'd been working since early morning, but I ran on adrenalin in those days. Ronnie and I set everything up the way he liked it. I got him a cup of tea backstage, then the band went on. It was the thrill of my life to see them all in their bow ties and monkey suits – they looked *so* good on stage. Then they started to play. Ronnie and Tubby Hayes together were fantastic, and I was so proud to be working for Ronnie. What a man! He was a born leader.' Ronnie's orchestra started to pack up and pile into the coach. George remembered: 'Jack Jones was talking to Ronnie and Ronnie said: "OK, Jack, I'll see you tomorrow." Jack responded: "No, no, Ronnie, you're riding with me. You don't have to ride in the coach." Jack had a limo standing by, but Ronnie said: "Sorry, Jack. I always ride with my band. See you tomorrow." And your dad climbed into the coach with the rest of the guys. It was a blast all the way home. He had everybody laughing and telling limericks and all kinds of crazy stuff. But that was Ronnie, completely unpretentious, and he couldn't stand anyone who was.'

Although Tubby and his band had played the club on several occasions, it had been a couple of years since Ronnie had spent any time with his old friend and co-leader of the Jazz Couriers. Tubby had written an arrangement for the band, and during the tour they travelled together and shared hotels, getting to know one another again. Tubby, who had always had an incredibly high level of energy, had suffered a massive heart attack and had undergone heart surgery, and although he was now able to play again the illness restricted his breathing and dissipated his energy. But my father thought he sounded better than ever and that the artist within Tubby now took precedence over the craftsman.

It was around this time that my mother stopped working at the club, having made the decision to start a small suede and leather clothing business with Hilary McNair. The plan was to design original outfits for performers. Ronnie was very supportive of the venture, and when they couldn't decide on a name for the new business he suggested 'Mallary', a combination of Mary and Hilary, and Mallary it was. The dining room became a workroom, and a regular and an industrial sewing machine, a stud machine and also a knitting machine were gradually purchased. Buddy Rich's band was performing at the club, and all seventeen of them ordered waistcoats. Cleo Laine and Annie Ross became customers, as did Tony

Orlando and his group. Ronnie promoted the business, telling all the musicians about it. The word spread to pop groups and Emerson Lake and Palmer became customers. The guys had an image they wanted to express through the medium of leather; their outfits were completely unique and flamboyant. Dad was fascinated with the direction that the business was taking. He loved leather himself and told me: 'I kept asking your mother to make stuff for me, but they were so busy with other orders I ended up only getting one jacket and a chamois shirt!'

Dad and Mum started looking for a larger flat. Because of Mallary Mum wanted to have a three-bedroomed flat so that her workroom would not become restricted. Since a baby was on the way they discussed buying a place. Dad liked the idea even though he had lived in rented houses or bedsits all his life. Neither one of them wanted to move away from Chelsea and over the next few weeks they looked at several places, but all of them were too expensive, so they decided to stay where they were and make the best of it. Shortly afterwards, Elm Park Mansions decided to go co-op and the tenants were offered the opportunity to purchase their apartments, and that is what Dad decided to do, becoming the first man in his immediate family to purchase a home.

As my mother's pregnancy progressed and my parents talked about the imminent birth of their baby, Dad expressed concern about bringing up a child in a world that was changing so drastically as far as drugs were concerned. They were already affecting people from every walk of life. My parents discussed how they would tackle this potential problem and decided that complete honesty and an early education would be the way they would handle the situation. There were two really poignant stories that my father shared with me in later years that I will never forget. The first one involved his own experience when he was about twenty-one and someone turned him on with heroin, although luckily it made him so ill he was never tempted again.

The other story was about Phil Seamen, who played drums with Ronnie and also played at the club many times over the years. Daddy used to say that Phil was one of the best drummers that England ever produced and what a shame it was that he was a heroin addict all his life. When Dad and Mum would be coming home from the club at four o'clock in the morning, and Daddy would stop off at the newsstand to pick up the morning papers, on more than one occasion an ambulance would come screaming past and Daddy would look at Mum as he was getting into the car and say: 'I have to follow that ambulance. I think it's Phil in the back.' So they would chase the ambulance and the pair of them would run into the hospital. Daddy was never wrong. It was always Phil. Mum used to say: 'It was as though Dad and Phil had some kind of radar between them.' Of course, they never left until they knew that Phil was OK. A week or so later Phil would come into the club wearing a new suit, looking all fresh, having put on a few pounds, and was always so glad to see everybody; he knew Mum and Dad had been at the hospital. But he was never able to kick the habit, and at the age of forty-six, in 1972, the year I was born, Phil Seamen died. It distressed my father deeply to see people get screwed up by drugs and alcohol. He made a point of telling me that he had lost too many good friends that way and had seen too many lives destroyed.

The Modern Jazz Quartet, which is still going strong, made its first appearance at the club, with Milt Jackson on the vibes, Percy Heath on bass, Connie Kay on drums – now replaced by Albert 'Tootie' Heath – and John Lewis on piano. Milt Jackson, an elegant, slender man, always wore a tailored suit with a red silk handkerchief in the breast pocket to match his four mallets, which were covered in red silk, the light catching them as they flew with incredible alacrity up and down the keyboard of the vibraphone. It was an exciting year musically, with Chuck Mangione, Weather Report, Chick Corea and Back Door all making their debuts at the club. The daytime activity was constant, between rehearsals and press receptions. Frank Sinatra would book the club for a rehearsal when he was in town. He actually booked about four different places to throw the press off the scent, turning up at only one. He never did show up at the club, but Sammy Davis Junior would stop by. Sammy was a very unassuming, laid-back, kind and extremely funny man, often staying most of the evening to listen to the music and hang out.

On one such afternoon Ronnie, immersed in his daily practice of placing bets with the bookie across the street, ran in through the side door to use the staff toilet, which was so minuscule it was hard to get up off the seat without banging your head on the door. George was actively engaged with the afternoon's activities at the club and Donald was working in the service area at the top of the stairs above the toilet, when they heard Ronnie shout out a stream of profanities, followed by a series of very loud stomps and kicking sounds. Eventually, Ronnie ran up the stairs, still swearing profusely, this time at Donald who had come halfway down the steps to see what was happening. It appeared that while my father was sitting on the toilet a mouse ran up his trouser leg! Donald and then George were held responsible because they were supposed to keep the club clean, and Ronnie was as fastidious in the club as he was at home. He made Donald go down and clean the toilet and the whole passageway. George said: 'It must have come in from the street, Ronnie, it had to have!' Wherever it came from, it was the first and last time a mouse was seen in the club. Donald said: 'He was rampant, but the next day it was OK. Ronnie could find humour where everyone else could find none.'

Because my arrival was imminent, changes had to be made to the flat. The workroom was to become my bedroom, so with Dad's consent my mother designed a wooden partition in their bedroom which actually became a floor-to-ceiling headboard for their bed and created a very compact workroom behind the partition. Together they purchased my first crib, and Mum made curtains and a lampshade and all the bed linens for the crib.

It was 4 September, my mother's birthday. Dad was taking a bath, and she had to leave for an appointment at the hospital. On her way out she stuck her head around the bathroom door and said: 'Ronnie, I'm leaving now. I won't be back today.' Dad looked at her in astonishment and said: 'What do you mean, you won't be back. Where are you going?' Mum was laughing, and replied: 'This baby is going to arrive soon. How would you like it if I came home with a little girl with dark brown hair all over her head?' My father was stunned. He said: 'But you're not in labour. You can't *possibly* know a thing like that. How do you know it's a little girl?' Mum left, saying: 'You'll see!'

Sure enough, while Mary was waiting to see the doctor the labour pains began. The hospital telephoned Ronnie to say she was being admitted. By the time Ronnie got to the hospital everything was happening very slowly, and the Olympics were on television. Since both of them were avid fans, they spent the rest of the afternoon watching Mark Spitz win several of the seven gold medals he won that year. The doctor was furious, saying that Mum should be tranquillised; the baby was too small to be born now and she should take the medication and have quiet bed-rest for the next two weeks! Mum assured Dad that all was well and the baby was going to be born. Ronnie left for the club, believing what the doctor had told him. He went to bed that morning and, as was his customary practice, left the telephone off the hook. Meanwhile my mother refused to take the tranquillisers, but she always told me: 'You decided to go back to sleep!' And it was not until the next morning that labour began again. My mother waited until the pains were two minutes apart before telling anyone. The hospital called the club when they could not get through to Ronnie, so the guys at the club, knowing that the telephone was off the hook, called the post office and had them send an incredibly loud siren-like sound down the telephone line. It worked, and Ronnie woke up with a jolt. Realising something of import was happening, he telephoned the club to find out what was going on. By the time he got to the hospital my mother was sitting up in bed with me next to her in a cot, weighing in at seven and a half pounds.

Mum told me: 'Your father came into the ward on the trot, with a huge grin spread across his face, apologising in mid-stride for not being there earlier, saying he believed the doctor, saying: "Mary, you were right. We have a little girl! How *did* you know?" Daddy went straight to the crib and looked at you with each hand resting on the sides of the crib, and said: "Look at her! She looks exactly like my grandmother! We *have* to call her Rebecca." ' Sitting on the edge of my mother's bed, Dad decided that I should be given two names so that if I didn't like one I could use the other. He liked the name Sally. When it came to registering my birth my parents discussed whether my last name should be Schatt or Scott. Since both names were legal Dad agreed that Scott would be fine, so I was named Rebecca Sally Scott.

Dad was enjoying his new family. Åke Persson and his girlfriend were in London and had brought a teddy bear from Germany as a gift for me. They came to the flat to meet the new baby and have dinner. Ronnie's trio was flourishing, playing at the club and doing quite a lot of touring. On one occasion on a tour of England Ronnie asked Mike Carr to drive him into Huddersfield; he wanted to buy a suitcase. As they drove into town Ronnie spotted a café and said: 'Let's pull in for a cup of tea.' The café was next door to a betting shop and Mike recalled: 'Ronnie pulled his newspaper out of his pocket and said: "Look at this. I have to place a bet on these two, Mike. Look at their names – Birdland and Club Talk!" Both horses were a long shot, fifty to one, each in a separate race. We went next door and Ronnie put a pound on each horse, and they both came in! I couldn't believe it!' It was a period that Dad really enjoyed. He said that they played virtually what they wanted to play and got good reactions from the audience. The three of them had the same kind of outlook on music, and their ability to communicate to the people the way they felt about things gave all of them a tremendous kick – that's what it's really all about. At the same time Ronnie was very involved with the running of the club. He and Pete collaborated on all the major decisions, the selection of artists – Ronnie often recommending musicians that he had heard while out on the road –

the lighting and décor of the club, the 'creation of atmosphere', the sound system, the choice of chef and the menu: all the critical ingredients involved in running a fulfilling and successful jazz club. Even with all this as well as being a working musician at the same time, because Uncle Pete took care of the day-to-day things, Dad felt that he was left fairly free to practise his craft.

Uncle Markie was not well. He had been in and out of hospital and was not up to coming down to the club any more, so my mother used to take me to visit him and Auntie Rosie. Uncle Markie was so thrilled with Ronnie's baby daughter, he said: 'I'm so glad he called her Rebecca. He's right: she does look just like my mother.' My mother told me: 'I took you over to see Uncle Mark quite frequently. It cheered him up considerably. He loved to sit you on his knee and play with you.' Six months later, Uncle Mark became critically ill and Dad could not deal with it at all. He couldn't bring himself to go to see Uncle Mark, who died in February. His cremation was on St Valentine's Day. Uncle Markie was the last member of Dad's immediate family, and Dad became very withdrawn for quite some time after his death. Mum had taken several pictures of us together, and after Dad died, in the front pocket of his telephone book, which he took everywhere with him, was a picture of Uncle Mark with me at a few weeks old.

In January 1973 my mother had decided that she wanted to get Dad an extra-special birthday present, and an investment for me. Tony Crombie told me the story. He said: 'We were all friends, Ronnie, Mary, myself, Beryl, Les Leston, who before he became a famous racing driver used to play drums for Ambrose Octet when they were all lads during the war, and Lenny Bloom and his wife Gundi, who ran a series of popular dance clubs. We were all interested in antiques and paintings. Les Leston had his own place. Beryl and I had a stand with Lenny Bloom in the Antiques Supermarket in Kensington, and Graham Hill, the famous racing driver, came for the inaugural opening of the stand along with some press.' Knowing all of this, my mother went to Tony for guidance in purchasing something that would eventually increase in value for Dad and also me. They discussed various possibilities and because Dad had such a love of cats Tony suggested that they should take a look at some Louis Wayne drawings. Tony said: 'So I took her to Abbot & Holder in Castlenau, Barnes, where they specialised in Louis Wayne's art.' Mum chose a huge drawing in black charcoal of a cat with a monocle and a fat cigar sticking out of its mouth, the perfect gift for Ronnie, and for me she selected a portrait of a marmalade cat done in red chalk. Dad always had the drawings hanging on the wall in the living room. We both loved them.

The fact that my mother worked from home now made things much easier all round. She used to take me to the suede and leather factories when she picked out the skins, but customers always came to the flat for fittings. A couple of nights a week Mum would go to the club to listen to the music and spend time with Dad, but life had changed considerably since Mum's pregnancy and my arrival. She and Hilary were busy trying to build the business, so the amount of time she and Dad spent together was cut by half. Tony Crombie's second wife Beryl, who was a close friend of my mother's, had given birth to a baby girl, Allison, the year before, and Mum had made little dresses out of chamois for her. Tony and Ronnie were proud fathers at the same time. Christmas that year was a very special one. Although not quite four months old, I was already sitting up and taking notice. Dad and Mum had bought me all kinds of gifts because it was my first Christmas, and the proud parents took pictures of me pulling the wrapping paper off some of my gifts, and Mum took a picture of Daddy showing me the ornaments on my first Christmas tree. It was a very happy time.

The music booked for the year ahead at the club included a return visit of Buddy Rich's band, Jimmy Witherspoon and Freddie Hubbard. After several years' absence due to ill health, Stan Tracey returned to play with his new quartet, a worthy performance that Miles Kington of the *Melody Maker* noted: 'You have to go a long way to find music that simultaneously gets the toes working and the brain cells tingling.' Stan was back in full force. There were some exciting new arrivals on the scene. Oscar Peterson made his first appearance at the club, as did Art Blakey's Jazz Messengers and George Melly, who has become a tradition at Ronnie Scott's, opening the evening's festivities every Christmas with Ronnie's band. George has kept up the good work for twenty-five years!

In spring 1973 Auntie Ella came to stay with us for a few days. She told me it was the only time that she had stayed with Ronnie since their home in Edgwarebury Lane had gone. My father enjoyed the visit immensely, and Auntie Ella told me that it was the first time that she had seen her half-brother this relaxed and for the first time seemingly content with everything in his life.

John Birks 'Dizzy' Gillespie made his first appearance at the club in 1973. It was an auspicious occasion. Ronnie was thrilled. He had known Dizzy since the days when he first visited 52nd Street in New York thirty years earlier, and finally to have Dizzy playing at his club was another dream realised. Dizzy, a larger-than-life personality, had a marvellous sense of humour, and in the inner sanctum of the club, between sets, he often enjoyed a game of chess with my father. They swapped stories, told jokes and held endless more serious discussions about music. My mother took me to the club one afternoon while Dizzy was rehearsing and Dad told me that was my first introduction to the great Dizzy Gillespie and his music. As a small child in America, I was fascinated with how huge Dizzy's cheeks became as they blew up like a pair of bellows when he played! Dad explained to me that Dizzy had not had formal trumpet lessons and so had developed his own unique method of controlling his breath and creating his embouchure.

During June Tubby stopped by the club to see Ronnie. His illness was not responding to treatment. Just before he left, Tubby made a point of letting my father know that his playing had influenced him in his formative years and that he held him in high regard. Dad always believed that Tubby wanted him to know this because he felt that his time was running out. Realising this, my father, who considered that Tubby's contribution to jazz in Britain was second to none, was a little embarrassed and let Tubby know that he had just paid him the greatest compliment Ronnie could ever hope to receive, because it had come from him, Tubby Hayes. Shortly after this, at the age of thirty-eight, Edward Brian 'Tubby' Hayes died.

One of my favourite stories was when we would go through the photograph album and Mum would show me the pictures of Daddy, me and Mum on the beach and under the palm trees in Palma. It was 25 June 1973 when we all went together for a month's holiday. I was nearly ten months old. Dad had rented a car, and we all piled in and Mum could not wait to show me the sea. She said that Dad was a little bit nervous about it all but went along with everything. Anyway, we checked into the Hotel Balle, which was where they usually stayed, dropped the luggage off, and we were on our way to the beach. Dad parked the car, and Mum was carrying me with Dad bringing up the rear. We rounded a corner, Mum talking to me all the time, and suddenly there was the ocean. It was a windy day so the waves were crashing and making a roaring sound. My face crumpled up, and I started to yell and cry and cling to Mum. Dad didn't know what to do and said: 'Oh, God, Mary. Maybe we shouldn't have brought her. She's too young. I think this was a mistake, for God's sake!'

Mum told him it would be all right once I got used to it. She told me I carried on so much she started to have second thoughts about it herself, but she just kept talking to me and eventually we reached the sandy beach and she let me crawl around. Soon I was playing with the sand, doing all the usual things like trying to eat it, and everyone heaved a sigh of relief.

We all went to the huge building where Hai Alai was played. The Spanish ladies were seated in groups at tables playing cards with money on the table. Dad pulled Mum over to one side and whispered to her about the old days. He got a tremendous kick out of watching the old ladies for a few minutes as they haggled over who had put what in the middle of the table. Dad would giggle to himself, his mind flooding with memories of his mother and her friends and their Saturday card games.

Daddy often told me that the best part of it all for him was watching me discover everything, and once I got wet I loved the water so much he would swim and play with me. My father bought a yellow blow-up dinghy so that he or Mum could give me rides in it, pulling it along the edge of the sea by a string. One day Mum was doing the pulling and in the split second that she looked up to say something to Dad I leaned over too far and everything turned upside down! There was a brief moment of panic, but all was well and I thought it was just another game and laughed, but Dad said he stayed really close after that because Mum was accident-prone and anything might happen! Everyone seemed so happy then, it was hard for me to understand looking at those pictures why Dad and Mum broke up just seven months later.

Back in London, life at home was well balanced. My father, who loved walking all his life, used to derive great pleasure from taking me for long walks in the pram, sometimes before he went into the club, or on weekends. Other times we would sit and watch old movies together. Several years before, Mary had bought Ronnie a video camera and projector along with reels of Charlie Chaplin, Laurel & Hardy, Buster Keaton, and Abbott & Costello. Back then our favourite was Laurel & Hardy. Dad would set up the reel and sit me on his knee. Mum told me: 'Daddy would talk to you, pointing out the insane antics as they happened on the screen, adding his own personal touch by gurning at the same time, and the two of you would giggle your way through a 200-foot spool!' I never lost my appetite for this kind of humour and continued to watch the comedians on TV in America. They remained a source of mutual delight for my father and me over the years.

It was during this summer that my father received a telephone call letting him know that his good friend Åke Persson had died. Åke had been living in Sweden and was suffering from depression. One night everything became too much for him and he drove his car straight into a river. Ronnie was so distraught by his untimely and sudden death that he agonised over whether he could bear to go to the funeral. My mother coaxed him into going, knowing that unless he said goodbye to his old friend he would be haunted by the circumstances of his death for a long time. At the last minute my father decided to go to Sweden for the funeral and was always thankful that he did.

That same summer Dad and Uncle Pete followed through on a dream they had shared as young men and became involved with saloon car racing, taking part in the celebrity races that were run at Brands Hatch and Silverstone, driving in formula saloon car competitions. Uncle Pete and Dad persuaded the breweries and other businesses to sponsor their cars, which had Ronnie Scott's Club advertised on each side.

Ronnie juggled his touring with the trio – by now Tony Crombie had left and Bobby Gien was on drums – with motor racing and running the club. During a gig in Brussels, at the Pols Jazz Club, Ronnie asked Pols if he knew where he could buy some racing driver's shoes; he was looking forward to driving in a celebrity race against TV personality Noel Edmonds on his return from Belgium. Pols told Ronnie he knew just the man; he would make a few phone calls and see what he could do. Within ten minutes he came over to the band and said: 'OK, Ronnie, Mike and Bobby, I want all three of you to meet here at 1 p.m. tomorrow. There'll be a chauffeured Mercedes here to pick you up and drive you out to the home of Jean Blaton.' Jean had been driving racing cars since he was fifteen. He was one of four brothers who made their fortune in construction and they were a very well known family in Brussels and Europe. When they drove into his driveway the following afternoon, they arrived at a magnificent mansion in the midst of a picturesque estate, which included a beautiful swimming pool. They were greeted at the door by a butler, who led them into a vast expanse of rooms, with loudspeakers in every corner filling the house with the sounds of Oscar Peterson's marvellous piano playing. Jean Blaton appeared in a luxurious robe, warmly welcoming everyone and offering drinks all round. Mike remembered: 'Bobby Gien enjoyed his scotch, and Ronnie had a cup of tea.'

A guitar player himself, Jean was a discerning listener and avid fan of jazz. He booked British, American and European musicians to play at his parties, sometimes sitting in himself on guitar. An extremely generous man, he paid top dollar and all expenses, lavishing his visiting musicians with superior wines, luscious food and gifts. Jean has an incredible collection of Formula One racing cars and Ferraris. My father was in his element and needless to say came back with a serious pair of driver's shoes. As far as winning the race against Noel Edmonds was concerned, the shoes did not help: that day Dad's car veered off the track. Jean Blaton always visited the club when he was in London, much to the delight of Dad and Uncle Pete, and Mike Carr has played at his home on many occasions since that afternoon.

The first cup that Ronnie won was third place, and a couple of races later he won a silver cup for second place. My father's favourite story about the celebrity races was of the 1 September event, a few days before my first birthday. The whole event was sponsored by Capital Radio. Daddy was the only jazz musician there and the only driver who was not in his twenties; he was actually forty-six at the time. Among the pop musicians he was racing against was Keith Emerson from Emerson Lake & Palmer and musicians from Slade. Dad took first place! The radio station did an interview with him proudly wearing the Laurel Wreath as he held his cup high for all to see, saying: 'I'm going to buy my mother a big house, but I shall carry on working!' He often told me: 'I got a tremendous charge out of doing it, and it really made me feel *so* good to have beaten all those young men!' There were times when my mother watched in horror as his car spun off the track and rolled over several times during the formula saloon car competitions, but Dad was lucky and each time he walked away unharmed. Uncle Pete was not so lucky: he had a really bad accident, seriously injuring his knee, and was hospitalised. Dad visited Uncle Pete every day and temporarily took over the day-to-day running of the club. Even so, George went to the hospital every day to report to Uncle Pete, who never had his finger off the pulse of the daily activities at the club. Even after the accident, as soon as he was well enough, Uncle Pete kept right on racing, but shortly afterwards Dad decided to quit while he was ahead of the game.

My parents had been living together now for nine years. My mother had become pretty adept at turning a blind eye when my father succumbed to the temptation of the fairer sex, and the ground rules were clear: there could be no intrusion on their home life. However, my mother was unaware that Ronnie had started an affair with a waitress at the club. Her name was Linda Poulton, a very pretty, petite, personable and vivacious young woman. My mother thought she knew her well. Linda was determined to become a singer. She also played a little guitar and enjoyed painting and sculpture. My mother told me: 'I knew nothing of her affair with Ronnie. It was a very happy period in our lives. We were both enjoying being parents, I was building Mallary with Hilary. Your father was about to buy me a yellow Mini, because I took you everywhere with me while I ran errands for our business. Life was full, and it wasn't until a very close friend of mine warned me that Linda wasn't my friend, quite the reverse in fact, and that I should no longer confide in her, that I found out.' Mel Lewis the co-leader of the Thad Jones and Mel Lewis Big Band had invited Linda to New York to sing with his band, but it soon became clear that there was no permanent job with the band.

Ultimately, the pressure became too much for both my parents. Ronnie was besotted with Linda and made the decision to move in with her. He tried to split his time between the two homes; he considered ending the affair and constantly assured my mother that it was over. He never actually moved his belongings out of the flat – instead he bought new clothes! Christmas came, and just as they had done every Christmas Eve for years, Ronnie and Mary, with me toddling along, went to visit old friends, Harry and Harriet South, for the evening, their three girls, Anita, Louise and Annabelle, playing with me. Their dog, a large and soppy bulldog called Buster, allowed me, with the help of the girls, to ride on his back. As was the tradition, Harriet had prepared a Swedish Christmas, the wide window seats spread with snow-covered Scandinavian village scenes and figurines, tiny white lights and lots of candles – absolutely magical, a world of wonderment for a small child. The huge Christmas tree with presents stacked underneath, the smell of roast duck, hot spicy Glûrg, which the grown-ups sipped from small mugs, making them giggle – there was no strain in the air that night. The jokes, bantering and hearty laughter in the company of loving friends made everything seem normal again. My mother often told me it was her last good memory of London.

Ronnie became frantic, trying to juggle family and girlfriend. There was no way this could be resolved. The fact that he was going back and forth between the two homes became too much for my mother, who made the decision to go to New York. Once her mind was made up she was anxious to leave as quickly as possible, and my parents' old friend Spike Milligan came to her aid, understanding that their relationship was in crisis and that my mother needed to get away.

Ronnie did everything in his power to stop Mary from leaving. But by the middle of January my mother was staying with a friend, going to the flat to pack only when Ronnie was at the club. One afternoon she knew he wouldn't be there and went back to finish packing, when all of a sudden she heard a key in the lock and froze in her tracks. Brian Theobald (who worked at the club) appeared in the hallway, as shocked to see Mary as she was to see him. She said: 'What do you think you're doing? Why are you here?' Brian, very embarrassed, muttered that he must have made a mistake, saying: 'Ronnie asked me to pick him up from the flat, but I must have got the days mixed up!' It was later disclosed that Ronnie had sent Brian to take the trunk and suitcases out of the flat in an effort to stop Mary from leaving.

The final weeks in London were fraught with anxiety. Mary, trying to sidestep Ronnie's attempts to prevent her from going, persuaded Henry Cohen, a massive man who could block a doorway and was a bouncer at the club, Keith McDonald, who worked the door, and a couple of the waiters to come and move the extremely heavy trunk and suitcases to a friend's flat in the same building. It was a clandestine operation that took effect at 4.30 a.m. after everybody had finished work at the club. One by one the shadowy figures arrived, each shuffling his feet and protesting: 'Christ, Mary, are you *sure* he's not here? God almighty . . . you *know* that if Ronnie shows up we're *all* going to get the fucking sack!' Mary pleaded, they moaned and huffed and puffed, struggling with the heavy containers on the stairs. Shortly, the mission was completed and four highly relieved friends scurried off into the night, still sure that they were going to bump straight into Ronnie rounding the corner!

It was a dark and gloomy day in London on 8 February, and because of the ongoing strikes in Britain the electricity was functioning only on opposite sides of the streets for designated periods of time, adding to the glumness of it all. A station wagon pulled into Elm Park Mansions, and my father stood watching as my mother's trunk and suitcases were loaded into the back. Dad looked crestfallen. He hugged me and kissed me and my mother goodbye and with tears running down his face begged her not to leave. My mother and I climbed into the car. By now her eyes were filled with tears, too, as my father right to the last second was still begging her to stay.

CHAPTER ELEVEN

BROKEN WINGS

Gazing into the faces of my husband and daughter, I realised that if love were the cure I would have been healed a long time ago.

MARTHA MANNING, *Under Currents*

Some nights of apprehension and hot weeping
I will confess; but that's permitted me;
Day dried my eyes; I was not one for keeping
Rubbed in a cage a wing that would be free.

EDNA ST VINCENT MILLAY

When bebop began it was blazing. We were all very privileged to be a part of this era, it's been like there was a bottle of medicine that's always in the cupboard, and whenever you get depressed, you take a sip and you're back the way you should be. Playing is what brought Ronnie back to us.   LAURIE MORGAN

THE FEBRUARY OF 1974 was bitterly cold in New York, with the Hudson River frozen over, but the vast city, unlike the London we had left behind, was ablaze with a billion lights. As the cab driver entered New York City, my mother was amazed at the rough terrain of the potholed streets, badly patched up roads making the ride very bumpy, not to mention the clouds of steam pouring out of grids from the subways below. She asked the cab driver what the steam was, and he laughed and asked: 'You've never seen this before?' Then he went on to explain its source, adding: 'That's why they call this city Gotham City.' He pulled into West 46th Street, outside the Century Paramount Hotel, and the bellboys proceeded to unload our luggage. The hotel was where my father always stayed when he came to New York. It was a favourite among musicians, with Woody Herman's Band and João Gilberto among their regular customers. We had two adjoining double rooms, each with bath, at a very special rate, and when we checked in there was already a message from Dad asking us to call him as soon as we arrived.

My father called every day several times a day. My mother had contacted the Getzes, and we were immediately invited to spend the weekend with them at Shadowbrook, their Westchester home which is surrounded by nine acres of land. It is a magnificent home which was originally owned by the Gershwin family. Uncle Stan's pride and joy was the circular music room. The wooden floor is comprised of a series of blocks laid in exact circles from the walls to the centre of the room ending with one perfect block in the centre, with a grand piano standing directly above it. Uncle Stan solicited help to roll the piano to one side then he stood my mother on the centre block and said, 'Now sing a note – any note.' It was incredible: the shape and structure of the room had been designed so that when you stood in the centre the sound was exceptional – the acoustics were absolutely *perfect*. Uncle Stan loved to stand on that spot and practise, and his group often rehearsed here when preparing for a recording date or a new tour. Under the tall stained glass windows encircling the room were window seats where the fortunate listener could sit and enjoy the full impact of this unique experience.

We became frequent guests of the family. The tranquillity of the surroundings and the comfort of friends were a little oasis in the midst of the turmoil that was in full swing between my parents. Dad often telephoned us during these weekends, ever hopeful that we would come home. Uncle Stan used to look at me and laugh and call me 'Little Ronnie'. Monica was so kind and thoughtful and Uncle Stan's daughter became my Auntie Bev. On Valentine's Day Uncle Stan came home with a white puppy under his coat for Auntie Bev. He had a heart-shaped nose, and she called him Whippet. We spent many a happy hour playing together.

Dad came to New York twice over the next couple of months. On the first visit he stayed for about a week and, getting down on his knees in traditional fashion, begged my mother to marry him. Still very much in love with Ronnie, she said no. Mary knew his true feelings about the subject and knew the formality was not necessary for them. When it came down to it, legally they were already common law husband and wife with a child; she was known as Mary Scott and marriage was not the issue. Although no one recognised the symptoms at the time, Ronnie actually was descending into a state of depression, fluctuating from phases of self-deprecation to acting on impulse, completely torn between his family and Linda, frantically trying to save both relationships at the same time. Filled with anxiety about the whole situation, he had already started to lose weight.

A few days after he returned to London, Mary got a call from Pete saying: 'Ronnie's had enough now, Mary. Come home. I think that now he's really ready to marry you.' Mary explained to Pete that she couldn't come home, that marriage was not the answer, certainly not while Ronnie was in such a state of confusion.

During one of our visits to Shadowbrook my mother received a phone call from England. Dad and the trio were booked to play the Edinburgh Festival, and without telling the band he had arranged with the promoters to add Linda's name to the fliers, billed as the band's singer. When Mike Carr and Bobby Gien found out, they refused to play if Linda was to sing, and all hell broke loose. My mother telephoned Dad and added her fuel to the fire, stating very calmly that if she *ever* found out that Linda sang one crotchet with his band he would never see me again. The outcome was that Linda never sang with my father's band and she left England and went to Australia.

In the meantime Mike Carr got a gig for the trio on board the P & O liner *Ocades*. They were to do a cruise to Casablanca, Barcelona and Madrid. Ronnie loved the idea, because they would not have to play that much and it would be like a holiday. When the *Ocades* left from Southampton, Bobby Gien was nowhere to be seen. Mike and Ronnie anxiously looked for him when from the deck of the liner Mike suddenly spotted Bobby on the quay. The trouble was the tugs were already pushing the liner out of her berth. Mike was yelling: 'Bobby! Catch the plane to Casablanca!' Meanwhile Ronnie was exercising his powers of persuasion with the captain, who sent a tug to pick up Bobby and bring him alongside and they hauled him on board! Even though Dad was distressed, his humour remained intact and one night they were all sitting in the Caz Bar in Casablanca and Mike recalled how Dad turned to Bobby Gien and surreptitiously said: 'Bobby . . . try not to look Jewish!' Bobby replied: 'I'm trying . . . I'm trying!'

The trio had a considerable amount of work during the year, but as time progressed Dad's depression increased and Mike and Bobby found themselves struggling with Ronnie's lapses into deep distress. Never having seen him or anyone else suffer from such plunges into misery, they often found themselves feeling helpless; nothing they could say seemed of any consolation to Ronnie. Mike sadly remembered when they were in Berlin sitting in a restaurant waiting for their food to be served. Ronnie was filled with regrets about Jock, Cissie and Nanna Beckie, haunted by things he thought he should have said or done as a young man. Sleep eluded him. Doctors had prescribed sleeping pills and he was depending on a combination of the pills and brandy to get any sleep.

As often as not during their telephone conversations, my parents talked about music. Carmen McCrae was performing at the club, and Ronnie used to go out front and listen to her sets. There was one song in particular that she sang which he said 'Always brings tears to my eyes, it's so moving'. The song was 'Poor Butterfly', a tune that became a part of his own repertoire. In New York, Frank Sinatra's latest release, 'Send in the Clowns', was being played on all the radio stations. Intimate with Dad's musical and lyrical preferences, Mary shared her thoughts about the song with Ronnie and sent him the sheet music. This, too, became a part of his repertoire, and he played it on both soprano and tenor sax, recording it on soprano in October 1977 on his album 'Serious Gold'.

At the end of July Ronnie came up with a plan. He phoned Mary and told her that he was coming to New York, explaining that he would be in town for only a couple of days. He would be arriving on 4 August and was looking forward to seeing us both. He loved walking in New York, so when he arrived Mum brought my pushchair along and we went out for the afternoon in Central Park, afterwards stopping at the Carnegie Deli for dinner, then walked home. Daddy was staying at the same hotel, and after I'd gone to bed he asked Mum if he could take me out by himself the following afternoon. Mum said: 'Of course you can. What time do you want to go?' Dad said that he would pick me up about 1 p.m. After they said good night, my mother could not shake the feeling that Ronnie was up to something. Mum told me that when she got up the next day the feeling was even stronger, so when Dad arrived to pick me up, slightly embarrassed, she quietly asked him to leave his passport with her. Dad smiled, took his passport out of his inside jacket pocket and handed it to her, saying: 'Don't worry. We'll be back soon.'

The afternoon came and went. Soon it was well into the evening. My mother's feeling of foreboding rapidly grew. The night passed torturously slowly, my mother pacing the floor, her thoughts racing in different directions. If there had been an accident, surely someone would have called. But then again she had Dad's passport, so maybe he had no identification on him. What to do? What to do? By the time the telephone eventually rang at eight o'clock the next morning she was beside herself. It was

Ronnie. 'Where the *hell* are you? What's happened?' she demanded. Dad very calmly responded: 'Everything's all right. Becky is fine. Guess where we are?' My mother was in no mood for guessing games and maintained a stony silence on her end of the phone. My father went on to say: 'We're home! At the flat in London!' Mum was absolutely flabbergasted. Worn out from worry and lack of sleep, she was grateful that we had not been involved in an accident, but this situation presented another set of problems. Ronnie said: 'Come home, Mary. Becky and I are here waiting for you. Everything is going to be all right. Just come home.'

It had been a well-thought-out plan. What actually occurred was that my father went to the passport office in London and declared that he had lost his passport, so they reissued one. He had my birth certificate so that he could put me on his new passport. In fact he hadn't lost it but travelled to New York with both passports, anticipating that Mum might sense something was wrong and would ask him to relinquish his passport, which she did. Dad handed Mum the old one then left with me and headed straight to the airport and to London.

It wasn't as simple as 'come home, everything will be all right'. Things had changed for my mother since I arrived. She felt that it was one thing to gamble with her own emotions but she was not about to do so with mine. She told me: 'By this time I knew that his relationship with Linda wouldn't last, but I wasn't prepared to take the risk of going through all the heartache again, and I thought it better to distance myself and you from that side of your father's life.' My mother knew the importance of creating as stable an environment for me as possible and was determined to maintain a relationship with my father that would work for all three of us.

My father had fully expected my mother to be on the next flight to London. When she stood her ground he responded with a stone wall of silence. Every time Mary called the club she was told he wasn't there. At the flat the answering machine was on all the time. She could not reach him or get any information out of anybody as to his or my whereabouts. The silence had the desired effect and she became frantic, finally consulting an attorney, who told her to call the club and leave a message for Ronnie stating that if she didn't hear from him within twelve hours she was going to call Scotland Yard and report him for kidnapping. Two *minutes* after Mary left this message, Ronnie called her back. The line of communication was once again open between them, and the phone calls went back and forth. Not yet two, I was missing my mother terribly. Finally accepting that Mary felt she could not return to England under the circumstances, but never really understanding why, my father made the necessary arrangements to take me back to New York. We arrived at the Paramount on 11 September. My mother opened the door and I ran into her arms. Our reunion was an emotional one, as was Dad's departure. I was quite a handful at that age, and during the long flight Dad had put his back out. As he stood in Mary's doorway with his hip at a forty-five-degree angle, in obvious pain, apologising profusely for the way in which he had disappeared with me to London, all the displeasure that my mother had been feeling dissolved and she instantly expressed her concern for Ronnie. My father, still apologising, insisted he would be all right, saying he was going straight back to London.

On 23 September 1974 Ronnie left London with his trio for Australia to do a tour with Stephane Grappelli (the famed Parisian violinist) and the Diz Dizley Trio. Linda was already in Australia, and they spent a week together. The relationship with Linda was in trouble by this time. She was no longer interested in being with Ronnie, so she left Australia and went to live with her parents in New Zealand. Ronnie was suffering from depression all through the tour, his drinking increased, and Mike was really worried about him by October when they were headed towards New York, first to play a concert at Carnegie Hall and then for a week's engagement at Buddy Rich's Club. Dad was looking forward to coming to New York, and we were all excited about them playing at Carnegie Hall. It was an auspicious occasion for everyone because Ronnie and Stephane were both making their debuts at the famous old hall. Ronnie was very nervous about it, and he said to Mary: 'Well, we can't expect too much, you know. The audience is here for Stephane, not us. They don't know us from Adam!' There was a major problem for Mike Carr, who had brought his Hammond organ with him only to discover that it was incompatible with the electrical system at Carnegie Hall, and so had to hire another organ. The anxiety level was quite high for all concerned. When the time came for Ronnie's band to open for Stephane and Diz, Dad was so nervous when he walked out on stage that he introduced the band twice. When Ronnie, with his lighted cigarette familiarly gripped in the scrolls of his saxophone, and his group started playing, it was hard for Mike, who was less than satisfied with his rented instrument. But the audience was oblivious to any of the problems as Ronnie opened with a few jokes that had the whole audience laughing, and by then everyone was relaxed. The music is best described by Michael Watts in his review about the concert for the *Melody Maker*: 'Scott plays like there's a big warm heart beating beneath that deadpan exterior; there's a large size humanity about his playing, whether it be his racy work on Kenny Burrell's "Midnight Blue" or the delicate, poignant soprano solo on David Gates' "If". The set ended on a strong note with Ronnie's own "I'm Sick and Tired of Waking up Tired and Sick".'

The response from the audience was wonderful, and Ronnie went into his comedy routine just as though he were at the club in London before bringing Stephane et al. on stage, which was quite a crowd-pleaser. Of course, Stephane was greeted with cheers, he was such a unique combination of elegance and flamboyance, and after he and the Diz Dizley Trio completed their set they received a standing ovation. But Stephane was not happy with the sound that night and afterwards said: 'The sound was a bit deesturbed. I couldn't 'ear myself, so I was not quite at 'ome. If I can 'ear me I am safe.' Stephane said he was surprised at the standing ovation but very glad of it, because then he knew that everything really had gone well. Everyone rushed to see the reviews, and Mum remembered being really put out by John Wilson's review in the *New York Times* because he didn't have anything to say about Ronnie. Most of the article referred to Django Reinhardt and the days when he and Stephane played together; there was very little about the actual music played that night. She told me: 'I was dreadfully disappointed, and it ended up where Daddy was consoling me! However, the review in the *Melody Maker* made us all very happy. We didn't know it then, of course, but as things turned out that was to be the one and only time that Ronnie played at Carnegie Hall.'

The week at Buddy Rich's Club was a highly successful one for all concerned. A number of well-known musicians, such as Woody Herman, Benny Goodman, John Lewis, Jo Jones and Tony Bennett, Monty Alexander and the comedian Milton Bearle, to name just a few, and Ronnie's old friend Lennie Metcalfe, all came to Buddy's place to listen to the music and chat to Ronnie and Stephane. Another old friend of Ronnie's, Joan Crewe, his serious girlfriend from the 1940s, who now lived in New Jersey, came to the club to see him. Ronnie sat and chatted to Joan for a few minutes and then he came over to Mary and told her he wanted her to meet Joan, so together they went over to her table and he introduced them. Ronnie had obviously told Joan that he and Mary were having problems because while they were chatting Joan said to my mother: 'Mary, do you think there's any chance of you and Ronnie getting back together? Maybe as time passes you'll be able to return to London and Ronnie. I really hope so. Ronnie really loves Rebecca, and it would be good for all of you if you could work things out.' Ronnie was feeling the effects of his depression and had to have a jug of iced water on the bandstand at all times because his mouth was so dry from the antidepressants and the sedatives, and he was drinking heavily, as he had been throughout the tour.

This was the first time that my mother had ever seen Ronnie touch hard liquor; when she met him he was teetotal. He could not stand the smell of drink on people's breath and really hated the effect it had on people when they drank too much. He felt very strongly about it. It was quite a paradox for her and everyone who knew him to see him suddenly take up drinking like that. The amazing thing was if you did not know Ronnie, the real person, you would not have known that anything serious was wrong. Somehow, when he was in public he managed to transcend the terrible inner turmoil that was bubbling just below the surface. The music and the joke routines went on, and under the circumstances it was incredible how he held it all together. However, Mike was extremely worried about Ronnie, as was my mother, because the trio also had to go to Rochester, New York, to do a radio programme, and Mike quite naturally was concerned whether or not Ronnie would be able to manage all of it in his present condition.

Old friends in New York tried to help. Dill Jones, a Welsh pianist who had also emigrated to New York, sat talking to Ronnie, who confided in him that he was really in trouble. Dill told him that Lennie and his wife had a place in Cape Cod – Lennie used to play up there all summer – and suggested that Ronnie give them a call. Ronnie rang Lennie and said: 'Dill tells me you have a place on the Cape.' Lennie told me: 'I hardly recognised his voice, he sounded so ill. Ronnie said to me: "I'm feeling rather down at the moment and I'd like to get away." I said to him: "Get your ass up here." I gave him the directions, telling him how to get here via public transportation. But he never did come.' Lennie had known Ronnie since he was a young lad in London and used to see him when he came to New York, sometimes at the Half Note. Lennie recalled: 'This was the first inclination that I had that he suffered from depression, because he was never like that. Ronnie was always the opposite, so alert and alive, so funny and great.'

Mum saw Ronnie every day during this visit. She recalled: 'Dad didn't see you. He was acutely aware of his illness. He'd lost a lot of weight and looked quite drawn, and, young as you were, he didn't want you to see him like that. We discussed it and decided that it was better for you not to see him. Actually, he would not talk to you either when he was really ill. He didn't trust himself, he was afraid that he'd break down and frighten you.' Although this was Ronnie's first breakdown, there would be more to come over the ensuing years and it was very hard for me to try to cope with the sudden and sometimes prolonged silences from my father during his battles with depression. As a child it felt like rejection to me, and Mum spent a lot of time reassuring me, saying that Daddy loved me but was ill and unable to see me. During these periods there really was no explanation good enough to stop me from wondering why my father had seemingly disappeared from my world.

Towards the end of November a package arrived from my father with a letter. It contained photographs of my grandparents, Jock and Cissie, and Nanna Beckie, group family photographs, and pictures of Daddy as a young man. In the letter he asked my mother to make sure I would always know who my father was. My mother was deeply disturbed. Even after speaking with Dad on the telephone she could not shake off an overwhelming feeling of dread. Dad was still taking a combination of antidepressants, sleeping pills and alcohol, and on more than one occasion had passed out while talking to my mother on the telephone. She had called Uncle Pete, who immediately sent someone or went to Ronnie's flat himself to make sure he was all right.

It was Christmas 1974 and Pete King called Mum and told her that Ronnie was in dire straits and would we come home? We left for London immediately. Ronnie had prepared to travel to New Zealand to spend Christmas with Linda and her family, but at the eleventh hour she told him not to come. It was the last straw. Already gripped in the relentless jaws of depression and believing at the time that being in Linda's company was the solution to all his suffering, with the sudden denial of his visit the wave of confused emotions that was threatening to drown him engulfed him completely and he swallowed everything in sight at the flat. Fortunately for all concerned, Brian Theobald was scheduled to pick Ronnie up that day to take him to the airport. Even though Ronnie had left a note for Brian on the front door telling him not to bother, instinctively he knew that something was badly wrong and, with the aid of Henry Cohen, broke the door down. Pete King immediately called Sydney Gotlieb, who took charge of Ronnie. My mother told me: 'When I saw your father he was desperately ill. I've never seen him look like that before or since. That time he lost *so* much weight he looked like a little bird, and he wasn't even fifty. Yet he looked like an old man of eighty. He couldn't even hold a cigarette for himself. I actually had to light the cigarette and hold it for him, he was so ill and frail. It was enough to break your heart to see him like that. It *did* break your heart.' Sydney Gotlieb had immediately made arrangements for Ronnie to stay at his house in Highgate, which is where my mother saw him, and from there he was taken to a nursing home in St John's Wood.

When Ronnie was moved to the nursing home he asked for his saxophone to be brought in. He always took it everywhere with him; the fact that he was ill was no exception. The other patients, however, were quick to complain, because he would practise whenever the inspiration struck, which likely as not was during the night when he would keep everyone awake. The establishment eventually felt obliged to take his reeds away. Nevertheless, Ronnie practised both the tenor and soprano without reeds and sat in bed fingering the keys so he would not lose his dexterity.

Once Ronnie knew Mary was going to stay in London he wanted her to cook for him. My mother always loved cooking, and Dad used to love eating her special meals. Mum began preparing those old favourite dishes for Ronnie. She always said: 'It was a joy to cook for your dad. He was the most appreciative, fun person to cook for. The very smell of the food would be greeted with him playfully smacking his chops with anticipation, and as he ate there were mms and ahs of satisfaction! It was a pleasure for us to share that experience again, and I felt that I was actually doing something constructive to help with his recovery.' Mum sent him meals twice a day to the nursing home via Brian Theobald, who was at that time driving a minicab (later he became a booking agent and worked very closely with Ronnie for many years, booking tours and gigs for Ronnie's group).

Mum used to go to the nursing home to see Dad every day. She remembered: 'Of course, it wasn't only you and me that he was pining for but he also desperately wanted to get Linda back into his orbit.' The doctors thought that it was important that Linda come over from New Zealand to see Ronnie, and after much pressure from Pete King and, ironically enough, my mother, who pleaded with first Linda and then her mother to encourage her to come, finally she agreed. Brian and Mary met her at the airport. Linda, even though now in London, was still reluctant to go to the nursing home. Mary, grateful that Brian was driving, agreed to accompany her in the cab. Her stay, though short, seemed to help Ronnie to a certain degree. Shortly afterwards he received ECT treatment. Dad was never sure whether the treatment actually helped him or not. During this period Ilsa telephoned my mother at the flat. Because of Dad's illness he had not been able to give her and Nicholas the usual support and they were running out of money. Ilsa asked my mother to come alone, leaving me at home. Mum explained that it was impossible, she could not get a babysitter at such short notice, and if Ilsa wanted her to come that night then I would have to come too. And so we went to see Ilsa and Nicholas, who was twelve at the time. We arrived with bags of groceries and some money. Ilsa made tea, and she and my mother talked while Nicholas and I played together. He was a kind and gentle boy and shared his toys with me. Ilsa was adamant about one thing: she did not want Nicholas to know at that time that I was his half-sister. Ilsa would give no explanation for this and, although my mother never understood why, she respected her wishes and nothing was said.

In the middle of all the worry about Dad I came down with the chickenpox, and as a result Mum's visits to the nursing home had to be reduced to evenings only, because, of course, I had to be isolated from other children until I was no longer contagious. In the meantime, the doctors had decided that Ronnie needed a new environment to return home to, in an effort to prevent him from sinking back into his original depression. He would not hear of moving, so Uncle Pete and my mother made a decision to refurbish the flat at 108 Elm Park Mansions. Dad quite liked the idea and participated in making decisions about the changes. Ultimately, they completely redecorated and refurnished the flat during his stay in the nursing home. Spike Milligan, who had great empathy with Ronnie's illness, paid for his entire stay.

When Ronnie came out of the nursing home, Pete and Stella invited all three of us to stay with them, giving Ronnie a chance to get acclimatised before returning to the flat and the club. Although much improved, there was still a long way to go before he would be completely recovered. Ronnie and Mary used to go out for long walks and equally long talks. Stella was warm and supportive, while Pete, worried about his friend and partner, was kind and gentle, his support as solid as a rock, and even when Ronnie was at a low ebb humour was ever present. Pete kept everything at the club running smoothly, anxious to get his partner back into the fold. Finally, Ronnie decided they should return to the flat. Gradually, he was improving and started practising again, this time with his reeds. Then he felt well enough to go to the club, and the pieces of his life began to fit together again.

Treatment for depression back then was different in many ways from what was available when my father was so ill in 1996. One thing that did not change was the fact that Dad found it very difficult to deal with therapy. He found talking about his innermost feelings embarrassing and any form of group therapy was impossible for him. Dr Riccio, who treated Ronnie at the Priory in 1996, felt that because of this he was never treated adequately for reactive depression which, if it is left to run rampant, becomes biological, and that was what happened to Dad at the end. Alcohol and antidepressants do not mix, and medication such as Prozac has to be taken for about a month before it begins to take effect. My father needed instant relief, and when the prescribed drugs didn't produce that effect he reached out for alternatives that he thought would bring him relief, albeit temporary. There is no one treatment that works for everybody who suffers from depression; what works for one may not work for another. The new theory about serotonin was not around in 1996; some doctors believe it to be very effective, varying the dose of medication according to the patient's own levels of serotonin. At least today there is a wider range of choices with new breakthroughs always on the horizon. Gradually, the illness is being recognised and understood for the agonisingly painful, devastatingly destructive, distortive demon that it really is.

My mother and I were in London for about five months. Many years later Mum told me: 'It was the thought of you that held me together through those months in London. I cared about your father deeply. It was so important that we help Daddy get back on his feet again, and I was determined that you would not be robbed of the opportunity of knowing him and having a relationship with him.' Given the histories that both my parents shared as far as their own biological fathers were concerned, and the fact that they had discussed their mutual loss in depth many times over the ten years that they had been together, the thought of history repeating itself yet again in their daughter's life was simply unacceptable.

By the summer, Dad, although still recovering, had put together a new band, this time forming a quintet, a powerhouse with John Taylor on keyboard, Kenny Baldock on bass, Martin Drew on drums and the amazing Irish guitarist Louis Stewart. Ronnie had always been drawn to the guitar in both the classical and the jazz arenas. After the John Williams/Barney Kessel run in the club Ronnie had bought himself a guitar, taken a few lessons and played around with it at home for his own pleasure. This was a band format that he had always wanted to play with, and they split their time between touring and playing at the club. Gradually, Ronnie's health improved. His ability to express his feelings through his music was a catharsis that psychotherapy was never successful at producing for him. He played his way through the latter stages of his illness, growing stronger every day.

Dad came to visit us in New York. By this time several well-intentioned friends of my mother's had convinced her that it was imperative that she and Ronnie should see an attorney and have an agreement of support drawn up as a precaution and a form of security. Dad agreed to the meeting and, to make it less formal, my parents and the attorney met at a restaurant in New York to discuss the situation. My father, who had a total aversion to any kind of contract as far as personal relationships were concerned, did not take kindly to the attorney's increasing insistence that it was the *only* way to handle the situation. The exchange between them became progressively heated until Ronnie sprang from his chair, simultaneously turning the dining table over, and amid the clatter of broken dishes he told the attorney what he thought of him in colourful vernacular then he flew out of the restaurant. Totally disregarding the attorney, who was left standing amid the disarray, Mary beat a hasty exit after Ronnie, who by now was halfway up the street. She called his name, he turned, saw she was alone and waited for her to catch up with him, his anger abated as rapidly as it had arisen.

They found another restaurant and Ronnie said: 'We don't need a lawyer, Mary. Do we? Isn't this something that we can settle between ourselves?' That afternoon was the beginning of a new relationship between my mother and father. They were loyal to each other, the one always there for the other when things went wrong; they were very close friends, and that afternoon a new measure of trust and a different kind of commitment that was to last for a lifetime was established between them. They were both nonconformists in a way, and once again they agreed that legal formalities were not necessary. Their relationship had taken on another dimension: they both felt deeply for each other, and they were secure within their own personal commitment to one another. My father could not understand why my mother would not come back to England. She always said: 'We both had the same friends, the club was our social life, and I wanted to stay involved in the music business. It was too painful for me to stay in London. I knew he was a free spirit and couldn't bring myself to take the risk of us going through another break-up. I knew our relationship would be more stable this way.' They became confidants, and the bond of friendship and trust only grew deeper between them as the years passed.

By September, Auntie Bev, who was eighteen at the time, came to live with Mum and me at our hotel, and Whippet came too. In August, Jimmy Rowles, who used to be Billie Holiday's piano player, was in town staying at the same hotel as us. He was playing for a couple of weeks at Bradley's, on University Place. One evening Jimmy, Mum and Auntie Bev, after arranging for a babysitter, all went to Bradley's together in a friend's car. Jimmy and Auntie Bev were sitting in the back and Mum and the girl who was driving were in the front. They came to a red traffic light and by mistake the driver slammed her foot down on the accelerator instead of the brake, the car shot across the lights at top speed and slammed broadside into an oncoming car. Auntie Bev and Jimmy were OK. The driver was hurt a bit, but Mum's seatbelt broke and she smashed the windscreen with her head. She was very badly hurt and was rushed to hospital. She was haemorrhaging behind her eyes and had injured her neck and spine. Mum was in hospital for several weeks, and so Auntie Bev took care of me. Sometimes Uncle Stan used to come to the hotel and drive us out to Shadowbrook for a weekend. Auntie Bev remembered: 'When you were cross, you used to furrow your eyebrows together, exactly like your dad would do. Uncle Stan laughed so much every time this happened, because you really looked just like your dad. You always ended up laughing with him.'

After a few weeks Bev had to return to work. My mother was still in hospital, so arrangements were made for me to stay with some friends, Val and Brian, who had three daughters of their own and lived in rural Connecticut. I stayed with them for a month until my mother came out of the hospital and a home help was assigned to take care of me. My mother's neck and back injuries were extensive and she could not take care of a two-year-old by herself.

It was during this period that, even if we'd talked during the day, Dad started the tradition of phoning up every night just as I was going to bed. It was his way of tucking me in, saying: 'Sweet dreams, Rebecca, good night.' Over the years the only things to interrupt our 'good nights' were travel or illness.

Mum and I often talked about this period in our lives because Mum had to have traction at home and wear back and neck braces on and off for years; in fact she still does sometimes to this day. She often told me that Daddy became very concerned and blamed himself because he said if it hadn't been for him we would never have been in New York in the first place. It was a very difficult time, especially for my mother, because she was incapacitated and became quite despondent and worried about not being able to work and hold things together. My grandparents in Wales wrote my mother a letter telling her not to give up and that things would eventually come together. Gradually, Mum got better, but we came very close to coming back to England. Daddy was very supportive throughout and wanted us to return. Mum seriously considered it but decided that if we were to return it would be for the right reasons and not because she was injured. After much soul-searching the decision was made for us to stay on in New York.

CHAPTER TWELVE

KEEPERS OF THE FLAME

Ronnie wanted to be one of the chaps. I don't think he realised how he was one of the most important postwar British jazz musicians – not just a musician.

PETE KING

Only Ronnie would have had the faith to stick with his gamble. He made it possible for British jazz musicians to walk as tall as the Americans. He killed our inferiority complex. STEVE ALLAN **(BBC jazz producer)**

I regard Stan Getz as much an artist in his field as Yehudi Menuhin is in the classical sphere. And even though Getz is such a fine jazz artist he has managed to establish himself in the commercial field – and therefore created a lot of work for other tenor players in that idiom. RONNIE SCOTT, quoted in the *Melody Maker*

EARLIER IN THE YEAR my father had received an invitation from Robert Graves asking him to bring his band with him and play at his eightieth birthday. Robert explained that the celebrations were to be held on 24 July 1975 in their orchard theatre, which was surrounded by huge and ancient olive trees. My father discussed the invitation with Mum. They both fondly remembered the amphitheatre and leisurely time passed there with Robert, recalling how proud Robert was that the stage and seats had been built by a great-nephew of his, Simon, with the help of his youngest son Thomas. Robert always likened his theatre to its ancient predecessors in Rome. It was without doubt the ideal place for such a celebration. Sadly, it was impossible for Ronnie to go; funds simply would not permit such an extravagance. It was something that Dad always regretted. It was his last chance to spend time with Robert before the tentacles of Alzheimer's disease stole the great man away from the present. His illness distressed my father deeply. During their many discussions, Robert had shared with Ronnie that he could stand just about anything as long as he had his mind and could write. That such a fate should befall so scholarly a man, a literary giant who, with a ready wit, was able to laugh at the idiosyncrasies of human nature and life in general, seemed to be the cruellest hand that life could have dealt. Robert ultimately died ten years later, at the age of ninety, on 7 December 1985. When Dad talked about his own advancing age towards the end of his life, he remembered Robert's demise. The thought of living with Alzheimer's filled him with horror, the same kind of dread that he had about not being able to play. I could not help but think of the irony, the cruel blow that life dealt my father, who had his mind but could no longer play. It was as though each man in his own way had been faced with what they each saw as the worst final scenario.

Afternoon business at the club was quite consistent; something always seemed to be happening. Donald recalled that one afternoon while the BBC was in the process of preparing for one of the programmes that was taped at the club, Simon Dee, who was a disc jockey for the BBC, ran downstairs to the bar in search of a packet of cigarettes, and at that precise moment Ronnie happened to wander in, also in need of cigarettes. As luck would have it there was only one packet left, so in true Scott form Ronnie declared the only way to resolve the issue was toss for the cigarettes — double or quits. Needless to say, Ronnie won and Simon Dee was, as Donald put it, 'Quite pissed off!' On another occasion George and Donald were busy preparing for a press reception for Roberta Flack; it was to promote the Donny Hathaway album with which she was involved and which included her well-known song 'Killing Me Softly'. One of Roberta's employees was a man of huge proportions in every direction, dwarfing George and Donald. To add to this he was also rude and obnoxious, showering the two young men with a torrent of verbal abuse. While he was at his peak Ronnie walked in, headed straight for the man and said: 'Get out! Get out right now! You can't talk to them like that. Not in my presence, you can't.' The man, looking somewhat startled, bellowed: 'And who the hell are you?' Ronnie's response to that was: 'It doesn't *matter* who I am. What matters is you do not talk to them or anybody else in here like that.' Ronnie threatened to cancel the reception and throw them out with all their stuff. As George said: 'He gave back to us what he expected from us, loyalty. No one was going to get away with treating his staff badly no matter *who* they were.'

Benny Green had been heard in the past to describe the club as 'a secret society for the propagation of good music' – a line that Ronnie loved. But times had changed and Ronnie Scott's had become a world-renowned jazz club. This was another fruitful year musically. Among the major names that were presented was the prodigious talent of Joe Pass, guitar, a return visit of Ronnie's old friend Zoot Sims, and Milt Jackson. Newcomers were Clark Terry, Roy Eldridge, one of the forefathers of the trumpet, Monty Alexander, a superb pianist, and the Count Basie Band. Ronnie was back in the saddle again at the club and busy with his quintet. Kenny Baldock had come up with a new name for Ronnie; it was Gunza Mucher which means 'the big maker'. The guys shortened it to Gunza. As Martin said: 'The musicians called him Gunza because he was such a great leader and he was a big man in so many ways.' The name stuck for the rest of Ronnie's life.

When they were on the road Martin Drew would drive. But he is the first to admit that his sense of navigation is not always the best and ruefully remembers Ronnie saying: 'Mike Carr was incredible! It was like he had a homing antenna in his head which would take us straight to the gig!' Ronnie would open the window and ask directions of the driver in the next car, mumbling: 'Momzer, can you help me?' The only audible words the other driver heard was 'can you help me' but everyone else in the car heard 'momzer', Yiddish for bastard! Everyone was doubled up with laughter while Ronnie with a dead straight face proceeded to get directions. Martin often found himself the brunt of Ronnie's oblique humour, because he spared no one, least of all himself, from his particular brand of levity. When they got stuck in traffic in a strange town on the way to a gig, Martin recalled: 'Ronnie would wind the window down, stick his head out and shout, "Excuse me! Excuse me! We're a *band*!", playing make believe that the traffic would magically clear on hearing this announcement.'

My father came back to New York twice that December, first on the fourth for a brief visit and then on the twentieth, when we celebrated Christmas a few days early. I was just three years old, and he bought me a whole menagerie of soft, plush, cuddly Disney characters to take to bed. Once again, Dad made a concerted effort to persuade Mum and me to return to London. My mother agonised over the decision, but as she told me years later something deep down inside held her back. All had long since been forgiven, and in many ways their relationship had strengthened, but she just could not go back.

By this time my mother had started her own business, called Hulin

Artists Management. She was working with several New York jazz musicians booking gigs and tours and securing record contracts, and in 1976 she booked Carrie Smith, who had a deep, rich, powerful contralto voice, a wonderful singer, into Ronnie Scott's. Stan Getz made a return visit that year, as did Oscar Peterson, Dizzy Gillespie and Horace Silver. Betty Carter, a unique singer, with her musical director John Hicks at piano, who wrote a lot of Betty's arrangements and collaborated with her on originals, made her first appearance at the club, as did Cedar Walton, a marvellous pianist who still appears at the club to this day. Then came Woody Herman and his Thundering Herd, as the orchestra was fondly referred to, playing to a full house.

Over the course of the years there were occasional flare-ups between Ronnie and Pete, a natural enough occurrence in any partnership. George remembered: 'The office door would slam shut and they would thrash it out between themselves, their voices raising the rafters. Then it was all over, the air was cleared and pretty soon things were back to normal.' The partnership was seventeen years in the making, and they had ridden some stormy seas together, but in some areas they could not see eye to eye. As Wally Houser said: 'Working so closely together as they did, they started to rub sparks off each other, so they both asked me to be a director. I held one voting share so if necessary I could mediate between them – a kind of interface, I think they'd call it now. It was OK. Ronnie was a fantastic man, a complete one-off, wholly unique. He was the leader of my generation.' The arrangement worked well, and over the ensuing years Wally was rarely called in to calm the waters. As Uncle Pete said during an interview for *Crescendo* with Mike Hennessey: 'I don't think there's ever been a point where a parting of the ways seemed likely. There are times when I'm sure I must drive Ronnie mad, and he can drive me mad – but never to the extent that you can't go home and sleep on it and come back the next day and work out a compromise. It would never have occurred to me to do all this without Ronnie.'

By now Dad had a new girlfriend. Her name was Françoise Venet, and she worked in the bar downstairs at the club. A keen jazz fan, Françoise used to bring her own records in to play at the bar. They became really good friends at first, Ronnie often stopping in at the bar to chat with Françoise, who was tall and slender with very pretty elfin-like features; she was also an accomplished photographer and painter. Over time their relationship progressed and Françoise eventually moved into Elm Park Mansions with Dad.

That summer Daddy came to visit us in New York. He wanted to get me something special for my birthday, which was not until September, so we went shopping together. We were out all afternoon, spending time in the village, and even though I was still very young I used to walk miles with Dad, and if I really got worn out we came back home by taxi. That day my mother could not believe her eyes when we walked in with three plastic bags, one with goldfish swimming around, another with multicoloured tropical fish, and the third with two frogs! I was so excited with my new collection of swimming friends, but Mum was not so thrilled because we had nothing to put them all in. Dad hadn't thought about buying a fishtank, and the frogs could not go in with the fish, so that meant two tanks were required. Those details were left up to my mother to sort out. We spent long afternoons together, meeting Mum for dinner at night. Dad also liked to have time to himself. He always played the horses, and often walked from midtown to the village and back, occasionally hanging out with musician friends.

During his stay Ronnie and Mary went to the Half Note. The Canterino family always welcomed them, and while they were sitting chatting to Sal Canterino, Woody Herman came in. He was pleased to see Ronnie and proceeded to sing his praises, telling my mother the story of when he and the band played for the United States' armed forces at an American air force base in Scunthorpe. Ronnie and his nine-piece band were on the same bill. Woody was absolutely knocked out; he recalled his surprise at finding a band of that calibre in England, saying that their musicianship was fantastic. He and Dad reminisced. Woody had raced around the perimeter of the airfield in an Austin, and Dad told Woody about his racing endeavours in 1973. Even though Ronnie had brought his saxophone with him – he *never* went anywhere without it – he always left it at the hotel, refusing invitations to sit in. He never felt comfortable playing in New York and played only on rare occasions, always a little embarrassed because there were so many saxophone players that he deeply admired and he felt somewhat intimidated playing on their turf.

Back in England, the following September, a week of jazz concerts was presented by the Jazz Centre Society at the Shaw Theatre in London. The opening night featured Ronnie's quartet, the *Jazz Journal* recording the event by saying: 'Louis Stewart on guitar shared the solo honours with Scott, no mean feat when the leader is playing so aggressively. Most of the numbers were up-tempo, but the audience reserved most applause for a version of Stephen Sondheim's "Send in the Clowns" which featured Scott on soprano saxophone.' Following Ronnie's group was the Stan Tracey Octet – Stan in full swing, the band playing his original material. On the fifth night Ronnie's good friend and one of his favourite saxophone players, Dexter Gordon, who had not played in London since playing at the old club, got a standing ovation from a full house before he played a note. The Pat Smythe Trio, which consisted of Ron Mathewson on bass and Martin Drew on drums, accompanied Dexter. One of the tunes that he played was a ballad that Ronnie loved called 'You've Changed', a song always associated with Billie Holiday. As Brian Davis of the *Jazz Journal* stated: 'Ballad artistry as only Dexter can portray, muscular never sentimental yet so *very* emotional.' All these ingredients for Ronnie were salient factors when playing a ballad. Dexter and Ronnie spent time together at the club after the concert was over, and he was booked to play the club in Frith Street the following year.

By December Dad was back in New York, arriving on the fourth. The city was adorned with Christmas trimmings, Fifth Avenue a splendid sight. The windows of Lord & Taylor were famous for their animated stories and my godmother, Auntie Jenna, an actress, had prerecorded the storyline and we warmed with pleasure as we edged slowly past each window, listening to her voice through the speakers. Daddy was as enchanted as I as we watched the mechanical figures perform, the men in their top hats and tails, the glamorous women in swirling gowns made of brightly coloured silks and taffetas, their freshly coiffed hair peeking out from beneath wide-brimmed hats, and bonnets adorned with ribbons, the skaters' scarves flying as they whirled around the frozen pond. Then we were off to the Rockefeller Center to see the biggest Christmas tree in the world sparkling with thousands of tiny coloured lights set above the skating rink, now filled with skaters of every creed, culture and generation. We were greeted by a host of heralding angels illuminated with the tiniest white lights amid great bows of furry white pine, and dark green prickly holly adorned with clusters of bright red berries set in the centre of the walkway. The smell of roasted chestnuts wafted past as vendors filled white paper bags to the brim for a dollar. Unable to resist, we sat on a wall contentedly munching the hot, soft and tasty nuts.

The next day the three of us went out to buy a Christmas tree, one that could stand on the tabletop, three feet high planted in a pot. Daddy bought tiny white lights and small ornaments and together we decorated the tree. Next on the agenda was a trip to Macy's to see Father Christmas. Dad loved Macy's and he left Mum and me queuing up while he went shopping. It was a *very* long queue and Dad was back in time to see me sit on Santa's knee and tell him my Christmas wish. He spent a lot of time trying to get me to tell him what I'd wished for, but I wouldn't tell because I thought my wish would not come true if I did. The night before Daddy left, we had Christmas together, my mother keeping one gift back so that when Christmas Day came I still had something from Daddy to open on the day itself.

Every year over Christmas and New Year's Eve Dad and his group played at the club, and since 1973 to this day George Melly became the other half of the annual holiday package. For as long as my mother could remember, on New Year's Eve the customers at the club were all served complimentary bottles of champagne, the ladies boxes of chocolates and the men cigars. At midnight the lights were switched off and my father stood to the side of the darkened bandstand, holding a microphone into a radio. The club was filled with the sound of Big Ben ringing in the New Year, the lights in the room simultaneously flashing on and off, people hugging each other and throwing streamers. Without fail, seconds afterwards Dad would ring us in New York and, although it was only seven o'clock in New York, we always brought the New Year in together to the background sounds of everyone clinking glasses, blowing their hooters and joyously wishing each other Happy New Year.

S arah Vaughan made her first appearance at the club in 1977. Prior to her visit she was performing in New York at Avery Fisher Hall. Dad telephoned Mum somewhat perturbed because Sarah had not signed and returned her contract. Anxious to get the formalities over with, he asked Mum to take a copy of the contract to the hall and get Sarah to sign it. We went to the concert together, and backstage afterwards Sarah signed the contract. That was the one and only time I saw her perform and met the great lady whom everyone affectionately called 'Sassy'. It was also tenor saxophonist George Coleman's first appearance at the club, sharing the bill with Tete Montoliu. It was the beginning of a lifelong friendship between Ronnie and George, who played the club about once a year for the next twenty-odd years, each time bringing Ronnie two or three boxes of Henke reeds which were his favourite. This year also saw return visits of Joe Pass, Stan Getz, Horace Silver and Dizzy Gillespie.

One afternoon during the Getz run George received a note that Stan had left for him the night before asking him to take his sax to Lewington's to get it fixed. George, in a bit of a rush, grabbed the saxophone case in the office and ran down to Lewington's, taking it straight to the workshop upstairs. The guys at Lewington's knew George very well by now and fixed the sax while George waited. About six o'clock that evening Stan came into the club wanting to try his horn before the evening's performance. He walked into the office, looked around and finally asked: 'George, did you get my horn fixed?' George said: 'Yes, Stan, it's right there.' Looking round, Stan said: 'If you mean this one it's not my horn, George, that's Ronnie's horn!' George had to bolt out of the club with Stan's horn in a frantic dash to catch the guys at Lewington's before they left. He made it by the skin of his teeth and all was well, and Ronnie also unexpectedly got his sax fixed!

One of Dizzy's pleasures was to play chess with Ronnie when the evening's music was over. Since the mid-1960s the game had become almost a nightly ritual. As soon as Jeff cashed in the money from the door, Dizzy and Ronnie got down to serious business at the chessboard. When Martin Drew started working at the club he joined the after-hours chess school and remembered many evenings when he joined Ronnie, Jeff Ellison and Giuseppe ('Joe') the chef, whom Ronnie used to call El Parasita, in a game of chess, commandeering the desk in the office, which would drive Pete mad because he couldn't close out his books for the night. Ronnie used to say, 'We won't be long', then would proceed to keep everybody waiting for hours. During the game, Ronnie would keep up an incessant mumble that would drive his opponent crazy, like: 'Yes. Hmm . . . hmm. OK. We'll soon see about that! Hmm . . . Yes, I see . . . Yes.' Martin said: 'It was all gamesmanship to distract our focus and get us to make mistakes, and it bloody well worked! But when it didn't and Ronnie lost, you should have heard the insults flying all around! All in good humour, *never* with malice. Ronnie was a great man, he really was.'

Ronnie and the quintet were back out on the road, and as was his habit Ronnie called into the club to check with Pete about business. Sarah Vaughan was due to open, and Martin remembered: 'There was a terrible hiatus going on at the club. Pete was pulling his hair out because Sarah was refusing to go on. Ronnie said: "Let me have her number." He rang her up and it turned out that Sarah thought the club wouldn't pay for her musicians to stay at the same hotel as her, and she wanted them to receive the same kind of treatment as her. Ronnie had found out that the guys actually preferred to stay at a different hotel, and he was able to explain the situation to Sarah. He sorted it all out and the gig was on. He was one of the hippest guys I've ever known, the way he could handle any situation.'

One afternoon in 1977 Ronnie was in the back office at the club when the telephone rang. He answered it, much to the surprise of the caller, who turned out to be Cynthia, his first love, who was phoning to make a reservation for her daughter Melody's twenty-first birthday on 2 June. Cynthia had never been to the club and had not seen Ronnie for thirty years. She had decided the evening would be a special celebration for herself and her daughter. Cynthia remembered: 'I wasn't expecting him to pick up the telephone, but I went ahead and made the reservation and Ronnie said: "Cynthia! Still talking to dead people, are you?" ' Laughing, they started chatting about old times. When Cynthia and Melody arrived on 2 June Ronnie was at the door to greet them. Making a special point of seeing that they were seated at a prime table, he sent a bottle of champagne over to them and there was no bill at the end of the evening. Cynthia said: 'We had such a *wonderful* time. Melody has such great memories about her twenty-first birthday. Ronnie rolled out the red carpet and made us feel like royalty.'

I clearly remember that summer. I was five years old and Daddy brought his new girlfriend, Françoise, to New York to meet us. Françoise had a distinct French accent which at that age I found hard to understand. Mum belonged to a pool club that was on the roof of a neighbouring hotel, and we were there practically every day after school. I used to attend the United Nations School. I loved the water and had been swimming since I was a baby and so had no fear. A capable swimmer, I was able to swim under water and was learning how to dive. Françoise and Daddy joined us at the pool, and we spent our afternoons swimming and playing in the water. I didn't really mind her coming along, she was fun. Afterwards we all met for dinner a couple of times. Too young to understand, I just wondered why she was there.

During this visit Daddy and Françoise took me to the Children's Zoo in Central Park, and afterwards we went into the little 'hole in the wall' juice bar where they sold one of Daddy's favourite drinks, Orange Julius, one of the things he looked forward to when he came to New York. Françoise took lots of photographs, and made sure that she had enough copies made for everybody. We all got along together very well.

Shortly afterwards Mum took me to see Max Roach play. I remember her telling me we went because it was the first time Max had played in New York in seven years, so it was quite a special event. The club was Storyville, on 58th Street at Madison Avenue. It was a big club and was fully booked. As soon as the first set started I was absolutely hooked on what Max was playing. Mum told me that she expected that we would have to leave after the first set, but I could not get enough of the drums that night and we ended up staying for all three sets. Mum was promoting an album for CBS at the time, and she did not know it but the president, Bruce Lundval, and several other executives were also in the audience. At the end of the evening Bruce called Mum over to his table and said that none of the adults in the audience had listened to the music with the same level of attention as I had. He was so impressed that he insisted on paying our bill for the evening! I was more interested in meeting Max Roach and getting close to his drum set. Mum took me to the bandstand and Max handed me his drumsticks, and while he and Mum were talking I tapped out rhythms on the edge of the bandstand. Max stopped talking and turned to me and said, 'Becky, would you like to sit at my drum kit?' He lifted me up and sat me on his drum stool, and adjusted it so I could reach, and I played on his drums! It was a magical evening for me. I was really impressed with him and his music even at that tender age. Of course, when I was older I realised that Max Roach is one of the most respected jazz drummers alive, a legend. I couldn't wait to tell Daddy when he called, and he was so enthused at my obvious fascination with the music.

By now Dad's quintet had a change in personnel. Kenny Baldock left and was replaced by Ron Mathewson, my father jokingly describing the ensemble as 'two Yids, a Mick, a Jock and a Yock': Ronnie and Martin Drew were the Yids, Louis Stewart the Mick, Ron Mathewson the Jock and John Taylor the Yock. On 18 October the group made the recording 'Serious Gold'. Before the actual recording session took place, Ronnie had called a rehearsal. Martin was the only one in the group who didn't smoke pot, but that particular afternoon the guys were able to cajole him into having a 'tote'. Martin said: 'I only took a couple of drags – that was it.' Everyone took their place on the bandstand and Ronnie counted in Kenny Wheeler's tune 'Hey-Oke Suite Ballad'. Everyone started to play when all of a sudden Martin got the giggles. It got so bad, not only couldn't he play but he ended up rolling on the floor doubled up with laughter. Everybody caught the giggles. It was hopeless: the rehearsal was temporarily on hold.

'Serious Gold' was a landmark album in more ways than one. In the first place it was to be one of three albums which launched Ronnie's and Pete's own recording label. Called Ronnie Scott's Record Productions, they had made a deal with Pye Records. Sarah Vaughan and Carmen McCrae were the other two recording artists, and the trio of albums was released in January 1978. Secondly, my father, who thoroughly disliked recording, particularly in a studio because he felt that his music was always in a state of flux, that whatever he had just played could be improved on the next time, describing his playing as 'a moment of fleeting emotions', would not record again with his own group until 1990. The quintet, which by then had John Critchinson on piano and Mornington Lockett on tenor, recorded the CD 'Never Pat a Burning Dog', the label's name changed to Ronnie Scott's Jazz House, and this, sadly, was the last recording that Dad ever made.

We spoke to Dad nearly every day, even if it was just my good night call. He would ask the usual questions about school and always inquired about the fish and frogs. I had a little friend who used to come to play with me. Her name was Monica, and we used to take the frogs out of the tank and try to catch them as they hopped all over the place. My mother would say: 'You're not supposed to do that, Rebecca. Be careful or you'll end up losing one.' Sure enough, it happened. As usual Dad asked me about the frogs, and I had to tell him what I had been up to and that eventually we found the carcass under a radiator.

Dad and Françoise came to New York again in the summer of 1978. They were on their way back from the West Coast and spent a few days with us before returning to London. I didn't know it at the time, of course, but one of the things they couldn't get over was that people bought pot by the branch on the West Coast. It was during this visit that Dad asked Mum what she thought about me going to London for Christmas. Françoise was happy with the idea and Mum agreed. She got along well with Françoise and felt comfortable with me spending time with her and Daddy.

That same summer two unique events took place in America within four days of each other. For the first time in the history of jazz the art form was acknowledged as America's most significant contribution to culture. In New York on 15 June the inaugural presentation of the Prez awards was held. To commemorate jazz, discs inscribed with the names of some of the jazz immortals were embedded into the sidewalk on legendary 52nd Street. The awards were presented to twelve musicians who helped create the renowned street. They were: Kenny Clarke, Roy Eldridge, Sarah Vaughan, Dizzy Gillespie, Miles Davis, Thelonious Monk, Coleman Hawkins, Billie Holiday, Art Tatum, Lester Young and Charlie Parker. The mayor of the city, Edward Koch, opened the celebration.

Just three days later President Jimmy Carter hosted a White House Jazz Festival, one of the most incredible evenings in the music's history. The occasion was to commemorate the twenty-fifth anniversary of George

Wein's Newport Jazz Festival. There were 40 performing musicians and 600 or so writers, politicians, musicians and assorted celebrities attended the event. On the White House lawn, gigantic kettles of a Creole dish called jambalaya were simmering; on the tables were huge bowls of salad and large pecan pies. President Carter opened the festivities with a ten-minute speech, saying: 'If ever there was an art form, one that is special and peculiar to the United States and represents what we are as a country, I would say that it's jazz.' He went on to describe the music as being 'vivid, alive, aggressive, innovative on the one hand, and the severest form of self-discipline on the other, never compromising quality as the human spirit bursts forth in an expression of song'.

Interestingly enough, the following year Ronnie found it necessary to make the distinction that jazz is an American art form. During a conversation with Les Tomkins of *Crescendo* magazine, published under the title 'The Ronnie Scott View Point', Ronnie set Les straight by saying: 'But you were talking about a British jazz sound. It's either jazz or it isn't – and jazz is an *American* sound, an American art form. A musician can have his own sound, certainly – sure, that's the idea, to develop that. He doesn't have to ape some of the American jazz musicians, note for note, sound for sound. Of course not – but he's got to play in that *idiom*. If he's outside of that idiom, then he's making a different music.'

Dad was to receive an award from the Songwriters' Guild, which organised the presentation ceremony at the Connaught Rooms in London on 4 October. The guild was presenting their Gold Badge of Merit to an eclectic group of prominent recipients. My father was awarded the medal and was named on the list of recipients as Ronnie Scott (jazz musician). Dad had become so well known as a club owner and raconteur that although surprised by the award he was really thrilled because it was in recognition of his musicianship, and he always considered himself first and foremost a musician.

All the arrangements were made for me to visit Dad. Mum took me to the airport. At six years old it was actually kind of fun but it was scary too, because although I knew who my dad was I didn't know him like I knew my mum. I remember that the stewardess was very nice and walked me off the plane and down the long corridor. I wasn't even sure if I would recognise Dad, but of course I did. He came on his own to meet me and we went to the club to see Uncle Pete. When we arrived at the flat, we had a lovely dinner together that Françoise had prepared. They had really cool big colourful cushions that we sat on in front of the TV, and the room was dim because Dad always liked soft lighting.

In the afternoons my father would watch the horse races, and say, 'Rebecca, you've got to give me fifteen or twenty minutes and I'll be back.' I knew exactly what he was doing, because during one of our afternoon excursions in New York he had taken me into the OTB, the largest betting shop in New York, so he could place his bets and we watched the races together on their closed-circuit TV. The first time he disappeared like this, I called after him, 'Dad bet on number five.' Five is my favourite number: I was born on the 5 September and there are five letters in my last name. Off he went to the betting shop, returning just in time to watch the race. I asked him: 'Did you bet on number five?' And he said: 'No, no, Becky. The odds weren't good.' Disappointed, I thought to myself, Oh, why didn't you put something on number five for me? You could have at least put a pound on or something. We watched the race, it was a good race, and as the horses were getting closer and closer, and number five was about in the middle of everything that was going on, all of a sudden number five came up out of nowhere and he won the race! Daddy was so pissed off, I kept saying: 'I told you. You should have listened!' He was pretty livid that he hadn't put the bet on.

Françoise remembered: 'When Christmas came around, it was fun to have the tree and decorations all over the flat, and for Ronnie to have time off to celebrate in a family atmosphere, which he enjoyed. I'd got you several dolls and other toys, but your preference was for an electric train which you'd asked for. The cat, Pussintat, was delighted to have so much wrapping paper to play with and boxes to hide in. On Boxing Day we went to visit Harry and Harriet South, where you found some playmates in their kids.'

After Christmas was over I was ready to go home. I packed up all my toys and stuff that I had been given for Christmas, happy to be going home because I missed Mum and I wanted to get back to her in New York. Dad took me to the airport, but when he presented my passport they would not let me through. My father got extremely upset and there was a lot of hysteria going on. At the time I did not understand what was happening, because I was still a little girl. Dad had no alternative but to take me back to the flat. When we arrived, Françoise and Daddy telephoned Mum. Everybody was very upset and at that point no one knew what to do. It was particularly frustrating for Françoise, who had taken two weeks off from the club to make my visit possible and was now anxious to return to work. My mother was beside herself in New York. Memories of Daddy whisking me off to London unannounced in 1974 rose to the surface, and her reaction was: 'Oh, my God. This *can't* be happening again.' Our immigration status was in the 'being processed' state. Mum told Dad that she would call a lawyer first thing the next morning.

The immigration lawyer made it clear that under no circumstances should Mum leave the country. The process of establishing residency in the United States was long and drawn-out, taking a couple of years to complete, and during this period they do *not* give you permission to travel. My own situation was a case in point. *No one* had dreamed that a child would be refused entry when her mother was in New York, but as far as the authorities were concerned I was just another case number. Mum begged my father to take me back himself since I was already on his passport, but for some reason he said that it was not possible for him to do that.

Dad discussed it with Mum and a decision was made to put me into a school because no one knew how long it would take to sort out the immigration problems. Françoise took me shopping because the weather was getting colder and I didn't have enough warm clothes with me and needed shoes. As a little girl I had my own sense of style, but unfortunately it wasn't the same as Françoise's. I hated the shoes and I hated the chequered bell-bottom trousers that she bought. As Françoise put it: 'Shopping for clothes for Becky was nice, but the classical English style I picked didn't really rejoice her as she was into a different look.'

Françoise dressed me up and took me to my new school, where all the kids made fun of me because of my accent, which by now was quite American. I seemed to be very different from the other children and very shy because I was in strange surroundings. One little girl became my friend, but unfortunately I don't remember her name. Most of the building was glass windows, so you could see in and out. The windows were covered with various paintings of flowers that the kids had painted, which made the school itself seem very appealing. Françoise took some photographs, in one of which I am leaning up against a window with the little girl who befriended me, and she is leaning over asking me something. The school had a real leather tepee up in the loft and the majority of my time was spent in that tepee. I used to sit there by myself, except for the times that one little girl would come and sit and play with me. All the other kids constantly taunted me. It was a miserable time.

Françoise, who had to stop working at the club to take care of me, had selected the school, which was quite close to the flat in The Boltons. Françoise recalled: 'I would take you each morning while Ronnie was sleeping. I should rather say drag you to school, as the idea of going there didn't really enchant you. Just as well that that modern, light and colourful school was only ten minutes away, because a lot of energy was required pulling along a child acting as if she were on her way to a torture session! I attended some of the classes so you wouldn't feel so insecure and to see myself how it was. But I guess that settling in among all those English kids and teachers wasn't easy for a New York kid.'

With Christmas over it was back to nightlife for Ronnie, and the ritual Saturday afternoons of betting, which meant getting up early, studying the newspapers, phoning the betting shop and watching the races on TV. As Françoise said: 'And absolutely no disturbance, please! So I had to take you out for the afternoon. We'd go shopping or walking around the lovely London parks.' We would take my 'invisible dog' out for a walk sometimes. I loved him, he was so obedient and clean. Ronnie had bought the collar and stiff leash for me in New York on one of our trips. This was the only dog that didn't have to go into quarantine on arrival in Britain! I really enjoyed that dog too, and Françoise took photographs of us out walking.

We often went into the club at night, but of course not staying until the last set. The guys on the door, Jeff Ellison and Jimmy Parsons, who had worked for the club's booking agency for years and is still there to this day, as is Monty – all the staff became like a second family, and I looked forward to seeing them. Joe the chef, who was Italian, had a son who used to come to the club too, and we played together. Joe knew I loved shrimps and would always conjure up a treat of some sort for me, welcoming me into the kitchen, which was where I preferred to be rather than sitting upstairs.

Time was passing and the tension was mounting. I was very unhappy and so was Françoise, who wanted her life back. I was not an easy child to cope with, especially when I found myself in a situation that I didn't want to be in. I got away with a number of things that I would never have got away with at home. Françoise remembered: 'Your father tried converting you to his taste for meat and two veggies, or bacon, sausages and egg, not forgetting the fried bread. But he had to admit defeat on each occasion. No matter the various ways of tempting you that were thought of, McDonald's and Coke was about all you allowed to enter your mouth.' My mother was *mortified* when she learned of this, because we *never* had Coke or any other kind of soda in the house. She was into very healthy eating; we never even had pre-packaged sliced bread! As far as hamburgers were concerned, they were an occasional and rare treat. It caused a war across the Atlantic, my father yelling at my mother for turning me into a junk food child, she yelling back at him for having no control. They were furious with one another, Dad because he thought that Mum should have found a way to get me home by now and Mum because she couldn't understand why he wouldn't take me back himself.

Life had become so tense at the flat that mercifully for all concerned Harriet and Harry South came to the rescue and I went to stay with them and their three daughters, Anita, Louise and Annabelle (we are all still good friends). Things were rapidly spinning out of control. No one seemed to know how to help my mother, who searched frantically for advice and help for weeks. Finally a solution was presented to her and arrangements were made for me to travel back home that February through Canada in the midst of one of the harshest winters that part of the world had seen in years.

M y father and Françoise bought a house in West Hampstead. Dad had the area checked out in advance of the purchase to make sure that he would not be woken up by any of his neighbours. The house was spacious. A music room was planned for Ronnie so that he could practise whenever he felt like it, and another of the rooms would be a studio for Françoise. It was a happy period for him and Françoise, the intention being that the house would be their haven. He was thrilled at the prospect. They took the cat with them and bought a beautiful big dog. As it turned out they lived in the house for little over a year.

There was much work to be done on the house to make the necessary transformation. This of course, required a tremendous amount of organisation and many builders to accomplish the rebuilding. It was not long before the place was filled with noise, debris and workmen – not a winning combination for my father – and the situation became increasingly irritating for him and Françoise.

In celebration of the twentieth anniversary of Ronnie Scott's, a gala concert was held at the Royal Festival Hall on 14 May, paying tribute to Ronnie and Pete. Ronnie and his quartet with John Taylor, piano, Dave Green, bass, and Tony Levin, drums, opened the festivities. Jimmy Staples of *Crescendo* wrote: 'Ronnie, when in his club, has a reputation for acid wit, but beneath this blasé façade lies a dedicated serious musician, a fact demonstrated at the concert. Ronnie proved his international class on tenor with a highly individual modern sound and a style that shows he has kept his ears open over the years. I particularly like his version of Freddie

Hubbard's "Sunflower".' Next on the programme was Art Blakey and the Jazz Messengers, followed by the Buddy Rich Big Band.

A decade earlier, my father, in an article he had written for *Melody Maker*, said: 'There's so much good music around now in *all* fields – yes, sir, even in the world of pop – that we want to be associated with it all, whether it's Sonny Rollins, The Who, John Williams, Blood Sweat and Tears, Clarke–Boland Band, John Surman, Ravi Shankar or the Thad Jones–Mel Lewis Band.' Ronnie and Pete followed through on this idea of experimenting and broadening the horizons of the club by booking all kinds of jazz fringe entertainers. Never losing sight of their original goal, they made sure the main artery of the club pulsated with the best of British and American jazz. Some of the fringe artists to appear during the 1970s were Jackie Cain and Roy Kral, a superb husband-and-wife vocal team, the very well-known Al Jarreau and Mose Allison, the Four Freshmen, and two great black American vocalists Ester Marrow and Esther Phillips. Exceptionally high standards of musicianship and artistry were maintained and the performers appealed to a wide cross-section of audiences.

Towards the end of May, Ronnie's quintet saw more changes in personnel. John Critchinson replaced John Taylor on piano, becoming a close friend of Ronnie's and staying with the group until the end, and Louis Stewart left to play with George Shearing. Martin recalled: 'Ronnie was very upset about the break-up of the band. John Taylor was an amazing player, and Ronnie and Louis were both intellectual guys and used to get along like a house on fire.' Until mid-1980 the group continued as a quartet.

The quartet, which was playing a tour of Wales, had just played a gig in Bangor. They spent the night at a bed-and-breakfast and were due to leave that afternoon to travel to Birkenhead. Ronnie, following his favourite occupation, was deeply entrenched in the local betting shop. Time was marching on, and Martin, who was driving, concerned that they were running late, went to pick him up. He remembered: 'I walked into the betting shop and as soon as Ronnie saw me he said: "Martin! I've just done me bollocks! I've done *all* the money, the band's money as well, and *everything* is riding on the last race. I've *got* to wait until it finishes!" So we waited . . . and waited . . . and finally the last race comes up. And he bloody well won! So we both did a war dance around the betting shop!' Ronnie had won all the money back – and some. Martin said: 'Bless his heart. When he won he nearly always wined us and dined us. He would say: "There you are. It's all on me." But we couldn't find anywhere to eat!

Birkenhead was shut! So we headed to the Blue Boar on the M1 and all had double bacon, eggs, beans, sausage, fried bread and juice.'

Back in New York, by the autumn of 1979 we had moved from Manhattan to Brooklyn. It was more of a neighbourhood lifestyle and there was an excellent public school, PS8, in Brooklyn Heights that my mother had selected for me to attend. Shortly after I started at my new school it was apparent that I was having trouble. My teacher, Mrs Kendricks, was very concerned because she had noticed that I reversed some of my letters and numbers. Mum was also very concerned because when we were working on my homework I became very frustrated and distraught. She knew something was wrong and arranged a meeting with Mrs Kendricks. They discussed my problems at length, and Mrs Kendricks secured a recommendation from the school for me to be tested for dyslexia. Dad was confused. Dyslexia was not something that he was familiar with, and he was anxious to get answers to all his questions. The testing process was an all-day marathon with several different specialists. We picked up literature that explained the idiosyncrasies of dyslexia and sent them all to Dad. The outcome of the testing was that I was indeed dyslexic. He was distressed by the news and wanted to see copies of all the tests, the results and relevant documents.

After he received the package Dad phoned and said: 'OK. So now we know Becky is dyslexic. Where do we go from here?' Mum explained that fortunately PS8 was set up with special remedial classes designed specifically for children with dyslexia. Also, Auntie Jenna's church had a special group of volunteers who coached dyslexic children one to one. Through Auntie Jenna we met a young man, David, who was a student at Columbia University. Because we weren't members of the church, Mum worked out a fee with him and hired him independently to work with me. David was an extremely intelligent young man with a very creative approach to the handling of dyslexia. He and I got on like a house on fire. I looked forward to my sessions with him, and he gave me assignments to do on my own. Dad wanted to know all the details and was fascinated, as was Mum, with the innovative way David set me on the right track.

David and I walked the streets of Manhattan together, with me, letter by letter, spelling out the words on all the neon signs. We would discuss advertisements that were running on TV and make a list of them, and he would send me home with the *New York Times*. My project was to find the same advertisement in the newspaper, cut it out and give it to him the next

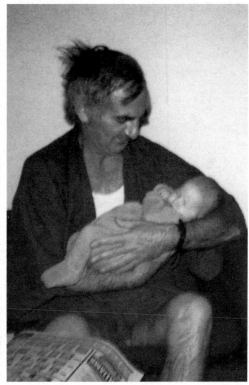

21. Ronnie and Mary in Mallorca in 1967 after receiving Robert Graves's 'blessing'

22. Proud new dad – Daddy and I waking up together

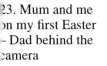

23. Mum and me on my first Easter – Dad behind the camera

24. Dad introducing me to the sea in Mallorca

25. At the school in the Boltons, London, with my one and only friend, 1978

26. Engrossed in music during a 1978 visit to see Dad and Françoise

27. Hanging out with Dad in New York, aged 8

28. Mother's Day 1987: Mum, Dad and me

29. Christmas 1989: Dad pulling one of his famous faces

30. Dad pretending to be a jockey on Shenanigans

31. Mummy and me at Daddy's flat

32. Me and my half-brother Selwyn

33. Ronnie and Pete King at the club

34. The club as it looks today

THE MET
(BOPERA HOUSE)
6, NEW COMPTON ST., LONDON, W.C.1
(TEM. 3003)
"Trustees" HARRY MORRIS, ALF SUMMERS, SONNY HERMAN

England's Foremost Bop Club Presents
at Each Meeting

RONNIE SCOTT
AND HIS QUARTET

PLUS ?

AT PRESENT FEATURING SUNDAY SESSIONS
FROM 3 p.m.—6 p.m. AT OUR PREMISES ABOVE

Admission: 3/6 MEMBERS - 5/- GUESTS

MEMBERSHIP AT: 6, NEW COMPTON STREET, W.C.1

SUPREME PRINTERS LTD. (T.U.), 13-15 NEW ROAD, LONDON, E.1

MON JAN 16th for one week
Latin American Jazz
GONZALEZ!
with
JANICE HOYTE
and supporting group

MON JAN 23rd for two weeks
McCOY
TYNER !
and his quintet
GARY BARTZ   JOHN BLAKE
JOHN LEE
WILBY FLETCHER
and
support group

MON FEB 6th for one week
the
LOU DONALDSON !
QUARTET
and
JOY YATES with DAVE MACRAE

MON FEB 13th for two weeks
GEORGE ADAMS —
DON PULLEN
Quartet
and
a guest singer
RUBY TURNER !
and her BAND
(for one week only)

MON FEB 27th for one week
"IMAGES OF BRAZIL" !
with JOHN ZARADIN guitar, and
DON RENDELL   JOHN SANDS
BILL LE SAGE   JOAO BOSCO
LES BOOTH   PETER BUCHAN
and
ronnie scott's quintet
dick pearce   von mathewson
john britishinson   martin drew

FUTURE
ATTRACTIONS
ART BLAKEY and the Jazz Messengers
JOE PASS, BARNEY KESSEL,
SACHA DISTEL
BUDDY RICH ORCHESTRA
etc. etc.
SPECIAL SUNDAY JAN 22nd 8pm
JAZZ with JIM MULLEN   see p?

MEMBERS OF
ronnie scott's
club are admitted
for only one pound
on MONDAYS to THURSDAYS
for almost ALL of
our attractions!
membership costs
£25 per annum —
ENQUIRE AT THE
FRONT DESK FOR
DETAILS.

membership is limited
— apply now !

ronnie scott's club
47 FRITH ST LONDON W.1
tel. 439-0747
FORTHCOMING
ATTRACTIONS —
MON JAN 2nd for one week
"SUPERJAZZ"
— a great sixteen piece
orchestra !
supporting group

MON JAN 9th for one week
NINA
SIMONE !
with her musicians
and
RONNIE SCOTT'S QUINTET
— BOOK NOW !

35. (*left*) Ronnie's first professional
gig as a bandleader, November 1948;
(*right*) Ronnie's own handwritten
posters, prepared for the printers. He
did this from the time the club opened
until the end of his life

36. Ronnie with Princess Margaret after being presented with the OBE, 1981

37. 'These are the jokes, folks!'

38. Studying the ever elusive reed
and mouth piece. How to
improve on it?

time we met. Gradually, we moved on to other things, always working the words out phonetically. My vocabulary expanded dramatically, and my teachers were amazed. It was then that Mum discovered that the method they used in the school to teach reading was not phonetic. This explained a lot, because since I was a baby Mum had used flash cards with me and taught me herself phonetically. All of a sudden I was exposed to a completely different approach, which was useless to anyone who was dyslexic. The teachers, when they saw how effective the phonetic method was, worked with me but could not implement the system in the remedial classes. Gradually, I learned how to manage my dyslexia, but to this day if I am exposed to emotional distress or anxiety the dyslexia manifests itself although now I recognise it and know how to deal with it. All through school and college, all my test papers and final exams were untimed. My father was very supportive of my rapid progress and was impressed with the way educational facilities in the United States provided extra help and training and made the necessary allowances for dyslexic children.

Although Dad phoned us frequently he had not been able to visit us in New York. It became increasingly clear that he was under stress, and Mum recognised the familiar signs of depression again. There were financial problems at the club, there was a constant, very tense communication going on with the VAT officials, a roller-coaster ride that ended with the club owing a large sum of money. George told me: 'Your dad would come into the club and pace up and down, up and down, thinking things through. Then he would say to me: "George, I have to make a phone call to New York. Make sure I'm not disturbed." I saw it over and over again. Whenever your father was in trouble, he'd call your mother. She was his lifeline.' As the depression took hold, my father, who had become a voice on the end of the telephone since my ill-fated Christmas visit in 1978, rarely spoke to me, able to cope only when he had periods of reprieve, which were becoming fewer and fewer. By now I was eight years old and missing him terribly. I could not understand an illness that prevented us from talking, and I knew he spoke to Mum frequently. Dad, in his desperate efforts not to hurt me, actually left me feeling really rejected. When he talked to Mum he would say: 'Mary, explain to Becky for me. Kiss her good night for me.' My mother spent a lot of time explaining, but it did little to alleviate the loss I was feeling. The financial situation reflected on us too, and during this period my mother had to do three jobs to keep everything going. I hated it because she was not at home until quite late. My closest companion was my cat, Tiger.

As the crisis was building in London, a major one was about to happen to me. My mother was on her way home from work, and I had decided to visit a friend of mine, Jon Jon, who, ironically enough, had recently broken both his legs when he was hit by a car a few weeks before. I was standing on the kerb, looking both ways, waiting to cross the street, and a lady stopped her car and waved me across. I reached the other side and was standing on the pavement when all of a sudden a car driven by an older woman came barrelling around the corner, swerving left and right as it came up the street. Neighbours watching from the end of the block were taking bets as to which parked car she was going to slam into. She swerved in between the parked cars, veered up on to the pavement, and struck me with her right mudguard. I was thrown up in the air and a hundred feet in front of her car. As I came down I landed on a parked car, banging my head and ending up partly underneath the car. The lady who had stopped to let me cross the street was an accident and emergency nurse, and she took charge of me. An ambulance and the police were called. I was drifting in and out of consciousness. By the time my mother's bus turned the corner the police car had arrived and the street was full of people. Although she could not see me as she looked out of the window, she had a dreadful feeling that I was the victim of the accident.

The chaos that reigned was unbelievable. The police had refused to wait for the ambulance and insisted on putting me into their car. My mother came running up just in time to jump in too. The hospital they took us to was an understaffed hellhole; six months later it was closed down. My mother's nursing experience saved the day. I was going into shock, there was no doctor in sight, so Mum took over. The nurses realised immediately that she knew what she was doing and followed her instructions. I clearly remember Mum cleaning out the huge gash on my forehead, trimming it and sewing it up. My mum knew what to do. They had to cut my clothes off me. My arm was broken in two places, and the two doctors, who by then were in attendance, ended up setting it incorrectly. Once they admitted me on to a ward, my mother was afraid to leave me for a second. She opened the drawer of the bedside locker and found it crawling with cockroaches. She was terrified of infection and God knows what else, so, determined to get me transferred to a Manhattan hospital, she went looking for a telephone and phoned my godmother, Auntie Jenna. Auntie Jenna called her doctor, who gave her the name of a paediatrician, Dr Gribetz, and a telephone number. The arrangements were made for me to be transferred to Mount Sinai Hospital in Manhattan. I was very badly injured, with my head swelling by the second, and the hospital we were in did not want to release me. Mum, who was working for a legal publishing company, knew our rights and got me out of there by ten o'clock the next morning. As we arrived at Mount Sinai Dr Gribetz and his team of specialists were waiting for us. He even arranged for an extra bed to be brought into my room for Mum. Dr Gribetz described my injuries to my mother, saying: 'It's as though she went a full round with Muhammad Ali.' While they were resetting my arm, Mum called Dad. He was unable to be of any help at all. The obsessive nature of his depression had him firmly in its grip, and he was incapable of applying himself to anything other than the intense pursuit of a young music student who lived in Brighton.

By now he and Françoise had broken up, and shortly afterwards she returned to France. Ronnie made arrangements to sell the house. He was now driven by a burning passion that he could not control, even though he was keenly aware that he travelled a path of guaranteed destruction. Now, as in 1974, he was mortified by the havoc his actions had wreaked and the pain he had caused. His own remorse at what was happening only added fuel to his ever-deepening depression. Once again in search of an anaesthetic he turned to alcohol, a false crutch that only compounded his agony, combined with sleeping pills and antidepressants. This combination and his music kept him going for quite a while, although by now he was forced to cancel some gigs. Critch was the elected driver when the band was on tour, and he and Ronnie spent hours together, month in, month out, in the confines of Critch's car. The extent of Ronnie's communication was short phrases such as, 'Aaah . . . *fuck*', the words forced out from the depths of his agony sounding like a deep groan of despair. Critch had great compassion and understanding of Ronnie's illness. His brother was a manic-depressive and Critch had spent a considerable amount of time with him in his darkest moments. At times Ronnie would say to Critch, 'Oh, God. I can't even talk to *you* now', as he retreated deeper and deeper into his illness.

The quartet was not playing full time any more, but the musicians had to earn a living and Critch worked with saxophonist Dick Morrissey's band. Even when he was desperately ill, loyalty within his band and family was of critical importance to my father. Realising that necessity rather than disloyalty to the band had prompted Critch to work with Dick, and also recognising his own imminent demise, Ronnie telephoned Critch and told him: 'You're the pianist I want to work with. I'm going into hospital now, but when I come out I'll be better and I want you there then.'

My father repeatedly asked my mother to go to London to help him, but this time she could not comply. I was still suffering terrible aftereffects from the car accident which had kept me in hospital for a month. After I came home it was several weeks before I could go back to school again. I had lost pieces of my memory. It was the strangest thing to live with: I knew who some people were but others, whom I had known all my life, I did not recognise. The doctors could not predict if my memory would return completely. Fortunately, the accident had not affected my short-term memory. But I was terrified to cross a street even holding my mother's hand, and for weeks it required a lot of patience and gentle coaxing before I overcame my fears. To compound the issue I had horrible nightmares night after night. I was living with a strange kind of fear. Mum tried to explain to Dad the severity of my situation, but he was too ill himself to understand and kept asking her to come to London. It was a heart-rending predicament for her.

Once again Ronnie's loyal and understanding friend Spike Milligan came to his aid. Realising that Ronnie would not come to visit him at his Barnet home of his own volition, Spike made arrangements for a car to collect Ronnie on innumerable occasions, bring him out to his house to listen to music, have dinner and a glass of wine and talk. Spike, all too familiar himself with the torture of mental pain, was of immeasurable help to Ronnie. Dad's good friend Harriet South helped him through many of his darker moments too, and Ilsa went to the flat to cook for him.

By the summer of 1981, Ronnie, with the help of treatment, friends and his music, was on his way back to good health. As Dad healed he gradually began to understand the serious implications of my accident. I could not remember half of what had happened before the accident and had not spoken to my father for so long that even though he was able to speak to me on the telephone again, and although I knew he was my father, I felt as if I was talking to a stranger. Anxious to see us both again, Dad made arrangements to visit New York, arriving towards the end of the summer.

It was quite hard for me. I was only nine at the time and had really wished that he had come to see me when I was in hospital. Mum had explained to me that Daddy was ill too, but it was impossible for me to comprehend his long silence. Just a child, it felt to me as if he simply wasn't there for me. So it was with some misgivings and more than a little apprehension that I went with Mum to meet Daddy at the Edison Hotel. He was waiting for us in the lobby, and as we came through the door he came running towards us, his face wreathed in smiles, saying: 'There you are, Rebecca! Mary! My God! It's so *good* to see you.' It was big hugs and kisses all round and in that moment all my resentment, doubts and fears evaporated. He was hungry, so the first thing we did was go to Kaplans on 60th Street. From that time on it became a favourite haunt of ours when Daddy was in town, and we called it our 'family restaurant'. I remember his concern for me and how gentle his manner was as he set about trying to explain not only his long absence but his long silence, constantly affirming his love for me. The fact that he was there helped me a lot even though I did not understand what his illness really was. But it did not matter any more because he was well and we were talking about everything. Dad was very concerned about the fact that I was still having nightmares and did everything he could to dispel the fear that was still just below the surface.

Dad stayed for about ten days, and we spent a lot of time together. Mum was working but I was on vacation from school. We explored the Village together, and I was amazed how Dad knew the streets like the back of his hand. The Village is a fun place to be, and Daddy loved the plethora of street vendors on street after street. The whole scene reminded him of Petticoat Lane in the East End, and he told me stories of how he would watch Nanna Beckie haggle over the price of things with the vendors when he was a little boy, saying to me: 'Come on, Becky, let's see if we can get a bargain.' We had great fun doing that, and when we met Mum for dinner at the end of the day we would brag about how we bargained with the vendors, making her guess what we had paid for the trinkets we had bought.

Knowing that Ilsa had helped Dad while he was ill, my mother thought it was a good time to talk to him again about telling me about my half-brother Nicholas, preferring that they did it together. Dad was adamant about not telling me. Whatever his reasons were, he thought it was a very bad idea and did not want to discuss the matter.

One night we all met at the Village Gate, a well-known jazz club. It was the first time I had been there. Dad liked it because it was open much earlier than the other clubs, and I liked it because it wasn't too smoky. Daddy started clowning around and we got into this thing where we were pulling one face after another, each of us trying to make the other laugh. My father's gurning skills were unbelievable. I asked him to explain how he did it. Laughing, he said: 'You can't do it, Rebecca, because one of the requirements is that you don't have any back teeth!' He was able to suck his cheeks in so far and jut his jaw out to such an extreme that his nose almost touched his chin as he pulled his eyebrows together and crossed his eyes.

We were laughing so hard and in between laughing we pulled and stretched our faces in every direction. My mother was crippled with laughter, as were several of the other customers. Not having a camera with her she asked a couple of Swedish tourists if they would take a picture of us. They did, but Dad and I were aware of it and stopped pulling faces and posed instead. This went on all night. We went from the Village Gate to a Chinese restaurant, where Daddy tried to teach me how to eat with chopsticks, all the time pulling these insane faces. The waiters were falling about laughing, and everybody had a good time that night.

Since our birthdays were just a few weeks away, unbeknown to us Dad had planned a special evening for all of us. It was a Saturday, and we arranged to meet Daddy at the hotel at 5.30 p.m. We jumped into a cab and went to the Village, where we wandered from street to street window-shopping and chatting until we came upon a very nice Italian restaurant on a corner with tables outside. Dad said: 'Anybody hungers? How about eating here?' We were all hungry by now and decided to sit outside, something we all loved to do. After we had given our order, instead of bringing food the waiters came out carrying beautifully wrapped gifts, singing happy birthday!

Shortly after he arrived, Dad had asked Mum if she knew anybody who would drive him to the airport. Mum's best friend, Frances Jackson, who was a schoolteacher and also a classical pianist, was happy to oblige. Aunt Fran was an integral part of our family and my father became very fond of her. She came from a family of educators who held a place in American black history. Dad was fascinated to hear her stories about her father, Beecher Arnett Jackson, who in the early 1920s was one of the first two black men to attend Harvard University. Aunt Fran had studied the piano with Irwin E. Hassell who himself was a life-long associate of Artur Rubinstein, a classical pianist whom my father revered. They enjoyed each other's company immensely and had many animated discussions. When the time came for Daddy to go back, Aunt Fran picked us up from Dad's hotel and we drove to Kennedy Airport. It was quite an emotional parting and a few tears were shed as we watched Daddy walk through the gate. Aunt Fran looked forward to my father's subsequent visits and whenever possible made herself available to drive him out to Kennedy Airport for his return trips to London.

Several weeks after Dad's return to London, my mother, after much reflection, made the decision in spite of my father's objection to sit me down and quietly tell me about my half-brother Nicholas. It was a complex situation to address because she had no idea when I would actually meet him. I received the news with mixed emotions. On the one hand I was pleased to discover I had a half-brother but on the other it didn't mean much as there was no contact between us. I understood my mother's not wanting me to grow up not knowing about Nicholas and then suddenly finding myself in the position of being confronted with the situation out of the blue at some unknown time in the future. The interesting thing was that when Daddy rang that night and she explained what she had done and why, he was very calm about the whole thing and actually seemed relieved.

During all these trials and tribulations, the club had celebrated its twentieth and twenty-first anniversaries. To mark the latter occasion, Ronnie and Pete took a full page in New York's *Variety* magazine, which was celebrating its seventy-fourth anniversary, to thank everyone who had helped them over the years. The subsequent pages read like a who's who of jazz. Various tributes appeared in blocks of all shapes and sizes, from the Newport Jazz Festival to musicians such as Sarah Vaughan and Stan Getz. One large block read in bold half-inch capitals:

HAPPY 21ST
ANNIVERSARY
TO
RONNIE SCOTT'S
THE DEFINITIVE JAZZ ROOM.
LOVINGLY, DIZZY

Woody Herman's read: CONGRATULATIONS TO MY MAIN MAN IN ENGLAND. Management companies, the artists themselves, bands and groups all published similar greetings. Ronnie had won his battle with depression, the club had overcome financial problems of gargantuan proportions. After going into receivership and more than a year of desperately seeking a way out, faith in human nature was restored by the generous actions of Chris Blackwell of Island Records, who, hearing of the club's problems, started the ball rolling by lending Ronnie and Pete £25,000. Brian Blain, Johnny Patrick and general secretary of the Musicians' Union John Morton arranged for the union to lend Ronnie and Pete £30,000. Then they went to Charrington's, the brewers, and finally the Performing Right Society came up with the last contribution. That this kind of help was forthcoming was a clear endorsement of the respect and affection that Ronnie's and Pete's twenty-one years of dedication to the jazz scene in Britain had produced.

Pete King conceded that his motivation came from love of his career and terror about his job prospects if the club went under. Uncle Pete was infused with a surge of new energy and determination to turn the club around and create an environment that not only paid off the loans and paid the bills but flourished. With Ronnie in the saddle again, they were back on course, into their third decade with a powerful calendar of talent in place for the following year.

CHAPTER THIRTEEN

MY HERO: PART ONE

Ronnie was a great companion. He had that rare ability to make things happen,
form things out of nothing, so you held on to his coat-tails and all these things
happened to you too.   BENNY GREEN, BBC broadcast, 1997

Ronnie was a marvellous musician; his playing was quite remarkable. People
always told me that I was underrated, but I always felt that Ronnie was
underrated, especially as far as America was concerned.
                              GEORGE COLEMAN, tenor saxophonist

O NE EARLY EVENING IN 1981, the telephone rang in our New York
apartment. My mother answered. It was my father. He was
chuckling with pleasure and said to Mum: 'You're not going to
believe it, Mary. They want to give me the OBE! For my
contribution to jazz.' Dad felt honoured but also a little mystified and
embarrassed that he had been selected as a recipient of the award. He said:
'It's all very nice really, of course. I'm honoured. But why me? It's
incredible really.' He thought that other people in the field of jazz were
equally if not more deserving of the honour than he. Ronnie invited his
friend and partner Pete King and Stella to be his guests, and on the day of
the ceremony, which was held in the afternoon at the Palace, Uncle Pete
remembered: 'There was a big hall for visitors and about four or five
hundred people were sitting there while a military band played on the
balcony. When Ronnie came through, the Queen was talking to him for
quite a while. She showed great interest in the club and asked him quite a

few questions.' It was a very special afternoon for both Ronnie and Pete. Even though my father was often heard to describe the OBE as the recognition of 'other bastards' efforts', the acknowledgement meant a lot to him, and on more than one occasion he told us that he wished his mother had lived to see the day.

As a child growing up I never realised that Dad was so well known and famous. It didn't mean much to me then, because I was growing up in America and he wasn't known to my friends. It was just that Daddy played the saxophone and had a jazz club in London, and that was what he did. It was no big deal to me; it was normal because I knew a lot of jazz musicians who were friends of both my parents. My father was the least pretentious person I knew; he really didn't think of himself as being famous and was always very low-key about it. Of course, as far as his playing was concerned, as I grew older I came to understand what a perfectionist he was and how much respect he had earned from musicians worldwide. But when he was talking to me, as a child, Dad mostly raved about the exceptional way other musicians played, people like Uncle Stan (Stan Getz), or Sonny Rollins and Zoot Sims, to name just a few.

I often listened to Dad's album, 'Serious Gold'. Mum had told me the story about 'Send in the Clowns'. I particularly liked my father's solo on soprano sax and would listen to it over and over again. At that time I was into gymnastics and dance, which I had loved since my first ballet lessons at Carnegie Hall at the age of four. A couple of times a year my school put on special performances at assembly, giving talented children an opportunity to do something original, and all the parents were invited. So I gathered together a group of my friends and choreographed a dance to Dad's recording of 'Send in the Clowns', which was my contribution to the assembly performance. I remember my father's joy. It really touched him that I had chosen his music for the performance. He was thrilled with my involvement with music and was very supportive. It was during this period that the great jazz pianist John Hicks gave me lessons on the piano. John was one of the artists my mother worked with for many years. He became a friend of the family; I had known him since I was two and called him Uncle John. My mother had bought the piano when I was about three. She used to write lyrics for various musicians and used the piano to work with the words and the melody.

Postcards came from all over the world. My father travelled extensively as a musician, and the cards came from faraway places like Hong Kong, Australia, New Zealand, South Africa (where Dad refused to play to all-white audiences) and all over Europe, including Finland and Poland. In the spring of 1982 he visited Gambia, and later in the year travelled through the Middle East. He travelled so much that year that he was not able to come to New York. It was exciting to receive the postcards, to see the pictures of strange places and the different stamps, but it ignited a longing in me to be there too. I wanted to be with my father. I yearned to travel with him and gradually became resentful of the fact that he was running all over the world and had no time to come to see me – when you are ten years old, a year can seem like a lifetime. I had a picture of Daddy hanging on my bedroom wall, and although we talked frequently, once again he had become a voice on the end of a telephone, repeatedly saying to my mother: 'Mary, explain to Becky for me.' He also told us that year that Françoise was coming back to England, but they were not going to live together again. My father had decided that living together did not work and he needed his freedom. But he cared a lot for Françoise, as she did for him, so they agreed to see each other frequently, and once again became very close.

My father was thrilled to pieces: my piano lessons with John Hicks were quite successful. Because they were irregular, he taught me chords and I learned how to build on them and was creating tunes of my own on the piano. My school was closing out the semester with an assembly concert of recitals performed by children who played instruments. I was invited to play the piano. I played my then favourite piece, the theme music from *Close Encounters of a Third Kind*. Dad knew about the recitals and that evening he telephoned and was really pleased that it had all gone well.

Ronnie and Pete had planned an autumn festival at the club. The eight selected groups produced an eclectic powerhouse of music. First came the Don Pullen–George Adams quartet. With Pullen on piano and Adams on tenor and flute, they played all original music written by Don and George, and the music ranged from the free jazz approach of the avant-garde to bluesy conventional jazz. The quartet was followed by Dizzy Gillespie, who among others played 'Night in Tunisia', a tune that Ronnie loved and frequently played himself. Dizzy, as always, played to a packed house, thrilling every member of the audience. A young French prodigy, Bireli Lagrene, just fifteen years of age, a gifted guitar player, took the stand for one night. In contrast came a powerful modern group called The La Four, followed into the club by Cayenne, a nine-piece band playing Latin fusion. Then came the great percussionist Art Blakey, otherwise known as Bu, who was renowned for seeking out the best of young unknown musicians to play with him: for many, working with Art was their springboard into the profession. If you had been a member of Art Blakey's Jazz Messengers, it was a credential that other band leaders were more than happy with. Many of the young musicians who got their start with Art ended up becoming band leaders in their own right, one of the most well known being trumpeter Wynton Marsalis, who was playing with Art that night. As Johnny Griffin, the 'little giant' and long-time tenor player with the Clarke–Boland Band, said: 'Bu lived beyond the system. He had so much imagination. Playing with him was like sitting on an atom bomb! Fantastic! Oh, man. Explosions! Everything was larger than life.'

A new approach came in the presentation of three American guitarists. Herb Ellis, Barney Kessel and Charlie Byrd, all highly individual jazz stylists in their own right, each soloed and then came back together as a group, a rare and refreshing combination. The festival closed with the George Coleman Octet, with Bobby Watson on alto, Mario Rivera on baritone, the irrepressible Sal Nistico on tenor, Clint Houston on bass and Billy Higgins on drums, with George leading with his full-bodied solos. The band was swinging, and the audience was clapping and howling for more. It was a great finale to the festival. Ronnie and Pete once again were well on their way to building the club back up.

I was excited too. Daddy was coming to New York, this time with his band. It was May 1983 when they arrived. Capital Radio, the independent London radio station, was hosting a programme called *London Salutes New York*, a week's festival held at quite a famous club in New York called the Bottom Line. Daddy's group played opposite Joe Morello, and, of course, Mum and I went to the Bottom Line to meet Daddy and hear the music. The well-known group Level 42 was also playing the festival, and they were staying at the same hotel as Daddy and his band. Dad took me to the hotel, where I met John Critchinson, Martin Drew, Ron Mathewson, and Dick Pearce, trumpet, who had joined the band in 1980.

Critch immediately noticed my American accent and said he thought I was a lovely young American girl! It was fun hanging out with Daddy and the guys. There was a lot of joking around, and Critch told the story of how Dick Pearce wanted to work at Daddy's club so badly he wrote a letter to Daddy and said that he would even do the washing-up just so long as he could work in the club, and he had enclosed an audio tape of himself washing dishes! Daddy, who thought Dick's whole approach was hilarious, was already familiar with his playing, so Dick not only played at the club but ended up playing in Dad's group. Everyone was telling stories, and

Critch reminded us all of the time that Daddy was in Birmingham and had gone into one of the nicer men's clothing shops to pick up a couple of shirts. He picked out his shirts and then queued and paid for them, but instead of walking out of the shop he started looking around again. He stuck a hat on his head, then he saw a tie he liked and another shirt and queued again. When it was his turn to pay he bought the tie and shirt and walked out with the hat still on his head! When he got back to his hotel room he caught sight of himself in the mirror, the price tag on the hat dangling down the side of his face. He could not believe that he had walked all around the shop, faced the cashier, and then walked out into the street and no one had noticed the price tag.

It was the first time that Critch had been to New York. It rained very heavily the whole time that they were visiting, but even so Dad still had a lot of fun showing him the city. He took the guys to the Empire State Building, and they went to Manny's music shop off Broadway, one of Ronnie's old haunts since his first trip to New York in 1947. Dad got Critch a really good deal on some accessories for his electric piano, and Critch was knocked out by the fact that wherever they went everyone knew my father. They all ended up at one of Daddy's favourite haunts, the Village Vanguard, where the Thad Jones and Mel Lewis big band played every Monday night for many years, and if Dad was in town on a Monday night he made a point of stopping by to hear them.

The visit flew by so fast. They were in town for only a week, and I did not see my father every day. When he returned to London, the feeling of loneliness that I had felt during his long absence and illness returned. A frustration was building up, and I began to blame my mother for their separation. We were in New York; Dad was in London. I could *not* understand why my parents were not together. I knew first-hand that their relationship was very close: they were best friends, always at ease with each other, they laughed a lot and shared confidences, there was a trust between them that each of them was very secure within. It just did not make sense to me.

My mother had always been very nurturing about my having my own relationship with my father, and whatever had gone wrong between them was not to cast a shadow over my relationship with him. Although my questions were answered honestly, Mum never belaboured any of the negatives, more often than not stating that none of us is perfect and that mistakes are made for us to learn from. She always stressed that I should make my own mistakes and not do a repeat performance of the mistakes she and Daddy had made. Mum did not want to tell me about Linda until I was much older, feeling the information at my tender age might do more harm than good, but my resentment now directed at my mother caused so much friction that she made the decision to tell me the truth in as simple terms as possible, trying to cushion the blow. Of course, I was furious that Dad had left us, but then I was equally furious because Mum had not gone back to him when he asked. My mother was right. I was too young to understand the complexities and nuances of the situation.

My father was definitely a part of my daily life. It was quite extraordinary that even though we were separated by distance we actually achieved a closeness during this period of our lives through the telephone, and the good night calls kept coming. If I had a problem, Dad was there with a ready solution, although there were times when I wanted to talk to him and it wasn't possible. Sometimes he was on tour and it was difficult to call with the different time changes and his schedule. I was often in bed and he spoke to Mum. During the summer I spent most of my time at summer camps, and we could not talk then, but Dad called Mum constantly and always knew where I was and what I was doing. I knew that, no matter what, his music came first, that was understood, then I felt the girlfriends came second and I was a distant third. But I wanted to be the most important person in his life. My mother was a very loving mother and she did anything and everything for me. Mum knew how much Dad loved me, worried about me, wanted the best for me, and she tried to assuage my growing feelings of discontent.

That same year John Critchinson was diagnosed with bladder cancer. By now he and Ronnie had become close friends, John as often as not driving Ronnie to out-of-town gigs. They had spent an immeasurable amount of time together over the past few years. Everything was happening at the same time: the band had gigs to play, and Critch felt that it wasn't possible for him to take time off – not only that, but he was terrified of what was happening to him. Never having been in hospital in his life, he was now suddenly faced with surgery. He said: 'Ronnie was wonderful when you were in real trouble. He was always able to bring a calmness and sense of stability to the situation. I was really anxious, and I said to him: "What happens if they lose me under the anaesthetic?" Ronnie said: "What do you mean, *lose* you? What are you going to do? Are you going to walk off?" He really made it into something very funny. Ronnie was the sort of person who could lift your spirits when things were bad.' Critch remembered that when he got to the hospital, all of a sudden he was calm, all the things that Dad had said to him came to mind and he was able to deal with the situation.

John Critchinson had seen my father have the same effect not just on his closest friends but also on many of the musicians who used to come into the club. They were all able to share their problems with him, often asking Dad's advice and receiving concise and apt information that made sense. Critch said: 'He gave the most astute advice, which was always considered. He was a sort of guru to everyone. Ronnie really *cared* about people. That was a very important part of Ronnie as far as the guys were concerned. It was one of the reasons so many people worked for him.'

The new year began with Ronnie and his quintet travelling to Bombay, Madras and Delhi for the Jazz Yatra '84, an international jazz festival featuring representatives from ten countries. They played Delhi first and then it was on to Bombay. Martin was sent ahead to scout out the hotel, which turned out to be appalling, with even dog excreta steaming on the hot floors. When Martin reached the rooms he found them smelly and musty, with the air-conditioner sounding like a truck driving through the room. Martin quickly decided: 'Ronnie ain't going to go for this!' So they headed for the Bombay Ovaroy, a very nice hotel where they had stayed on previous trips, Martin picking up the tab because he had his credit cards. Dad was back in London before the postcards arrived from India; they took weeks to reach Brooklyn.

I was in my second year at junior high school. My mother had managed to get me into a school that had a reasonably good music programme, and naturally I enrolled for the dance class. The teacher was excellent and exposed us to jazz dancing as well as more formal programmes. She recognised that I was talented and called my mother with a recommendation for me to join a dance studio. It was about this time that I really rebelled against music. I decided that as music was Daddy's passion it was not going to be mine and withdrew from all my musical activities. Nothing anybody said to me at the time made a difference. Mum tried to tell me that even if I just played the piano for my own pleasure, I should keep it up. I lived to regret giving up the piano, and by the time I reached my early twenties I began to wish I had stuck with it. Also my grades began to suffer. Mum and Dad were worried out of their minds, and Mum discussed what was going on with Auntie Jenna. One of the things that Auntie Jenna loved to do was ride. She was a member of a stables at Central Park in Manhattan, and she suggested to Mum that I should go riding with her, then we would have dinner and talk. Mum, who had grown up with horses and was a good rider herself, thought it was a marvellous idea. Dad said: 'If you think Jenna can help, go ahead.' The outcome of that afternoon was that I fell in love with horses and wanted to take lessons myself. My best friend, Moji Rotibi, whom I had known since I was about six and a half, also rode and attended a summer camp called Camp Winamac. I pleaded with Mum and Dad to let me go. They discussed it and told me that if I brought my grades up by the summer they would find a way for me to go riding. Much to Dad's and my dance teacher's disappointment, I stuck to my decision to drop my musical activities, but my school work gradually improved.

Mum spoke to Moji's mum and made enquiries about Camp Winamac, which was a family-run business in New Hampshire owned by George Athens. After satisfying herself that it was the place for me, she telephoned Daddy and told him all about it and also sent him a duplicate set of brochures and relevant information. It was quite an expensive camp, so Dad and Mum agreed to split the costs between them. It was a Saturday, and Mum took me out to dinner. We went to our 'family' restaurant, Kaplans. After we had finished our meal, Mum pulled an envelope out of her bag and said: 'I have a surprise for you, Becky.' Handing me the envelope, she said: 'This is for you.' I was puzzled — it wasn't my birthday or anything. I opened the envelope and there was a beautiful card with a picture of a magnificent thoroughbred galloping, mane and tail flying, through a paddock surrounded by trees. Inside, the card read: 'Have a wonderful summer at Camp Winamac with Moji and all the horses! With all our love, Dad & Mum.' Out of the card fell a colour brochure from the camp. Never have I been so excited. I was actually going to ride all through the summer!

When Dad came to New York that August he wanted to know everything that had happened during the summer. I told him we were taught to take care of the horses and did stable duty, which consisted of mucking out the stalls, feeding and grooming the horses and cleaning the riding tack. Every day we had riding lessons in the ring, then once we were good enough we went out on trial rides too, and afterwards we went swimming in a natural freshwater pool. At the end of our stay we received a certificate stating what level of riding we had achieved that summer, so that the following year you graduated to a higher level of instruction. I was fortunate enough to go every summer until I was about seventeen.

Both my parents and my godmother were thrilled and proud of the accolades I achieved that summer. Now I was asking for riding lessons and wanted to attend the riding stables in Brooklyn. We had recently moved and now lived within walking distance of Prospect Park and Culmitt Riding Stables. Mum and Dad discussed it but could not afford any more lessons, but Auntie Jenna decided that for my twelfth birthday that September she would give me ten riding lessons at Culmitt. I was told there would be no more lessons because no one could afford them, so I had best make the most of what I had been given. Delighted with my gift, filled with resolve, I went for my first riding lesson. After it was over I explained my predicament to Jimmy Culleton, the owner, who was always ready to take on a willing and eager stable hand and in return was happy to supply me with the lessons I so desperately craved. I telephoned Mum from the stables that day and said: 'Mum, I'm sorry but I'm going to be late home today.' She responded: 'Why? What's happened, Becky? Are you all right?' My reply was: 'Couldn't be better. I'm starting work at the stables today and in return I'll get my lessons.' Overjoyed, Mum immediately called Dad, who said: 'That's fantastic! Now we know she's really serious.' It was my first lesson in taking responsibility for myself and something I really wanted.

Peter Ind, a bass player and friend of my father's since 1947, decided to turn a recording studio that he owned in Oxford Street into a club. Called the Bass Clef, it was to be a place for British musicians to play at. Peter asked Ronnie and Pete for advice, and they willingly gave him all kinds of tips, one of them how to handle some of the guys who delivered the beer. Peter remembered: 'One of their favourite tricks is to take out a full barrel when you aren't looking and sell it to you again!' Ronnie and Pete advised him to chalk up his barrels. They also gave him all kinds of information about brewery loans and were very supportive in every way possible. Peter said: 'There were guys who always complained about Ronnie and Pete booking American musicians even though they always booked a British group opposite them. I think that Ronnie thought to himself: "After all these years of guys moaning at me, here's a guy who is actually going to have a club that will be a place for British guys to play." When the Bass Clef finally opened, Ronnie's quintet played the opening night.' Peter ran the club for ten years, until it finally went under due to problems with VAT. He recalled: 'Ronnie was very helpful then, phoning up various influential people to drum up support, but the VAT had stripped the club of everything so we couldn't recover. Ronnie had a heart, more than most, and that made him special.'

We had been attending a Baptist church in Brooklyn since I was six years old. It had an excellent after-school programme for children whose parents were working and a daytime summer camp for the part of the summer that we were not away at camp. Dad had always known this and never had much to say about it, but for some reason it started to bother him somewhat and he telephoned Mum and said: 'Mary, if you're going to attend a church and get into all of that, why don't you take Rebecca to a synagogue?' New York is full of synagogues, many of which welcome people of all faiths. Mum, who always believed that there is only one God, had no qualms at all and agreed to Dad's suggestion. It so happened that I had a couple of friends at school who were Jewish and their Bat Mitzvah ceremonies were to be celebrated within the next few weeks. One of them wanted me to attend her classes at the synagogue with her, and I came home shortly after Dad's call and asked Mum if I could. Perfect timing. Mum decided this would be the best solution, and I attended synagogue with the family on Saturdays too. After the Bat Mitzvah was over, I asked Mum: 'Do you think I could stop going now, Mum? I don't really like it that much.' She asked me why and my response was: 'It's OK, but I like the music at our church much better.' The church we attended had an excellent music director and we had two very good choirs, gospel and classical. At times that place rocked! Mum told me I should tell Daddy myself. I was more than a little apprehensive about telling him, but when I did he laughed and said: 'That's a very good reason, Becky! I don't have a problem with it at all if that's what you want to do!'

Ronnie had been asked to form a special big band for a Duke Ellington tribute that was to be played at St Paul's Cathedral. It was a massive television epic, with Rod Steiger and Douglas Fairbanks Senior officiating and Tony Bennett and Phyllis Hymen singing. They were to perform the Duke Ellington Sacred Works that he had written specifically to be performed in cathedrals. Ronnie asked his old friend Vic Ash to play in the band; this time, instead of playing his clarinet, Vic was on tenor sax and sat next to Ronnie. There were three days of rehearsals, and the two tenor players hung out together for the duration. Vic remembered: 'It was three of the funniest days I have ever had in my life! That incredible humour of his – he was just a joy to be with. He was a born comic as well as a great player.' Dad had never got over his anxiety about reading music; not being a session man he never got into heavy reading, and Vic remembered: 'There was a pause in the music, and there were some very tricky bits in Ellington's work, and once or twice Ronnie would get lost and he would say out of the corner of his mouth: "Where are we, Vic? Where are we?" And I used to crease up and fall about. Here was one of the greatest tenor players in the world and here he was saying to me: "where are we, Vic." Needless to say, he got through the show just fine and played some *wonderful* solos.'

That October Ronnie Scott's celebrated its twenty-fifth anniversary, which was covered by British TV. It was a very positive celebration, and Ronnie and Pete had met the goals they had set themselves back in 1980–1. The club was flourishing and a prosperous future lay ahead.

Suddenly, in November, my father suffered the loss of a friend, teacher and mentor, whom he had revered since his youth in the East End: Denis Rose died. There was many an afternoon when Dad walked into the club and Denis would be sitting on a stool at the closed bar reading the racing pages of the newspaper, waiting for him, and they would spend a couple of hours together with Denis at the piano and Ronnie with his sax, or sometimes they just sat at a table and talked, always about music and horse racing. Back in the war it had been Denis who had explained the mechanics of the music from America that consumed Ronnie and his friends in their youth. Without that intensive instruction, Ronnie doubted that he would have understood by himself all the complexities of the music. Dad telephoned my mother. He was deeply distressed: Denis had died un-expectedly, and the shock was immense. They talked frequently over the next week or two, reminiscing about times with Denis. Dad, Uncle Pete, Jeff Ellison and several other musicians went to the funeral in New Southgate, North London, on a gloomy, rainy, relentless kind of a day. My father was particularly touched when Denis's family gently placed a toy piano on his freshly dug grave.

Since Jock's death in 1958, Ronnie and the family had lost touch with each other, although the cousins in America always knew that things were going well with the club, following Ronnie's career as a musician, sending each other newspaper cuttings and keeping up with the news that way. Cousin Sydney, who lived in London, would stop in to listen to the music, sometimes not letting Ronnie know he was there because every time he did Ronnie insisted on picking up his bill. Auntie Rose, who had married her childhood sweetheart Bernie Krane, came to London to visit other members of the family and came to the club to see Ronnie. It was a grand reunion, my father so pleased to see her and her husband after so many years. It turned out that they were living in Brooklyn, so Dad told them all about Mum and me. When Dad called us that night he chatted about his cousin

Rose and Bernie, giving Mum their telephone number so that we could all meet when they returned to New York.

Shortly after, Cousin Ziggy and his wife Blanche walked into the club. Ronnie could not believe it. Their visit brought back a flood of childhood memories of when as small boys they had played together at Grandfather Morris Schatt's house. Ronnie had not seen Ziggy since he and his family had left for Belgium, and later made their ill-fated move to Zurich. It was an emotional reunion and the first time that he had met Blanche. They talked a lot that night, Ronnie taking them to the bar downstairs, where they could talk in private. He told Blanche and Ziggy about Mum and me. Blanche told me: 'He was very emotional that night, and missing you and your mother terribly, so much so that he asked me to write to you when I got back to California and see if I could influence you to return to London. I promised him I would.' Blanche is a very warm person who is very family-orientated, and she told me she wrote us a long and warm letter, just as she had promised, and could never understand why she never heard from us. The letter never arrived. My father told my mother to expect a letter from Blanche and kept asking if we had heard from her, but somehow that very important letter got lost in the post. Eventually he stopped asking about the letter, and we never knew what was on his mind during those weeks until after his death.

R onnie discovered for himself Dizzy Gillespie's passion for the colourful rhythms and textures that Cuban musicians brought to jazz when he and the quintet played at the country's sensational annual music festival. It was, however, a miracle they arrived in time to play, having taken a British Airways flight to Madrid, where they had to change to a Cuban airline for Havana. Ronnie and the guys boarded the Cuban flight and sat waiting on the plane for what was an interminable length of time. Eventually the plane took off, flying east instead of west – there was apparently a Russian delegation aboard. Twelve hours after leaving Heathrow they were flying over Scotland on the way to Prague, where they ended up landing in the middle of a snowstorm! When they finally arrived in Cuba, Ronnie's quintet had been travelling for twenty-four hours. When he came back to London, Ronnie told Pete that the cultural agencies of Cuba were anxious to welcome Pete as an honoured guest, believing the visit would help promote trade. Ronnie told him that the musical quality on the small island was incredible, and that he should go seeking out new talent for the club. So Pete and

Stella decided to make a holiday out of it and went to Havana. The outcome was that Pete struck a deal with the Cuban cultural agencies to present a festival of the country's music at the club the following summer.

Shortly after Pete's return to London, the first American musician to play at the club, and Dad's very good friend, Zoot Sims, who had suffered from cancer for some time, died on 23 March 1985. Dad immediately called us. Zoot had been a close friend for so long and was just fifty-nine when he died and Dad felt the loss deeply. He and Zoot had a lot in common; they shared the same kind of humour and were able to laugh at themselves and find comedy in situations when life threw a 'curve ball'. Musically, as tenor players, they shared a lot, swapping mouthpieces, playing around on each other's saxophones, discussing the more elusive nuances of their craft, and Ronnie was an absolute fan of Zoot's whole approach to the music and his style of playing. Zoot could really swing, always leaving the audience feeling uplifted, re-energised and happy after listening to one of his sets. Zoot was another friend that, as Dad said, he 'could not afford to lose'. Upset, he was not sure if he would be able to make the service, which was to be held at St Peter's Lutheran Church on Lexington Avenue in Manhattan.

My mother had already left for the service when the telephone rang. I answered. It was Daddy, and he asked me: 'Rebecca, where's Mummy?' I told him that she was on her way to Zoot's memorial service, and Daddy said: "Well, that's where I'm going too. If she calls you, don't tell her I'm here."

The church was packed, the service run by Dr John Garcia Gensel, pastor, legendary for his ministry to jazz musicians of every creed and culture, and well known as the pastor to the jazz community. Mum told me afterwards she had already greeted Louise, Zoot's widow, and was waiting inside for Annie Ross to arrive, chatting to Dan Morganstern, jazz historian and writer. Dan was telling my mother that Zoot's obituary in the *New York Times* had mentioned Ronnie when in mid-sentence, out of her peripheral vision, she saw Ronnie walking towards them and could not believe her eyes. My father always relished the element of surprise bringing a little levity to the sadness of the day. Louise had expressed to Mary how much she wished Ronnie could come, so Mary took Ronnie over to where Louise was sitting. Her face lit up and they hugged; it meant so much to Louise to have Ronnie there. Then they took their places in the church, which was filled with musicians, writers, fans and friends from all walks of life and different parts of the world; people were crowded outside looking in through the large windows. Hundreds were in attendance.

Reverend Gensel was inviting certain people out of the congregation to get up and say a few words. He looked straight at Ronnie, announcing that he had just flown in from London, and talked briefly about his friendship with Zoot, and invited him to the lectern to share his remembrances of Zoot. Ronnie shrank down into the pew and whispered in Mum's ear: 'Oh, God! I can't get up there! There are so many people here who spent much more time with Zoot than I did. What am I going to say?' Mum gently persuaded him that it would be all right, saying: 'Once you get up there you'll find the words. Do it for Louise.' When Ronnie started speaking, his direct honesty came through as he apologetically told the congregation that he really wasn't the one who should be speaking, acknowledging that there were members of the congregation that he felt must have known Zoot much better than he had. With that out of the way, he spoke straight from his heart, putting into words his feelings of love, respect, admiration and gratitude for Zoot as a man and a musician. As always, Ronnie was very articulate, his delivery heart-warming and leavened with humorous reminiscences that brought appreciative laughter to the occasion.

It was a flying visit. Mum had a cab pick me up and take me to Kaplans to meet them, so we could have dinner together. Dad was pleased to see me, asking lots of questions about the stables and school — all the normal things — but he talked a lot about Zoot that night. The next day he had to fly back to London but would be back in the summer for a longer visit. He was coming to New York about twice a year now, which stabilised things for us. The absences did not seem so long, and there was always the next visit to look forward to.

After returning to London, Dad frequently telephoned Louise to see how she was, and after a year or two had passed he tried to persuade her to come to London and visit the club again. When Dad was in New York, he always rang Louise, and if her schedule permitted they would see each other. I went with him on one occasion and we all had lunch together. After Dad died, Louise told me: 'Ronnie was so kind and considerate to me. After Zoot died, he was very solicitous about phoning me and *always* managed to make me laugh. We wrote to each other too, and he made *such* a difference in my life. I looked forward to our conversations and sharing that wonderful sense of humour of his.'

One of the things that Dad used to enjoy when he was in New York was slipping quietly into a jazz club and listening to the music without anyone knowing he was there. George Coleman recalled: 'I would play my sets and it wasn't until the whole thing was over that I would discover Ronnie sitting quietly out in the audience.' There were many times when he would slip out quickly at the end so that he did not have to meet people. Dad really liked to keep a very low profile when he was not working.

Ronnie Scott's, with some financial backing from the Musicians' Union, presented a short season devoted to British jazz players, featuring young musicians. This was followed by Charlie Watts, drummer with the Rolling Stones and a serious jazz fan, who assembled a big band of British musicians from several different schools of jazz and spanning three generations. Charlie had been a swing band fan since childhood and wanted to present to the audiences a complete cross-section of the growth and diversity of jazz performed by British musicians since its conception four decades earlier. It was a phenomenal event. Charlie Watts, the leader of the band, sat astride his drum stool flanked on either side by drummers John Stevens and Bill Eyden, who played with Ronnie and Tubby in the days of the Jazz Couriers. Charlie relied on his fame and fortune to make his dream a functioning reality; the whole venture cost him £30,000. It was an event that is still talked about to this day by those who were there, and my father often told me how he got a great deal of pleasure out of that adventure and often marvelled at Charlie's devotion to jazz.

Dad had fallen in love again. Dave Green, who was playing bass with Charlie Watts, brought his friend Jill O'Doherty, who was the manageress of a restaurant where Dave used to play, to Ronnie Scott's to hear the Charlie Watts band. During the intermission, Jill, a vivacious, pretty blonde with velvety brown eyes, was sitting in the downstairs bar chatting with friends. Ronnie bought her a drink, they chatted and he asked for her telephone number. The next day, to Jill's surprise, he called her. They started to see each other quite frequently and Jill, who was much younger than Dad – just twenty-nine at the time – soon found herself falling in love with him. Jill resisted his invitation to work at the club, deciding that her independence was very important to her. A former art student, she had other ideas about what she really wanted to do with her life; at that time her goal was to become an interior designer.

My father was not sure about living with someone again. He had not lived with anyone since 1981 and was mindful of the turmoil that would ensue if they were to break up. But their relationship was flourishing, and by 1986 he took the plunge again and Jill moved into Elm Park Mansions with him.

Françoise was still very much a part of Ronnie's life. They shared a friendship that, even when Françoise finally left England and returned to France to live, remained steadfast.

Ronnie's quintet also played at the club during this season, and Martin Drew recalled: 'We had played a couple of numbers and Ronnie called the title of the next tune. Turning to Dick he said: "Do you know this one?" Dick replied: "No, I don't know that." Ronnie responded: "Oh yeah. Well, fuck it. It goes like this . . . One, two, one two three four . . ." After a few choruses had gone down, Dick got it. He had no choice. It was amazing.' This was what my father did: he led his musicians to the extent where there was no laying back, he had them performing tunes and tempos they would never have done had he not led them into them. Martin said: 'I wouldn't be the musician I am today if it hadn't been for Ronnie. He told me when he played with Phil Seamen, Phil would say, "Do you want a night?", referring to playing *very* fast tempos. So Ronnie and I got into that, and we'd see how fast we could do it. I've *never* played faster with anybody, not Oscar Peterson or George Coleman or *anybody*. Legitimately, Ronnie didn't miss a trick. Very, very seldom did he screw up. He was an amazing saxophone player. Occasionally we'd just sort of disappear in a metaphorical cloud of smoke trying to keep up with him!'

One night during the intermission Ronnie was doing his fifteen minutes of jokes and a man in the audience started to heckle him. They went back and forth with a series of witty rejoinders until Dad dried up. When he did, the man leaped out of his seat and ran over to Ronnie and hugged him. Dad came off the bandstand and immediately had a bottle of champagne sent over to the man's table. He had enjoyed the battle of wits immensely and, recognising his opponent's worthiness, conceded graciously. Dad never forgot that man and often told the story with a chuckle, marvelling at his quick comebacks.

I found myself talking incessantly to Dad about my work at the stables; he was quite proud of the fact that I took my responsibility of caring for the horses so seriously. One of my favourites was a ginger thoroughbred called Scotty. It was a Friday afternoon when Scotty fell seriously ill. I telephoned Mum and said: 'Mum, I have to stay at the stables all night tonight. The vet has insisted that someone must stay with Scotty.' I wasn't on my own; a couple of us stayed. Dad wasn't too sure that it was such a great idea, but Mum, having spent much of her childhood on my grandfather's farm in Wales, growing up with a horse of her own and watching my grandfather bring umpteen calves, lambs and piglets into the world, persuaded Dad that it couldn't do me any harm. As the stable housed between thirty and forty horses, the vet was frequently called on and I used to help him a lot. The experience made me want to become a vet myself. Although my father was fascinated with the direction my life had taken, he wondered if one day I would return to my interest in music.

Shortly after Scotty died, Jimmy Culleton came back from the auctions with four new horses. One of them, a two-year-old dark grey that turned to a silver dapple colour as he matured, was a very spunky horse that Jimmy named Shenanigans. Nobody could ride him – he bucked off his back everyone who tried. Consequently, Jimmy used to keep him in his stall all day and let him out to exercise in the ring when all the lessons were over. One afternoon Shenanigans got away and galloped up the street and on to a main thoroughfare, where he got hit by a car. He was badly injured in the chest and legs. I used to take care of him and developed a soft spot for Shenani, and as he healed we bonded and he became my friend. I loved his spirit and used to sneak him extra food and give him treats, harbouring a secret yearning to ride him. As I groomed his hindquarters he would give me back massages with his nose, nibbling my ear and giving me kisses. I knew I could ride him and was determined to prove to everybody that I could. I used to beg my trainer, Karen, to let me ride him, but she said he was too dangerous. This went on for several months. My riding was of course improving all the time, and by now I was taking customers out on trail rides. Finally she caved in and said: 'All right. You can ride him, but if anything happens you *have* to get right back on him again.'

Every day I was dumped by Shenanigans. He had a trick whereby he would come trotting into the corner of the ring and then, suddenly, swing round fast and charge into the centre of the ring. Of course, I came flying off and was dumped in the corner while he stood looking at me from the centre. I would feel his body tense and knew he was about to buck and rear, but I got used to his tricks and eventually learned how to handle him and we became a team. Mum knew everything that was going on. She was not perturbed because she understood that it is impossible to be a good rider without taking a few falls, but at that time we kept that side of things away from Daddy because he was already anxious about my safety. I had begun to drive my mother mad, begging her to buy Shenani for me. In the meantime my grades in school had suffered, and Mum and Dad were both highly concerned about this turn of events since high school was next on the agenda and good grades were essential to qualify for a decent school. Dad and Mum discussed the possibility of purchasing Shenanigans. Mum told Daddy she could afford to buy him but the monthly upkeep, stable fees, vet, food, and so on were way beyond her means. They talked about the pros and cons on and off for several weeks.

Daddy decided to come to New York. He had told us about Jill and wanted to bring her with him to meet us. But because of everything that was going on in my life we did not think it was the time to meet a new girlfriend and asked him if he would come alone this year. There was too much for us to sort out as a family, but of course if Dad wanted to bring Jill next year that would be great. Dad agreed. He wanted to come to see the stables for himself, meet Jimmy and see Shenani. My parents agreed that working at the stables and with the local vet was a constructive, positive way for me to spend my free time and were considering agreeing to buy me the horse, thinking that it would also be a good motivation for me to improve my grades in school.

In the summer of 1986 Dad arrived in New York. Mum and I were at the hotel when he arrived. He looked at me and said: 'Well, Rebecca, I see you are all in one piece!' He was always a bit concerned about the safety factor and constantly enquiring after my welfare. Over dinner we talked a lot about Shenanigans and the stables. Mum agreed to arrange for a taxi to pick Dad up at the hotel the following afternoon and we would be waiting for him at Culmitt. It was a Saturday, and Mum arrived at the stables about an hour before Dad was due. I was preparing Shenani so he would look his best. I took him into the ring for a warm-up and had set up some jumps so I could put Shenani through his paces and show Daddy what we were capable of. Mum came into the ring and was holding Shenani for me. I turned around and realised she was talking to him seriously. She had his head between her hands and said: 'Shenani, you *have* to behave yourself. We want to buy you, and Becky's Dad is going to want to ride you this afternoon, so *no* tricks. If you buck him off we won't be able to buy you!' She loved the horse almost as much as I did. The other kids at the stable thought my mother was stark raving mad talking to him the way she was, and for such a long time too. I had to admit that I had similar fears myself, and I said to Mum: 'Will Dad really insist on riding him?' Mum said: 'You can be sure of it. That's one of the great things about your father, Becky. He loves an adventure and will try practically anything at least once!'

Dad arrived, and I was surprised by the way he greeted Shenani, rubbing his nose, talking to him and patting his neck. Shenani nuzzled him, which was a good sign. Dad could hardly wait for me to finish doing my rounds in the ring, saying: 'OK, Rebecca, that's enough! It's my turn now. Come on, give me a ride!' We started out with me leading him around the ring at a walk, when Dad said: 'Come on . . . for God's *sake*. He can go faster than this. I'll be *all right*, Rebecca. I want a proper ride!' It was remarkable: Shenanigans would do nothing but walk! I couldn't believe it, Dad was getting really frustrated, I was tugging at the reins, and Mum said: 'OK, go faster but be careful!' Shenanigans reluctantly broke into a trot. Dad said: 'That's more like it! Now we're moving! Becky, let *go . . . let go . . .* I'll be *fine.*' I let go of the reins and held my breath. Dad pretended to be a jockey, lying flat against Shenani's neck, holding the reins up, pulling one of his famous faces and looking for all the world like a kid in a Thurber cartoon! He said: 'Ah, you see, Rebecca, it's a fine kind of madness!' We were in hysterics. It was amazing, really. Dad had never ridden anything but a donkey when he was a little boy, and it seemed as though he and Shenanigans were made for each other. It was a marvellous afternoon. Dad really enjoyed himself and loved the horse. I cooled him off and put him back in his stall, Dad met Jimmy and my trainers, Karen and Heidi, and went on a tour of the stables. By the time he had finished I was ready to leave too, so we took a cab into Manhattan and went to our family restaurant for dinner.

Dad was thrilled with the horse. He asked me a lot of questions, satisfying himself that this was something I really wanted to do. I had already shown some of Jimmy's horses and won some blue ribbons, and I explained that I wanted to show on my own horse. It was then that Dad told me: 'Rebecca, your mother and I have discussed buying Shenanigans. There's only one problem, you see. You're not doing as well as you should in school, so we have decided that if you can get yourself on to the honour roll by graduation, then Mum will buy Shenanigans for you and we'll split the other expenses between us. Do you think you can do that?' All stops were pulled out. Mum told me that now was the time to tell her if I needed any extra help in certain subjects, and Dad agreed: 'Do whatever is necessary. Just get those grades up.'

In November that year my grandfather, Cyril Hulin, was very ill in Wales. Long since retired from farming, he had remained an active journalist up until his hospitalisation. Grandad desperately wanted Mum to take me to see him. I was still unable to travel because the attorney who was handling our immigration papers several years before had died of cancer. His wife made every effort to get all his cases concluded before his death, because if he died before the process was complete then his clients would have to start from the beginning again with a new attorney. Somehow my papers got lost in the shuffle, and it was not until six months after his death that his wife found them. Consequently, Mum had to get a new lawyer for me, and I was still in the processing stage. She tried to get special permission for me to travel, but it was not forthcoming and in the end she made arrangements to go alone and for me to stay with friends. My grandfather died four days before she was due to arrive. I will never forget my mother's distress and how Dad was there for her every inch of the way. He recalled all too clearly Grandma Hulin's battle with angina and ultimate death not so long after my ill-fated Christmas visit in 1978, and how because of immigration neither my mother nor I could return home to see her or attend the funeral. We held special services for her in New York. After my grandfather's funeral, Mum stayed with Dad for a couple of days before returning to New York.

A t the beginning of 1987 George Coleman, who was one of Ronnie's favourite saxophone players, was playing his annual gig at the club. George always played with a British rhythm section. He remembered: 'I never did bring my own band with me, but I always loved to play with British musicians. The quality of musicianship among the British guys is very high. Sometimes if Ronnie's band wasn't working I had the pleasure of playing with them.' George always played the club in January or February and had often encountered freezing cold weather with snow on the ground. George recalled one of his visits: 'The pipes in my hotel in Marble Arch broke, and it was too cold to fall asleep in the room. So Ronnie, who absolutely hated the cold and always sat in the office with the electric heater blowing directly on him, lent me his heater out of the office.' The weather had little effect on the jazz audiences in London, however. George chuckled with pleasure as he recalled: 'In spite of the cold I always played to a full house, even when the traffic was bogged down with snow.'

When George walked into the office, Ronnie was either fingering his sax or sitting behind his desk with the saxophone out. It was always obvious that he had been practising. They would greet each other and start chatting about music, different styles of playing, and what other guys were doing musically. They often talked about Tubby Hayes, Ronnie's tenor partner from the Jazz Courier days, swapping jokes and stories. When they were not doing that Ronnie would be sharing some of the finer points of snooker with George as they watched the game together on TV. George told me: 'I had great admiration for Ronnie as a musician and as a man. I always felt he was responsible for my being at the club, even though Pete was the one to call me. Pete and Ronnie always treated me like royalty. I was always very well taken care of and looked forward very much to playing at the club.'

A steady stream of jazz luminaries continued to appear at the club. Ronnie remained the perfectionist in every area: if the microphone was turned up a decibel too high or there was a dirty ashtray on a table, the guilty party was subject to a dose of Dad's sardonic humour. The staff always accepted the criticism in the spirit with which it was delivered; they had great affection and respect for my father. I think that Daddy really summed up the way he felt about the club and the reason for its being there in an interview that he gave for the *Melody Maker* when he was talking about jazz in Britain and the legendary musicians who had played at the club: 'If we have helped raise the standard of jazz played here, I think it is because people have been able to understand the approach of some of these great players and their music – you can get the content off the records, but not the approach. It never stops being an education to me.'

That May Daddy brought Jill to New York to meet us. They stayed at our old hotel, the Century Paramount on West 46th Street, and we arranged to meet them at the hotel. I was not particularly looking forward to it, and Mum was a bit apprehensive too. When we arrived Daddy was waiting for us in the lobby but Jill had not yet come down. We chatted for about ten minutes and then Jill stepped out of the lift. She was young and pretty, warm and outgoing, with a ready smile. My mother and Jill got along well right from the beginning; they really liked each other. I was a little slower to warm towards her because I resented having to share what little time I had with my father with his girlfriend. But Jill turned out to be great. She enjoyed spending time with us, and consequently we saw a lot of them for the two weeks they were in town.

On Mother's Day we all went to South Street Seaport. It was a gloriously sunny day, there were all kinds of shops and restaurants to wander through, and we decided to take the Circle Line boat that takes you around Ellis Island, which was where the first immigrants landed and is now a museum, and the Statue of Liberty. Daddy started his antics on the boat, pretending to be Long John Silver, we got into our gurning session, and Jill and Mum were in hysterics. We had a wonderful time and a raging appetite by the time we got off the boat, so that night we ate copious amounts of seafood sitting at a table outside one of the restaurants on the broadwalk.

During the last week of their visit we introduced Jill to our family restaurant, Kaplans. Dad wanted to know the details of how I was doing at school. The report was good – my grades were much improved by this time and I was actually doing very well. My father was really pleased, and Dad and Mum firmed up the promise that, if I graduated on the honour roll, Mum would buy Shenanigans and Dad would help out with the upkeep. I was overjoyed, and we started joking around, Daddy coming out with a one-liner that was an old favourite: 'Just remember, Becky, I've been known to stop a runaway horse dead in its tracks . . . just by putting money on it!' Mum said this would be one time the money wouldn't go down the drain and took a picture of Daddy and me holding a fifty-dollar bill between us to mark the occasion. After dinner we walked down to Carnegie Hall on 57th Street and took pictures of each other standing outside the great hall. Before Dad and Jill left, they invited me to join them in Orlando, Florida, later in the year for a vacation. I was really thrilled at the prospect. It was the first time I had been invited on one of Dad's vacations.

On 23 June 1987 I graduated on the honour roll from junior high and was accepted into Edward R. Murrow High School that September. My mum bought Shenanigans the following weekend and he was finally mine. The first thing I wanted to do was put him on a special diet to build him up, because I wanted to train him for shows, and the vet had to do some work on his feet, which were not holding the shoes properly. It would take a couple of months to get Shenani into shape before I could start training him.

Daddy and Jill spent a couple of weeks on their own in Orlando before I was due to join them. A few days before I left, the phone rang. It was Dad, who said to me: 'Becky, we have a slight problem, nothing to worry about, but let me talk to Mummy for a minute.' I handed the phone to Mum, and Ronnie said, 'Mary? Look, there's a bit of a problem. Well, you see, I thought I'd make us a bit of extra money for the holiday, and I'm afraid it didn't quite come off.' It turned out that he had been betting on the Hai A lai (otherwise known as Fronton) and had started out on a winning streak and thought that he was well ahead of the game. He got a bit carried away and his luck turned, and not only were his recent winnings lost but also the holiday fund had severely diminished. So the request was for my mother to send money with me for the remainder of the holiday. In the meantime Daddy and Jill had to move out of their hotel into a less expensive lodge until I arrived with new funds from Mum! Then the remainder of the holiday got upgraded with Mum's help. Dad reimbursed Mum after he returned to London.

Mum and I were looking for a fun little gift for both Daddy and Jill. Jill loved toy pigs and had a large collection of them at home, and, although

Daddy and I loved what Jill called 'toilet humour', Jill did not really like it, so we decided on a compromise. We found a cute fat pink pig with a grin on its face but – surprise – when you pulled its tail it farted! I wrapped it up in a box and said the front half was for Jill and the back half was for Daddy. I think he and I had much more fun with that pig than Jill ever did. But she and I got along really well. She was able to relate to me. We had common ground with clothes and music and suchlike, maybe because Jill was a young thirty then and seemed closer to my age and we were able to be girlie together. Things were somewhat strained between Dad and me then because I was a bit of a rebellious teenager, but Jill was able to act as a buffer between us and my relationship with Dad blossomed with her encouragement.

Knowing my propensity to burn when sunbathing, Mum had given Dad strict instructions to make sure I applied plenty of sunscreen lotion before lying out by the pool. All Daddy had to do was look at the sun and he turned brown, but much to my frustration I had not inherited his complexion and have fair skin like my mother. However, I was determined to get brown fast and ignored the sunscreen, instead sneaking on some of Dad's tanning oil. I burned myself so badly it was unbelievable. I actually had sunstroke. I was nauseous and had a headache during the whole trip. I tried to keep it from Dad, but that was impossible. He had no idea what to do and felt badly for me. I just told him that I did not feel too well so he and Jill should go on to dinner without me. As soon as they left I called Mum, crying. She told me to get some Aftersun from the gift shop downstairs, and some aspirin, and to drink lots of fluids. I also had stomach cramps, so she reminded me that hot sweet tea always helped. The next day we went to Disneyland. I was burned so badly it really hurt to walk, and Dad always walked miles and miles – it was one of his favourite occupations. I kept asking for soft drinks, trying to rid myself of the ever-increasing sensation of passing out. Dad started to get worried when all of a sudden I saw an information centre, a huge air-conditioned area where you could sit and relax, and I said: 'Dad, I'm just going in there to sit down for a bit. You and Jill go and see the things you want to see. I'll wait for you in there. I'll be OK.' It was *such* a relief – I was absolutely on fire! Gradually, after sitting in the air-conditioning for about half an hour I began to feel better, but Dad was worried and kept coming in to see if I was all right. Somehow I got through it. Dad really was mortified when he realised how bad I was, especially after Mum had made such a point of telling him to make sure I did not do something stupid.

That summer Dad taught me how to drive. We had a rented car, and he taught me in the huge car park next to the hotel. When he drove into the entrance of the hotel he said: 'All right, Rebecca, we'll switch seats and you can park the car.' Dad would let me pull out and drive the car up to the gate, and round the car park, and he taught me how to park, but that was it. He was a bit nervous and wouldn't let me drive in the street. I was too young so he had to be careful. But he gave me a good start. Our holiday was coming to an end and the night before we left Daddy and Jill invited me to go and stay with them for Christmas.

It was when I went to stay with Jill and Daddy in London for Christmas 1987 that the flat really became like a second home for me. Now that I could finally travel, my visits to Dad became a regular event. That Christmas we had what we call a 'Charlie Brown Christmas tree', and the flat was decorated with lots of candles. It was warm and cosy. I loved the red-brick fireplace in the living room, and I sat and watched the flames dance over the artificial coal that everyone thought was real as we chatted after the delicious Christmas dinner Jill had prepared and we all pulled crackers. I had my own bedroom, which was always there for me. Dad had kept the leather-bound books my mother had bought for me years ago, all classics: Dickens, Pushkin, Tolstoy, etc. My toy box had become a linen chest, and many things went back to the days of 108 Elm Park Mansions. My favourites were the cat drawings that hung on the living room walls. In the daytime the light streamed in through the uncovered living room bay windows that looked out over the treetops and down on the pretty town houses with their little gardens lining the opposite side of the street and the church directly opposite. My father's flute lay on top of a chest of drawers. He would take it down and try to show me how to coax some notes out of it. His guitar leaned against a wall next to the sofa, and we would take turns strumming it. Dad had taken a few lessons and tried to teach me what he had learned. In the kitchen on the shelves of the Welsh dresser proudly sat dainty cups and saucers with tea plates from my great-grandmother, Charlotte Mercer, whom Mum called Nana in Wales. It was good to be there and time passed all too quickly. The New Year had come and gone and I was headed back to New York.

February 1988 saw the first appearance of a wonderful saxophone player from Chicago. His name was Earl Lavon 'Von' Freeman, who came to perform with his son Chico Freeman, also a tenor player, who had already made a name for himself, with Kirk Lightsey on piano, Lonnie Plexico on bass and Don Moye of the Art Ensemble of Chicago on drums. Ronnie

MY HERO: PART ONE

became a lifelong friend of both father and son. Von Freeman, whom Ronnie had great admiration for both as a man and a musician, rarely played outside his home town, but on this occasion had come because of his son. Chico, who still performs at the club, like many of the musicians, had a special relationship with my father. When he first arrived from America, Chico and Ronnie quickly got caught up in a banter based on the differences between American and English language and culture. One night Chico walked into the office, where Ronnie was watching snooker on TV. Chico had never seen the game before and said to Ronnie: 'What the hell is that? Don't you guys have any football or basketball over here?' Ronnie shot him a look that we all described as the 'are you fucking mad look' and responded: 'Are you taking the piss?' Chico collapsed laughing: 'Taking the piss? Now what the hell does that mean? If I take a piss I go to the bathroom. I'm happy to get that stuff out of me, man! You're mad . . .! What kind of logic is that? You've got to learn to speak English!' By now Ronnie was laughing, seeing he had a partner in crime. An affinity for wordplay was quickly established between them, and crazy exchanges and wacky sayings were something both men looked forward to each time Chico played at the club. Chico remembered: 'Ronnie flipped out. He had so many of his quick responses. One time I played opposite Professor Irwin Corey, and when those two got started in the back office they were way out of my league. Man, I didn't say a word. They were *unbelievable*. The repartee between them was incredible.'

During one of his visits Chico said to Ronnie: 'I want you to meet a friend of mine. Now, when I bring him back, don't you mess with me!' Ronnie chuckled. A few minutes later Chico walked back in with Avery Brooks. Chico said: 'I could see he recognised him, then Ronnie said: "Aren't you Hawk . . . Hawk from Spitfire?" Of course, now he's well known for his role in *Star Trek*.' Chico was one of the saxophone players who joined Ronnie in his search for that 'magic horn'. They were both constantly trying out different horns, and on one of his visits Chico brought over one of his Selmer saxes for Ronnie. He played it for the duration of Chico's visit but then returned it, deciding that his horn 'of the moment' had a better sound. Chico recalled: 'I had a mouthpiece that my father had given to me. It was an Otto Link, and I'd bitten through the plastic so took it to Lewington's to get it fixed. Ronnie lent me a mouthpiece to use on the gig, and when he saw how much I liked it, he gave it to me. I cherish that mouthpiece.' Every time Chico played at the club he always brought Ronnie boxes of reeds and always spent his break with him in the inner sanctum.

They talked a lot about music, swapping tunes, discussing chord changes. Ronnie and Critch gave him 'But not for Me'. Chico said: 'Ronnie was a fine saxophone player, a great musician, and *nobody* can tell jokes like he told them, with that dry sense of humour. I used to like his delivery, it was *so* unique. I never tired of hearing his jokes.'

From as early as I can remember comedy and humour were always a common ground for Dad and me. As I grew up our favourite comedians were guys like John Cleese, Peter Sellers, Jacky Mason, Victor Borge (especially a piece of his called 'Punctuation'), Mel Brooks, Spike Milligan, Woody Allen, Dudley Moore; then there was Professor Irwin Corey who on stage always wore a black jacket with long tails, a grubby pair of jeans or trousers and very old sneakers with holes in them, and he had long grey hair that stuck out all over the place. Just watching him walk was funny before he even spoke. Dad used to do such a great take off of him for me that by the time he got through I thought I had seen the real Irwin Corey. It wasn't just the one-liners; we were into body language, weird noises. I think that listening to Daddy take off actors and comedians and do different accents started me off trying out different accents. I would hear him do it and think to myself, I could do that, and I started doing it and found that it came very easily to me. I could always make Dad laugh when he listened to me do Jamaican, Spanish or colloquial American accents, and we would go back and forth with insane exchanges between us until we were laughing so hard we had to stop.

One of the accents he loved was Indian. One afternoon we were looking for a map of Cape Cod at a newsagent's stand. The man running the stand was Indian, and my father asked him: 'Do you have a map of Cape Cod, please?' The man said: 'One moment, please, I will find.' He started rummaging around in the back of the stand and finally came up with a map that he handed to my father. Dad looked at the map and said: 'But this is a map of New York City. I asked you for one of Cape Cod.' The Indian gentleman replied: 'Yes, yes, but this is verri nice map . . . verri, verri *nice* map . . . You will like it!' My mother had to turn away so the man would not take offence; she could not control her laughter. Then Dad responded: 'Yes, yes, and here I am standing beside myself!' delivered with the exact accent of the gentleman who was offering the map. We were laughing hysterically at this point.

We also loved doing a play on words. We had made up our own language, almost. When it was time to eat, Daddy would say: 'I don't know about you, but I am stavaration!' or 'Hungers are you, Rebecca?' Cats were called

Pussintats. He told me about the British comedian Stanley Unwin, who had made up a language, a play on words. Dad thought he was marvellous and had been listening to him and imitating him for years. It's all about rhythms and cadences of speech, really, and it's very funny. Stanley Unwin knew that Daddy really loved what he did so he wrote and taped a small piece especially for Dad and sent it to him. It was called 'A Talk about the Origin of the Saxophone' and goes as follows:

> Adolph Sax eighteen thrifty fold
> the woodwilly tilted hormones there
> eeeee-nnnck, lovely sound as you press tit-el-ode buttons
> of that old joyfold, and people dancing upaload dowda
> a little ensembla and gathy for a little session
> a jam session if you wold, all saxaphobia there
> harmonisey, contropolled puntle improviseo.
> Oh there's a joyfold, all in the jazzy mood
> deep joy, oh deep joy!

We loved this kind of stuff, and although I never heard or saw some of the comedians, Dad made me feel like I really knew the people. When he was taking them off he was so good at it he would become that person.

There was a side to Dad's humour that was really irreverent. My first sight of this was a cartoon that a friend had sent him. He liked it so much he had it framed and hung it up in his living room. It was a drawing of a monk working in calligraphy on a scroll that was half-finished, another monk leaning over him showing obvious concern about the fact that he was only halfway through his work. The caption underneath reads: 'Deadline? What fucking deadline? Nobody told *me* about a fucking deadline!' When I was young Dad was careful about the kind of humour we shared, but as I got older things loosened up a lot, and one time when he was visiting us he bought a phrase voice box. It was really bad: if you pressed a button a voice would yell, 'Fucking asshole'. The effect it had was kind of like the whoopee cushion's in a way. There were four similar phrases on the box, and again Dad got the best effect from his timing. He carried it in his pocket and in the midst of a conversation would press the button when you least expected it, and everyone had to laugh, you just couldn't help it.

Dad often said that his sense of humour really developed from travelling so much, being on the road with his bands. He just made up funny lines and stories about the hotels, towns and people he met on the way. As he said: 'To lessen the boredom of the long hours of travel, I would have gone bloody potty if I didn't!' And then he started putting the stuff together and it became the well-known routine that he did in the club. He always managed to make a joke somehow – that's one of the things that I miss the most. Daddy could take the load out of a heavy situation with his humour which somehow always managed to put a different perspective on things. He had that knack of being able to laugh at himself and life in general. One of his routines was about being Jewish and it goes like this:

> I was born in a room over a Jewish pub in the East End of London called the Kosher Horses. Ours was a very poor family, and my father was always out of work . . . he was a shepherd. But my parents used to go around the house all day singing the blues. Used to drive me crazy. Then one day I heard Mantovani – and I said to myself, That's my music – these are my people.
>
> Actually I'm not a Jew . . . just Jewish. And Jewish people have very strong bonds of affection for one another. But my Uncle Reuben and his wife were constantly at each other's throats. I remember my aunt saying to Reuben after a particularly violent argument, 'What would you do if you came home from work one day and found me in bed with another man?' And my uncle said, 'I'd kick his guide dog!'

There were times when we would be talking and maybe I had spoken out of turn about someone, said something that was a bit unkind, and he would put me in my place by saying: 'H'm . . . I hear he speaks very highly of you, Rebecca.' Since I have had to live without him, I have come to realise that there really is no one quite like Dad. My mum has always said and she used to say it to him: 'They threw away the mould *before* you were born, Ronnie.' Now I understand exactly what she meant.

CHAPTER FOURTEEN

MY HERO: PART TWO

If there is anyone here whom I have not insulted, I beg his pardon.

JOHANNES BRAHMS

Music. It is the only sensual pleasure without vice.   DR SAMUEL JOHNSON

Ronnie was deadly serious, preoccupied, his concentration was intense . . . it was very deep. Every night he put himself on the line, trying to stretch. It was his sustenance, his inspiration, his life.   BENNY GREEN

One evening in the early Spring of 1988, Mum had just come home from work and I was coming in from the stables when the telephone rang. It was Dad, in a state of shock. Uncle Pete had suffered a major heart attack and was in intensive care at the Wellington Hospital in St John's Wood.

We were stunned. It scared all of us. Dad was deeply concerned, because he had never even considered the possibility of life without his partner and friend. Uncle Pete recalled: 'He was a great guy, Ronnie. As soon as he heard he came straight over to the hospital. When he arrived, there was a woman going mad in intensive care. I remember, she was screaming her head off at the top of her lungs. Ronnie grabbed the doctors and got me put into a private section all by myself.' Ronnie was at the hospital every day and took care of the day-to-day business at the club. Uncle Pete had many visitors, among them Art Blakey and Dizzy Gillespie. Pete was concerned about how the staff were managing without him at the club and wanted daily reports. The doctors finally put a restriction on his visitors, allowing only Stella, his son Christopher, daughter Sharon and Dad to visit.

Dad and Mum talked at length. My father was worried that Pete would not recover sufficiently to return to the club. Dad confided that there was no way he could shoulder Pete's responsibilities, confessing to the fact that he just did not have the patience to handle the day-to-day business on a permanent basis. Uncle Pete learned something about himself too. He had never been good at delegating, feeling that he was the only one who could run things efficiently. But for a while at least he had to step back and discovered that even if things were not done exactly as he would have done them, they were still handled efficiently, albeit in a slightly different way. When Uncle Pete did return to the club, he followed his doctors' instructions and cut down on the number of hours he worked.

Once Uncle Pete was out of hospital and well on his way to recovery, Dad saw no reason to cancel his trip to New York in May. The weather was magnificent, as it often is then, and Dad was here once again on Mother's Day. We had lunch in a deli-restaurant. Both my parents loved the deli rice pudding, which is creamy and thick and served cold in old-fashioned tall sundae glasses; eating it became a ritual. Then we grabbed a cab and wandered around his favourite haunt, the Village, passing by the Blue Note, on 3rd Street, checking to see who was playing there, picking up the *Village Voice* to see who was playing at the other clubs. We went window-shopping, and Dad would disappear into a weird shop and try on way-out gear just for the fun of it.

Finally we wound up at a restaurant. It was always either Chinese or Italian, and this time it was Italian. We sat down and ordered our food and while we were waiting for it to come Daddy and I were fooling around as usual and we had started to arm wrestle when all of a sudden Mum noticed that Dad was not wearing on his little finger the ring that he had always worn since she first met him. Mary asked him why he wasn't wearing it, and Ronnie told her that he had lost it on his travels somewhere. His finger felt so odd without it that he had bought himself a silver ring when he was in Cyprus to take its place. Mum looked so sad when Dad told her he had lost the ring that it led me to ask why it was so special. Daddy explained that when Grandma Cissie died he and Auntie Ella had her wedding band cut through the middle, so they each had half, and he had added a band of silver to the gold so that he could wear it on his little finger. I was wearing rings on every finger and thumb. Dad said: 'Oh, my God, Rebecca, you look like a jewellery shop!' We compared rings and I said to Daddy: Why don't we exchange rings?' Dad really liked the idea and asked me which one he could have, so I spread out all my fingers and told him he could have whichever one he wanted. He chose a silver and turquoise one and put it on his little finger and I wore his ring. His mother's ring was so special to him that it really meant a lot to us to make this exchange. Now he had a ring again that was special and so did I. He wore his until the day he died.

There was a steady flow of new talent into the club during these years, groups whose music was a skilfully woven combination of African, Latin and American influences. A group that became very popular and still plays at the club is a Brazilian band led by Airto Moreira on percussion, with Flora Purim on vocals, and the colourful rhythms and joyful nature of their music is appreciated by a wide range of fans. Pete had accepted that areas of his workload had to be distributed among others and permanently adhered to his doctors' instructions of shortening his hours at the club. Bonnie Blair, who had worked with Ronnie and Pete for many years, became more involved and handled the promotion, publicity and advertising, as she still does, and also took care of the banking and the payroll, while Dorothy, also a long-time employee, organised work permits for visiting musicians and made their hotel reservations too. These days Pete has help with the bookings from John Ellson, an independent agent, and John Cummings of Serious Music.

The work for Ronnie's quintet was steady at home and abroad. Occasionally Ronnie drove his own car to out-of-town gigs and often Dick Pearce rode with him, but John Critchinson frequently picked Ronnie up from Elm Park Mansions, remembering: 'The pick-up from the flat was always hilarious. You'd press the buzzer and there'd be the voice, sometimes a dead ringer of Peter Sellers' Inspector Clouseau, or a British agent. Ronnie would say: "That you, 87?" I'd respond: "Yes, yes, coming down, 43, are you?" Other times it was a stream of pure gibberish, the tonal inflections making it hilarious, always rounded off with, "I'll be right down, Crite-chers." My response was, "OK, Schatters" and we'd be on our way.' Dad *never* wanted to leave in time to get to the gig an hour early. He would say to Critch: 'I want to get to the gig, play, and then come home.' Wandering around Marks & Spencer for an hour, killing time before the gig started, was not something that Dad could be bothered with at all.

When they were headed out for a Saturday night gig, Critch used to try to get him to leave early and arrived at about 2 p.m. to pick Ronnie up. He would get in the car and say to Critch: 'We have a problem!' Critch said: 'That meant that he had to go to the bookie. It would be either the one on King's Road or the other one on Fulham Road. It made me anxious because time was rapidly running out.' Finally, they would be on their way headed out of town, but as they neared Warwick Road or Brompton Cemetery Ronnie would say: 'Pull in!' And he would dive into the betting shop. Critch recalled: 'I would sit there seething because I was worried about us getting to the gig on time!' It was one of my father's greatest pleasures to play the horses, and as Critch remembered: 'Ronnie really was a very, very generous man with his winnings. When we were in Australia, a friend of his had taken him to the races and Ronnie won. That night he took us to a fabulous Chinese restaurant in Melbourne and we all had an amazing meal. We came out of there bursting!'

My mother and I had travelled to Hillsdale, New York, to spend Christmas with Auntie Jenna and her new husband, Uncle Charles. They had purchased a beautiful little house, and when I wasn't in London we visited them for Christmas. Daddy always telephoned us while we were there. Shortly after we arrived the phone rang and it was him, terribly upset. He had just learned that his friend, Harry Flick, had just lost his son Clayton and his fiancée Clare in the Pan-American air crash at Lockerbie, in Scotland, on 21 December. My mother knew Harry well too, and even though I didn't it was impossible not to be affected by such a devastating tragedy. They were so young, just twenty-five years old. Because of the investigation that surrounded the crash the families were not able to hold services until the beginning of February the following year. Dad attended the memorial service, which was held in Coventry Cathedral.

D ad was fascinated with Shenanigans. It had been a year since he had seen him, and Dad was anxious to see for himself how the training had progressed. By now Culmitt Riding Stables had changed hands and we moved to Bergen Beach Stables. I had worked very hard with Shenani, and he looked like a different horse. He had matured into a gorgeous silver dapple grey, the training had built up all his muscles and we had won many accolades together in innumerable shows. I was teaching lessons myself now to the younger children. Shenanigans had learned to listen and also had an innate understanding of the small children and was very gentle with them.

The day that Dad came to Bergen Beach, it really was remarkable. He and Shenani greeted each other like old friends, my father giving Shenani a big hug around the neck. Dad could not believe how well developed he was now; somehow he looked a lot larger than he did when we first bought him. I asked Dad if he wanted to ride again, but he looked at me, then at

Shenani and chuckled: 'Not this time, Becky. I'm not sure if I could handle him now! He looks marvellous!' We had sent Daddy loads of pictures of Shenani and me competing in the various shows, and later that night, as we all sat in Kaplans, he admitted: 'I found it very hard to believe it was the same horse in those pictures. I really wanted to see for myself. You've done a remarkable job with him, Rebecca.' That night he also wanted to know if there was any possibility of my becoming involved with music again, and I said to him: 'You have to understand, Daddy, Shenanigans is to me what your saxophone is to you.' At that time it was the absolute truth, although there is no doubt this was not what he wanted to hear. But Dad remained very supportive of my riding.

I had completed my first year in high school. It had been a difficult year. The school was structured along the lines of a university, with little or no discipline. It was very easy to cut classes, as many of the kids did, myself included; at that stage of my life I had not learned the art of self-discipline. Consequently, academically I was heading for trouble, and once again my parents were highly concerned. Unbeknown to me, Mum had already talked to Moji's mum about the New York Military Academy in Cornwall-on-Hudson, upstate New York, which was where Moji went to school. My mother called Dad and told him what she was doing. Initially he hated the idea and said: 'Mary, isn't this a bit drastic? Why does it have to be a military school?' My mother explained that it was one of the best schools in New York with a very high average of college acceptance; the curriculum was excellent, the classes small, and it was a highly structured, disciplined environment.

My father really wanted me to buckle down and do my school work. He used to rattle off maths questions at me, which I hated. As far as English was concerned, he was always on my case. When he received all the information about the Military Academy he finally agreed with Mum that it was the best thing to do. The admissions officer told Mum that Johnny Mandel, trumpeter and trombonist, a jazz musician who had toured with the famous jazz violinist Joe Venuti, and later on became well known also as a composer writing for Woody Herman's, Artie Shaw's and Count Basie's orchestras, was a graduate of the academy. This information helped to soften the blow a little for Dad. Jill remembered Dad talking to her about it, and he told her he was going to help my mother as much as possible with the school fees.

Even though Moji was there, I found the initial adjustments very difficult but after a few months I settled down. They had a stables on the compound

– the academy owned several horses – so Shenanigans came with me and we were in Troop D. I rode Shenani at all the ceremonial occasions; in my last year I also joined the band and played drums. Academically I had some catching up to do, but it was definitely the right environment for that. The teachers all lived in houses on the academy's compound, so they were always there to help you no matter what time it was. They were excellent teachers who really cared about all of us, and we knew it. Consequently, I regained my desire to learn. Dad was really pleased when I took a business legal class with Major Roberts. The subject came easily to me, and my teacher encouraged me a lot, and I grew in his class and learned about contracts and the legalities of business. I was very fortunate to go to such a school.

One thing that I was really grateful to Dad and Mum for was agreeing that my last name should be Scott. I cannot imagine what it would have been like in public school in America if my last name were Schatt. At the academy, your last name is worn on your uniform and you are always addressed by your surname. The other kids in school or the cadets in the academy would have made my life hell. Aunt Rose told me that when she and her brother were growing up in the 1940s some of the things that the kids said back then were really bad. It was relentless.

That summer I flew into Fort Lauderdale and Daddy and Jill met me at the airport and we drove from there to Orlando and all over Florida. While we were in Orlando we visited Disneyworld again. Dad and I were wandering around a rather large gift shop, where everything was so expensive that we were really just looking, when I saw a grey stuffed horse on one of the shelves. Dad came and stood behind me and said: 'You really like that horse, don't you, Becky?' I was so biased when it came to horses. I always wanted to be the one to stand out, because in horse shows all you had were bays and chestnuts, so everyone mingled together, but I was riding a grey and we really stood out. The stuffed pony was unusual, just like Shenani. It was absurdly expensive, but it had beautiful suede hooves and was soft and fuzzy. It was a lovely little thing, and I really wanted Dad to buy it for me. I never asked him to buy me anything, and I didn't want to start now, so rather wistfully I just said: 'He looks *so* like Shenanigans.' Dad walked around the store for a bit, looking at things, then he came back to me and he sent me off to the other side of the store to look at something else. About five minutes later he sauntered over to me and then we just walked out. When we got back to the car Dad pulled the stuffed horse out of his pocket, handed it to me and said: 'Don't tell your mother, now, don't tell your mother!' I couldn't *believe* he had just taken it! Dad said to me: 'Now, don't you ever do that, that's bad. *Promise* me you'll never do it, Rebecca!' This was a lot of fun for me, because Dad and I had a secret. He never told Jill either. When we were together, he was always doing silly things.

I didn't tell Mum for quite some time about the stuffed pony. When I did, she said: 'What? What do you mean, he took it?' She wasn't too happy about it, and I asked her not to tell Daddy that I had told her. But Mum was really concerned, because I was at such an impressionable age, and confronted Dad, who was very apologetic and knew that he was in the wrong. The pony sits on a shelf in my bedroom to this day, and I still tease Mum about it!

Uncle Pete and Critch told me stories about Dad walking into stores like Barney's and strolling around for a while looking at this and that. Selecting a cap or a hat he would put it on his head and walk out wearing it! He ended up with a drawer full of caps. It was just the excitement that made him do it.

In September 1989 my Uncle Richard, Mum's brother, had a massive heart attack. When Mum telephoned Dad and told him he immediately made arrangements for her to fly home and visit Uncle Richard. Mum stayed for about a week. That was the last time she was to see her brother because in November Uncle Rich died suddenly of another heart attack. I was upset, but my mother was quite devastated. I will never forget how Daddy was quietly supportive of us. In a gentle way he was able to give Mum strength somehow. He had prepaid tickets waiting for us at Kennedy Airport, and although we went straight to Wales without our usual stopoff at Dad's in London, he was in daily contact with us by phone. It was during one of these calls that he gave Mum the sad news that Harry South, a long-time friend and fellow musician, had just been told by his doctors that he did not have much longer to live. This was a real blow to both of us. I had some happy memories of staying with Harry and Harriet and their daughters Anita, Louise and Annabelle when I was six, and during my Christmas visits with Dad and Jill or Françoise the three of us would spend Boxing Day with the family. It was a tradition for Daddy. Harry was a kind and gentle man with infinite patience and a wonderful sense of humour. On our way back from Wales, Mum and I stayed with Daddy and Jill for a couple of days. The day we arrived, Mum and Harriet went to see Harry in the hospital and afterwards Daddy took Jill, Mum, myself and Harriet out to dinner, and we all found comfort in each other.

Harry was a highly respected composer and a very fine pianist. In the

1950s he had played with Tubby Hayes, and they made several recordings together, and although Tubby was also a great composer, many of the compositions that they recorded together were Harry's. In later years he wrote scores for television and films. A benefit concert was held at the 100 Club in Oxford Street in February for Harry. Most of the musicians who had played with Harry over the years performed that night, my father among them. But sadly, on 12 March 1990, Harry died. Even though he had been ill since November it did not lessen the shock. Harry's death was a great loss to the world of music on both sides of the Atlantic. To name a few, he had written for Buddy Rich, Sarah Vaughan and Jimmy Witherspoon, and was also music director for Annie Ross. For my father the loss was great; Harry was a personal friend and Dad was deeply saddened. After Harry died, Dad telephoned Harriet regularly and often invited her to come to the club. Their friendship deepened, and as Harriet has said many times: 'Ronnie was always a really good friend to me, but when Harry died he was marvellous. He was there for me right to the end.'

George Coleman was playing at the club when Harry died. He told me: 'I'll never forget when Harry died. Ronnie talked to me at great length about him. He was torn apart, Harry was his man. He and his wife Harriet meant the world to Ronnie.'

At the club, though, things were going well. All the gremlins of the early 1980s had been put to rest. Ronnie and Pete had overcome every obstacle that they had been presented with, and the club was prospering and world renowned as they celebrated their thirtieth anniversary. Of the club, Martin Gayford wrote: 'The club has remained reassuringly the same, as good clubs should. Generations of fans have gone to see the masters of the music playing – as they play their best – under relaxed, informal circumstances. It is also, like all the best clubs, an extension of the personality of the proprietor.' Ronnie said to Martin: 'We paint the place every now and then, change the lampshades (always keeping the same style); the waitresses change, but that's all. Why alter something that works?' The BBC's *Omnibus* programme made a sixty-minute documentary to mark the occasion. Sonny Rollins, Dizzy Gillespie, John Dankworth and Georgie Fame were among the musicians who appeared in tribute to the club and Ronnie and Pete.

While I was on holiday with Daddy and Jill in Florida in the summer of 1990, we decided to go to Disneyworld again for a day. This time we headed for the rides. While we were queueing to go on one called Space Mountain we noticed signs posted every few yards saying: BEWARE! IF YOU HAVE HEART PROBLEMS DO NOT TAKE THIS RIDE! Every time we came to a warning sign, Dad contorted his face so that he looked like a very old man with no teeth, and he would tremble from head to toe, turn to me and say: 'Oh, Rebecca! You don't love me any more! You're trying to kill me on this ride! Why are you making me do this? Why?' Dad had everyone in the queue cracking up. They were all a little nervous anyway so Daddy carrying on relieved the tension and folks were glad of a laugh. The Roller Coaster was a very fast and scary ride and we hung on for dear life. I loved it but I think Dad was glad to get off!

During the holiday we made arrangements for me to stay with Dad and Jill in London at the flat later in the year. This was my junior year at the Military Academy and I was looking forward to my junior prom, which was a very special event, and Daddy promised to buy me my first evening dress. I was, of course, very excited about the whole thing and was really looking forward to my visit to London. Dad met me at the airport as usual, and when we got back to the flat Jill had made us dinner and we planned my shopping expedition. Dad said he would give Jill some money and then she and I could go shopping the next day and take as much time as we needed.

We looked in a couple of shops and then Jill took me to Laura Ashley's on Kensington High Street, and together we selected a gorgeous, classically designed elegant dress. The boat-necked bodice had long sleeves and was made out of black velvet, with a full knee-length skirt of peacock-blue shot taffeta. Then we went looking for accessories, and Jill realised that we did not have enough money for everything. But as she felt that the accessories were a must to complete the outfit, she said we would have to ask Daddy for some more money.

That night after the club had closed and we were all at home, I put on the dress for Daddy. And as Jill said, that was when Daddy realised his little girl was rapidly becoming a young woman. Daddy looked at me and said: 'Jill, look at her, my God, she's stunning.' And he caught on quickly to how important the right shoes, bag, stockings and jewellery were to make the outfit a success and happily gave us the extra money needed. The next night he couldn't wait to see the complete picture. It was like a dress rehearsal for the junior prom. To this day I still have the entire outfit.

In the autumn of the same year my father and his quintet were in the process of recording 'Never Pat a Burning Dog' when Dick Pearce had a bad motorcycle accident. Ronnie brought in Mornington Lockett, tenor sax, to play on the last number on the CD, 'Sunflower', written by Freddie Hubbard. The CD was recorded live at the club, on Ronnie's own label, the tapes rolling every night for the duration of the gigs in October and November. If there was an ideal situation for Ronnie to record in, this was it. At times he forgot the taping was in progress and he was as free as a bird. The unique sound of my father's sax assimilated everything from the days when he first heard Coleman Hawkins to everything in between. His choice of tunes was a compilation of times past and present: Jimmy Dorsey's 'I'm Glad There Is You' – the ballad that all through the years was a special bond between my parents – Cedar Walton's 'When Love Is New', McCoy Tyner's 'Contemplation', and 'All the Things You Are' by Kern and Hammerstein.

As Benny Green said when he was talking about Ronnie's playing: 'He was deadly serious, preoccupied, his concentration was intense . . . it was very deep. Every night he put himself on the line, trying to stretch. It was his sustenance, his inspiration, his life.' A summation of this is captured on 'Never Pat a Burning Dog'.

The quintet had outlasted Ronnie's lifespan of three to five years for his bands. Critch, Martin Drew, Ron Mathewson and Ronnie had been playing together since 1979 and with Dick since 1980. Even so, the band never fell into a musical rut; for Dad, the music always had to be shifting and changing as he tried out new ideas in his constant and unrelenting search for perfection. There were times when tempers would flare and arguments would erupt but the incidents were short-lived and soon forgotten. That the relationship between Ronnie and his musicians was special is clearly reflected on the disc they had just completed. Mornington Lockett is a tenor player my father had admired for quite some time, and after Dick recovered from his accident Mornington stayed with the band.

Dad loved playing with Mornington Lockett. It was a rejuvenating experience, reminding him of his years with Tubby and the Jazz Couriers. When they shared the bandstand Ronnie and Mornington were reminiscent of the legendary 'cutting contests' of Kansas City. Martin Drew recalled: 'Ronnie had a stopwatch and used to time Mornington. He played *so* fast, Ronnie loved it.'

That December Stan Getz, who was now divorced from Monica and was living in Malibu, California, learned that a cancer he had sent scuttling into remission a couple of years earlier had reawakened. Auntie Bev and her daughter Katy had spent time with him in Malibu and were very much a part of his initial fight with the disease. When we told Dad what was going on he constantly asked about Uncle Stan's renewed battle with the disease. Mum spoke to Uncle Stan several times at length during this period and conveyed to Dad that Stan would like to hear from him. Finally the illness took over. Mum called Dad and told him that he should call before it was too late. Uncle Stan and Dad had not spoken to each other for a long time. They had had a serious disagreement in the past, but as my mother knew only too well they both still cared about each other deeply. Auntie Bev had gone to Malibu to be with her father and Mum spoke to her every night.

One night Dad rang and Auntie Bev answered the phone. She explained to Dad that it was hard for Uncle Stan to talk, so they chatted for quite a while, then Dad said: 'Bev, do me a favour. Please tell Stan that I love him and I don't want him to be angry.' When Auntie Bev relayed the message to Uncle Stan she remembered: 'Dad got this little smile on his face. It was as though he was embarrassed in a way because they hadn't mended their bridges before this, and he said: "Tell Ronnie everything's cool. I love him too." So the next time I spoke to Ronnie I told him what Dad had said.'

In the afternoon of 6 June 1991 Dad telephoned again. This time the telephone was answered by someone unknown to Dad, so he asked to speak to Stan but was told that Stan could not speak because his illness was back. Dad was given no indication that death was imminent. When Mum phoned him shortly afterwards to tell him that Uncle Stan had died, Dad struggled with the information, saying: 'Mary! How can that be? I just spoke to someone at his house. There was no indication . . . it can't be . . .' Gently, Mum affirmed that Auntie Bev had just called her seconds before and it was indeed the case. Dad was stunned. Memorial services were held for Uncle Stan in California and New York on the same day, Monday 1 July 1991. My father had been anxious to find out when the services were but because of commitments he was unable to attend. This time Mum and I went without him.

Dad asked Mum for Auntie Bev's address and phone number, and shortly afterwards he wrote her a letter which she cherishes to this day, remembering: 'Your dad's letter stood out from all the other cards and letters of condolence. It was so touching, so beautiful. This was the first time that I saw that side of Ronnie. He was always so reserved and private. For him to reach out to me like that meant *so* much.' Dad also phoned Auntie Bev, and they talked at length. He really understood and brought her great comfort.

The previous May I graduated from the New York Military Academy. Special invitations were printed for the occasion and we sent one to Dad. He came especially for the occasion, arriving in New York the night before.

Aunt Fran and Mum drove into Manhattan early that morning to pick my father up from his hotel and then on to Cornwall-on-Hudson. It really was a splendid occasion, called Alumni Weekend, with special events going on for three days – presentations of awards, open house, luncheons, dinner-dance, the works – ending with the presentations of our diplomas. I graduated as a sergeant in Troop D. It was a proud day. Both my parents were so happy, and Dad presented me with a magnificent silver fountain pen as my graduation gift.

The families of my friends had made arrangements to go to a restaurant in Little Italy in Manhattan. Dad and Mum and Aunt Fran were invited to join in the fun. Our trunks had been sent home the previous Friday, so suitcases and books were stashed in the boots of cars and we all left in a procession for New York. The top floor of the restaurant, which was like a loft, had been reserved for the graduation party. The meal was splendid and the wine flowed all night. It was a wonderful evening; everybody got along with each other, a great celebration. Dad and Mum were anxious to contribute to the expenses of the evening. But there was no sign of a bill – everything had been handled very discreetly. Even so they both agreed that they should talk with the host, a member of one of New York's 'families'. When Dad's offer to pay was refused, he said: 'Please, we were three extra people. Allow me to at least contribute something . . .' Our host, in a level tone that brooked no contradiction, said: 'Do not insult me.' Dad said, 'No, of course not. Thank you very much. It's been a wonderful evening', and returned to our table. When we were leaving, our host was sitting with several other men on a long seat against the wall downstairs, and we stopped to shake his hand and thank him once again. All the men looked at Daddy as though he had just flown in from Mars. I knew the whole family very well and had often visited their home. They were very warm and always kind to me, but they did not quite know what to make of this English gentleman, my father.

Dad was proud as punch when early that summer we learned that I had been accepted into Johnson and Wales University in Providence, Rhode Island. I was all set to begin my studies to become a vet. Wanting to specialise in horses, I had signed up for Equine Science as my major and a business course. They had an excellent stables on campus and Shenanigans came with me to college.

In the middle of July Dad returned to Florida. This time he was on his own for a week, staying at Fort Myers, then I joined him for two weeks. It was fun, and he had such a great apartment in the Great Western Complex right on the beach. We each had our own large bedroom with a TV and a bathroom, there was a huge living room and a decent-size kitchen. We had a beautiful view of the ocean, and a marvellous balcony where we would sit and watch the sailing boats glide by, gulls circling around them, and fast motorboats zooming past leaving a great wake behind, yachts like stately queens in their moorings. We talked about what was going on in his life and in mine and how things were with Mum. We took lots of pictures, especially as the evening drew to a close and we watched spectacular sunsets, in awe of the magnificent beauty of the deep crimsons and golds, sometimes purples and magentas, spread across the sky and reflected in the ocean, the colours flickering and dancing on the waves; other evenings the water was so calm it looked like sparkling glass. We would watch that perfect sphere of molten red slowly seeming to slip into the sea itself. It was glorious.

Sometimes there were storms. We had never seen anything to compare with those in our lives. It was kind of scary but thrilling as we sat on the balcony watching amazing bolts of lightning flashing across the vast expanse of sky, then shooting down through the clouds and over the sea. There were moments when the whole sky seemed to be fractured as multiple bolts flashed simultaneously, shooting out a network of smaller, thinner linked bolts spread out like great veins of light across the sky. Sometimes it was sheet lightning, and massive areas of the sky were momentarily transformed into vast brilliant sheets of blinding white light, reflecting on the dark churning sea, highlighting the peaks of the waves like millions of sparkling stars. It was absolutely spellbinding.

We spent our days on the beach. Sun-worshippers both we were content to lie on the sand and get a tan, occasionally running into the ocean to cool off, and then take a long walk along the beach. My father tanned so fast, and now that his hair was silvery white on his chest as well as on his head the contrast against his tan was amazing. Dad cut a striking figure as he stood at the edge of the sea, arms outstretched to the multitude of seagulls that flocked towards him. As they surrounded him, on the sand and in the air, it seemed as if he had a special affinity with them.

One afternoon we had been watching people on jet skis and Dad said: 'Come on, Becky, let's try them. What do you think?' I was thrilled, it looked like so much fun. We rented the skis and quickly got the hang of them. Dad yelled out: 'OK, Becky, let's have a race!' We flew across the waves. I turned to see where Dad was and he was right there, pulling one of his faces. Then he became a pirate, shouting: 'Ahoy! Ahoy, me hearties! Ahrrrr ... it be a fine day to walk the plank!' How we didn't have an accident I will never know. I couldn't stop laughing, and the more I laughed the more he carried on and the harder it was to keep control of the water skis! It was hilarious. The next day I wanted to try power sailing but Dad said: 'This one you'll have to do on your own, Becky. There's no way I'm going to float around in the air in that flimsy contraption!' He would lie on his back on the beach watching me. It was the most fantastic sensation – once you take off it really feels as though you are flying, and the view is unbelievable.

In the evenings when we talked Dad spoke enthusiastically about his new project. The city of Birmingham had put in a bid to host the Olympic Games, and Dad had read that the city council were rebuilding the central area, their focus firmly set on the arts. Through a contact of Uncle Pete's, he and Dad met Alan Satori and Barry Sherwin, who already ran the Rep Café Bar in the new Rep Theatre. They got along well, and a franchise deal was struck: there was to be a Ronnie Scott's Club in Birmingham. Dad shared in the artistic control and also agreed to play at the club when he could. There were some wrinkles to iron out. For instance, Dad did not like their original concept for the décor at all; in fact he could not live with it, and some adjustments were being made. Part of the plan was that some of the bands that performed at Frith Street were to be booked into the Birmingham club. Dad talked about the whole concept with great eagerness. He was exhilarated by the prospect of a new challenge. The new club was scheduled to open in the autumn.

Peter King, the phenomenal British alto saxophonist who as a young man had opened the first Ronnie Scott's Club in October 1959, now played at the opening of the Birmingham club in a small band with strings accompaniment that was formed by Rolling Stones' drummer Charlie Watts. Ronnie's sextet played opposite the band, and the new club was launched. It soon became clear that because of the preferences of the local audiences, if the club was to remain solvent slightly more R&B and pop-orientated jazz music than was originally planned would have to be performed. However, a successful balance was achieved, and the club is thriving today.

By now Ronnie and Jill had agreed to go their separate ways. Dad was feeling down. At sixty-four he decided once again that living with someone was never going to work for him. His relationships always seemed to reach the point where either marriage or living together became an issue. He suffered slight depression and was taking antidepressants during 1991, but he was in control and very few people even realised. It was like Benny Green said: 'Ronnie worked very hard at being cool. He was a great actor.'

It was an accurate observation. Only the people who really knew my father were aware of the fact that Dad could get very upset about things. As most people in the public arena do, my father had created a public persona and worked very hard at maintaining it, often using his humour or presenting a cool exterior, speaking in a rather terse matter-of-fact manner designed to keep people at a safe distance. Behind the façade Dad was actually a very vulnerable, complex man, who rarely exposed his full character, rather choosing to present different facets of himself to each of his many friends according to their activities and characters.

Eventually Jill ended up settling in Wales, but she and Ronnie had established a firm friendship and in the summer of 1992 Jill came to London for a few days and stayed with Ronnie at the flat. On several occasions over the course of the next few years Jill travelled to London for various reasons, and Ronnie always made her welcome if she wanted to stay a couple of extra days.

It was during the course of 1991 that Ronnie contacted some of his friends in Australia to make enquiries about the possibility of living there during the winter. He had always loved Australia and discussed it with us, describing the adventure as a form of semi-retirement. The idea was to fly out the rest of his group to join him when there was work available, and he would have time for himself in between gigs. I loved the idea. We always had such a great time in Florida together, so staying a couple of weeks with Dad in Australia appealed to me immensely. As we both detested the cold, a couple of weeks in Australia during January sounded pretty good to me.

As the year drew to a close Dad telephoned to tell us that he had met a new girlfriend. Her name was Jo Bailey. Ronnie was in love again. He brought Jo to New York to meet us in the summer of 1992. She was in her early fifties, very elegant, tall and slender, very pretty, with beautiful blue eyes. She had two adult daughters, Laurie and Dani. Jo had gone through a tough divorce. It is said that opposites attract, and that was definitely the case with Dad and Jo. One of the main conflicts was that Jo hated smoking and he was literally a chain smoker and had been all his life. Also, Jo was not a sports fan, was a vegetarian and did not have much time for TV. We got along quite well, and Dad was happy with Jo. Cooking was not one of her greatest pleasures, so they selected restaurants that became favourite haunts for them and often enjoyed a Wednesday evening, Dad's night off, at the Barbican in London listening to opera and classical music.

In March 1992 Dad received a letter from the Birmingham Conservatoire, notifying him that he had been elected a Conservatoire Fellow –

Fellowship of Birmingham Schools of Music. Dad responded by saying that he would be honoured and delighted to accept. The award was in recognition of Ronnie's initiative in bringing Ronnie Scott's Club to Birmingham. The graduation ceremony was held on 3 July. In his opening remarks the dean, Professor Kevin Thompson, said: 'Not only is Ronnie Scott known for his consummate skill as a tenor and soprano saxophonist but also for his warm sense of humour.' On hearing of his fellowship, Ronnie was heard to remark. 'My mother would have been very proud!' Dad hated to have his picture taken and after the ceremony was over he was very nervous about posing for the formal photographs. Professor Thompson recalled: 'After the pictures were taken, Ronnie said: "If you'd wanted one of those you could have asked for a mug shot at Wormwood Scrubs!" '

And so Birmingham's bid to host the Olympic Games . . . resulted in the city gaining Ronnie Scott's. The club was less than five minutes' walk from the Conservatoire and became a venue for the students. Professor Thompson remembered: 'I was very impressed with the way Ronnie related to the students. He was very down to earth. When he was at the club a number of them went down there to meet him. Ronnie often spent time with them at the club and encouraged the students to perform there. There was one student in particular whom he helped. Her name is Katherine, a jazz violinist, and she went to Berklee in Boston to study.'

An aspect that Dad really enjoyed about having the club in Frith Street was the nights during the week when they offered specially reduced prices for students. It gave him great pleasure to look out into the audience and see the students sitting there upfront. They were a knowledgeable audience, there to learn, and their rapt attention reminded him of the old audiences at Gerrard Street. Dad related well to young people. He was open-minded about music, and we had many long discussions, especially when we were in Florida together. We often drove quite long distances with the radio on, and Dad would say: 'Put on a station that you would like, Rebecca.' I knew what he *didn't* like, so I would find a station that played groups like The Cure and U2 or Morrissey and The Smiths, some R&B, Howard Jones, and I liked the Beatles a lot too. As we drove I used to sing along. Dad loved that and got a kick out of the fact that I knew all the lyrics.

My father was *always* interested in what was going on in popular music. Some groups he discarded as 'kiddy pop' or just plain 'pitiful' but he said: 'The good pop groups, Rebecca, whether they know it or not, borrow from jazz just as the jazz musician will assimilate and use the best things in pop. Music is constantly evolving, and one day the division between the two will be indistinguishable. Then we will *really* have some popular music. What do you think of that!'

I remember saying to Dad that the market is *so* contrary that it's hard for groups to make it on their own turf; they have to go abroad first and make it there, then they can come back home to huge audiences. He told me that audiences for some inexplicable reason do not recognise their own home-grown talent. He said: 'It's not as predominant in the world of popular music as it is in jazz or even opera. That was *always* one of our problems with the club: there are some *marvellous* players in England, but audiences won't come out for their own talent. You're absolutely right, though. I know a lot of American musicians who have real trouble getting enough work at home and yet they are idolised abroad.' He went on to say: 'I would really like to see a place open up solely for British jazz and flourish. We tried to do it with the Old Place and we couldn't even break even; it always cost us money. Maybe in the future someone will be able to do it, and the public will wake up to the reality of the incredibly high standard of its own British musicians.'

We talked about the reality of racism in our worlds. Dad summed it all up by saying: 'I'll tell you how I see it, Rebecca. When the historians a couple of thousand years from now look back at our time, as far as racial problems are concerned we will be seen as the equivalent to the way we see the Stone Age now. We still have a very long way to go, I'm afraid.'

I was devastated. Shenanigans was diagnosed as having an incurable bone disease. We did everything possible – X-rays were sent to Cornel University, a treatment was recommended – but there was little hope for Shenani. He certainly could not keep up with the rigours of training for shows, and the vet said that he should not jump any more. Shenanigans loved to jump and gallop full pelt on the flat, so it was more than I could handle. Dad was there for me every second, telling me not to worry, that we would find a way, then he would phone Mum trying to work out how to save Shenani. I was so upset. We had been through so much together, Shenani and me. I cried on the phone to Dad, who was very calm and gentle yet strong, quietly talking to me, and somehow he managed to make sense where there was none, slowly easing me into accepting the situation. Any major problem that we had, Dad was always right there. Even though physically he was three thousand miles away, there really was no distance between us.

The vet said that Shenani could still do flat work and it would be all right for young children to learn to ride him as long as the injections were kept up on a regular basis. His treatment was unbelievably expensive, and in the end Mum explained his situation to the owner of a stables close to the university who promised to take care of him. She had young riders who could ride him, and that way Shenani would earn his keep, so we ended up giving him to her. At least I knew he was happy when he was around children, and from time to time I would go and see him in the paddock. But all the time at the back of my mind was the knowledge that one day he would have to be put down. The more I thought about it the more I realised that I was completely incapable of putting a horse or any other animal down. It was then that I recognised I could never be a vet, and so I dropped my Equine Science studies.

I was so close to Shenanigans that I gave up riding. Periodically, Mum would try to encourage me to ride again, and she used to discuss it with Dad. One day he said to her: 'You ought to think about it carefully, Mary. Do you really want her to get seriously involved again? It's bloody dangerous, you know. Look what happened to Christopher Reeves.' Dad was very protective of me; his own daredevil side watered down considerably when it came to me. When Mum told me about his reaction I was surprised, because he never expressed that kind of concern about my riding to me.

I always admired his daring. In a way it gave me the extra courage to go one step further and do some things that horrified Daddy, like diving off a thirty-foot cliff in Jamaica and sky diving in the desert in California. But to save him some heartache and myself a long lecture, I told him only after the fact. He would immediately pick up the telephone and blast Mum to kingdom come, first for not telling him and secondly for letting me do it. But I think that deep down inside he was quite chuffed that I have my own daredevil streak, and he definitely enjoyed telling stories about my escapades.

The New Year began with a great universal loss to jazz. One of the originators of the evolution of bebop who woodshedded at Minton's Playhouse, the great John Birks 'Dizzy' Gillespie died on 6 January 1993 at seventy-six years old. A service in celebration of his life was held at the Cathedral Church of St John the Divine on 12 January. Dad had telephoned as soon as he heard the news and talked to Mum several times over the next

MY HERO: PART TWO

few days and made arrangements to come to New York for the service.

My father and mother met and went to the cathedral, which was filled to capacity. The processional led by Wynton Marsalis and Jon Faddis, musical sons of Dizzy's, played the most moving funeral march ever heard, the trumpets themselves sounding as though they were crying. There could not have been a dry eye in the cathedral and vast as the congregation was the only sound to be heard was that of the music. There was a Baha'i tribute for Dizzy who was an active member of the Baha'i faith, which teaches that one day all mankind will be united in peace. Many times during his life Dizzy explained: 'Baha'i teaches that music is a form of worship.'

Dad was deeply touched by the service. Although many people there knew him and greeted him, he slipped away with Mum as quickly as possible, and they found a quiet restaurant where Dad quietly wept. It seemed as though so many friends and mentors were gone and so few were left. Over the years Dad had many discussions with Mum about religions, mysticism and dogma, but he had never found anything that could entice him to believe; he needed scientific proof. But on this evening he talked to her about Dizzy's faith and, as he had done in the past, expressed his wish that he could believe. The interesting thing was that Dad had been exploring Judaism, reading books on the subject, searching for answers, but, as he shared with Mum, once again he was just not able to make a connection.

As a child I had never liked the smoky atmosphere of jazz clubs, but after I left college I found myself drawn back into the world of music and began working in Providence at a club called the Strand. I started out as a bartender and took care of the visiting bands' hospitality. I learned to put up with the smoky atmosphere and found that I loved working with the bands. We had everyone from Bob Dylan to Marilyn Manson, from BB King to Korn. I told the owner of the Strand that I did not want to be a bartender for the rest of my life and asked him for the opportunity to work in the office, saying: 'I'll run all your errands and get your coffee if you'll just show me the ropes and how things work.' He gave me my chance and I started working in the office during the day and began to learn about the business side of things, eventually becoming an assistant booking agent and promotions director.

In the beginning, when I was handling the artists' contracts, Dad was a big help. If there was something that I was not sure about I telephoned him and he would set me straight. At times things went wrong – everybody screws up from time to time – but Dad taught me not to freak out. He used to say: 'OK, Becky, start from the beginning and tell me everything. Now we know what the problem is, what do *you* think the solution is?' If there was a better way of handling the situation then he would tell me.

When I started working with the bands the guys would say to me: 'Your father is Ronnie Scott?' And I would say: 'Yes. How do you know him?' The response was always the same: 'What do you mean, how do I know him? He's a famous jazz musician and a legend in his own time. Of course I know who he is!' Dad would giggle when I told him that I had spoken to someone like Noel Gallagher from Oasis, who had been in the club many times and thought Ronnie was just great. My father would be all chuffed and pleased. The list of admirers went on and on, and they were all knocked out to meet me because I was Ronnie Scott's daughter. I began to really appreciate what he had done with his life and how important it all was. What I really admired about Dad most was the way that all his life he always helped other musicians as much as he could in every way that he could. Actually, it was not just musicians; I have heard his friends say how he changed their lives in this way or that, but always for the better. I think he had a gift of being able to bring the best out in people in a constructive way. Also, he always knew what he wanted to do: play the saxophone and have a club. Although I know he had many periods of self-doubt in his life, somehow he always managed to stick to his goals. Even though he was multi-talented he never lost his sense of direction. He was always a leader and became the very best at what he did.

I also wanted to be independent and make my own mark in the world. While I was working at the Strand I made two new friends, Linda Lorenzo and Michelle Oakes. It all started with a radio show on a college radio station. Michelle and I had our own show called the Michelle and Stoney Show on which we played some new bands. When we heard a band called Kilgore Smudge that had just come out with a CD on Revolution (later on they called themselves just Kilgore), bells went off: this group was really something special and we both knew it.

The three of us were all on the same wavelength. There was a chemistry between us which created an environment for our creative ideas to flourish and grow. I wanted to start up my own production company and asked Linda and Michelle to become my partners. I ran our ideas past Dad, who was very supportive and gave us constructive advice, and in January 1996 Pastie Productions was launched. At the Strand we met Gruvis Malt, a six-piece jazz, rock, funk, hip-hop band. For the next two and a half years Pastie worked as Gruvis' management company and booking agent. During this period Gruvis released a four-song EP and a compilation CD of their first recordings called 'Cromagnetid'. Gruvis Malt and Pastie Productions formed their own record label named Solid Pimpz, LLC, and released 'Sound Soldiers' by Gruvis. Pastie Productions no longer exists, all our energies having been channelled into Solid Pimpz and our separate careers.

A really cool thing happened. The three of us went to California for Foundations, which is a three-day music festival featuring about thirty different bands. Dad happened to be in California at the same time and met the Pastie Productions team in full force. Dad knew some of my favourite artists, like Sting, who used to go to the club; Ronnie had recorded with Phil Collins and years ago on 'Lady Madonna' with the Beatles. A group called the Black Crowes recorded one of their albums at Ronnie Scott's Club, and when they came back to America I ended up going on tour with them for a week, taking care of hospitality. Dad did not really like the Black Crowes; at the time he thought they were a bunch of 'arrogant Americans'. Now they are all older and married with families and are much more mature! But Dad could see that I was rapidly learning all aspects of the business and was behind me one hundred per cent.

This was really common ground between Dad and me, and I met lots of people who knew him, or of him, or of the club, or had actually played in the club and had met Ronnie. They were flabbergasted that they were meeting Ronnie Scott's daughter in the States. Through my job and all the networking we were doing, I started meeting managers and A&R reps and tour managers. Everyone was saying to me: 'You know, Becky, this is your niche. You've got a good mind for it, you really should get involved a little bit more and build up some more experience behind you.' Dad agreed. He recognised that I knew what was the hottest thing that was up and coming and told me that I had a great ear. I would say: 'Well, I got my ear from you.' That would put a smile on his face.

My father was very up to the mark with what was going on when it came to younger generations. He was always able to appreciate the boldness of youth, although he didn't always agree with it, especially when it came to me. I was going through a phase with my hair when I was constantly changing the colour to different shades of blonde or red and putting sun streaks in it. I went to visit Dad in London and he telephoned Mum to let her know I had arrived safely. When she asked him how I was, he replied:

'Your daughter is *very, very* blonde, and she has a silver hoop through her eyebrow!' Dad was expecting me to step off the plane as a bright redhead, but instead he got a lot more than he bargained for. He had yet to discover that I had also pierced my tongue. It took him a day or so to find out and then he said: 'Ugh . . . what did you do *that* for?' I said: 'It's no big deal. You can take it out and it heals within forty-eight hours, so no one is the wiser. It doesn't leave a hole.' Dad asked: 'Why? *What* was the purpose of you doing that?' My response was: 'Just to see if I could do it, if I could actually go through having a needle stuck through my tongue so I could wear a jewellery stud. It's fun to play with. It's like a pacifier, I suppose. When I'm really focused and have to concentrate I used to bite my lip a lot, and this has prevented me from chewing my lip.' It reached the point where he would call me up and say, 'Hello, Rebecca, what colour is your hair today?' or 'What have you pierced this time?'

My father was really good about it with me and didn't give me a hard time. But Mum told me later on that he gave her a *very* hard time about it. Dad rang her up and asked: 'Why do you let her do stuff like that?' I wasn't living with Mum, so of course she didn't know about it until it was done. But Dad never scolded me. He would just ask me from time to time, 'Why, Rebecca, why?' but he never freaked out at me.

In all the years I had been visiting Dad we never went sightseeing. We would drive through a park and he would say, 'This is Hyde Park' or 'That's the Palace . . . right there'. We would walk through Soho Square and on to Oxford Street. He loved to window-shop but rarely bought anything. Dad was a man of simple tastes. He never would have anything extravagant; the only luxury he ever really had was his car. He used to drive a Ferrari Dino, and one night he was pulling into Frith Street when a taxi driver rolled down his window and yelled at him, 'You rich bastard!' and Ronnie stuck his head out of his window and yelled back: 'Well, it's better than being a blue bastard!' But the Ferrari was long gone, and now he was driving a Peugeot 305 GTA. Although not a sports car, it's still very fast.

We were in the club every night, and as we walked in Jimmy Parsons would leap to attention, click his heels and say in guttural German: 'Guten Tag, mein Führer.' Dad would promptly click his heels, assuming a very erect posture, extend his right hand and with an impeccable teutonic accent shout: 'Today Soho, tomorrow the world!' Jimmy responded with: 'Sieg Heil.' All this while customers were milling around the lobby and walking in. It was hysterical. Dad would turn to an unsuspecting customer and say: 'They must be taught who is master, nein?' The repartee was absolutely marvellous; Jimmy and Dad had been doing this for years. Whenever Dad was touring, Jimmy would do the announcing. He also has an excellent sense of timing and is still one of the few people who can make Dad's jokes sound funny. Today, as well as working on the door, Jimmy is master of ceremonies at the club and always shows great deference to Dad when using some of the Guv'nor's material.

Monty and Dad also had an ongoing patter between them, but this time it was in 'African', which really confused the punters, who could not understand a word of what was going on. They would stage an angry exchange right at the door. Ronnie would walk in and Monty would politely say: 'Habari?' (How are you?) Ronnie would look at him with piercing eyes and snap: 'Nende kabisa!' (Piss off!). The exchange would become rapid and their voices raised: 'Omungu lake je je' and 'Jambo' or 'Onjele – ojenge.' Startled customers would give them a wide berth, watching from what they considered to be a safe distance, convinced there was going to be a serious altercation. In the blink of an eye Dad would revert back to being a gracious host: 'Good evening, sir. Can I help you?' The baffled jazz fans finally caught on that it was all an act, but everyone else had been rendered helpless by now, their sides aching from laughing so much.

Dad introduced me to Dani, Jo's youngest daughter. We used to hang out together, and sometimes I would spend the night at her place. I did not see much of Laurie because she was married, but on occasions she and her husband would come to the club. Occasionally, I had dinner with Jo and Daddy, but they did not live together and Daddy did not see her every day. As much as my father smoked, Jo would not allow him to smoke in her house. If he wanted to have a cigarette he had to go out into the garden. He never did stay overnight at her flat, although sometimes she would stay at the Mansions. The arrangement seemed to work very well for them, and things were really good between them. They did things together and laughed a lot.

By the end of 1993 Dad decided to slow things down a bit as far as his group was concerned. Andy Cleyndert had replaced Ron Mathewson on bass in 1992. Martin remembered: 'Ronnie decided to cut the band back to a quartet, but he couldn't really face Dick and Mornington, which was really unusual for Ronnie, so they found out through me. Finally Ronnie did talk to them about it, even though it wasn't easy to let them go, and we became a quartet again.'

On Saturday 1 January 1994 the Ronnie Scott Quartet began the New Year by playing on BBC Radio Three in *A Jazz New Year*. Among the tunes they played was an old favourite of Ronnie's, 'Bye, Bye, Blackbird', followed by 'Dancing in the Dark' and 'I Can Dream, Can't I?'. It was a great session, and afterwards they went for a quick cup of coffee. Martin recalled: 'Ronnie was ordering and he asked: "Waiter, could I have a coffee without cream, please?" The waiter said: "Sorry, sir, we don't have any cream." Ronnie's response was: "In that case I'll have it without milk!" '

Dad telephoned Mum with some sad news: Jimmy Deuchar had died. He had been a marvellous trumpet player and composer and had played many times with Ronnie in various bands, and written many of the arrangements. Ronnie and Jimmy were kindred spirits since before the days of the nine-piece band in the 1950s. They went back a long way, and had shared the marvellous experience of working together in the Clarke–Boland Band. Jimmy was another tragic loss.

Ronnie had arrived home from the club in the early hours of the morning and was unwinding after the night's work when the telephone rang. It was Marge Ellison, calling to let him know that Jeff Ellison, his friend and confidant of many years, had just died. Jeff was almost like a permanent fixture at the club. He had worked on the door for many years and played chess with Ronnie whenever he was in town. Marge remembered: 'Ronnie cried while he was on the telephone with me, and he said, "I'm not crying for Jeff, Marge, because now he must be at peace. I'm crying for myself. I've lost a good friend." They shared the same birthday, and were very close, like brothers.' The next day Dad went to see Marge and the children, Gavril and Anna. Marge recalled: 'He spent the whole day here. People were coming and going. Ronnie talked to all of them. He said to me: "Marge, you must invite people to come to the club and we'll organise a celebration of Jeff's life." Ronnie made it happen.' Marge had seen very little of Ronnie over the years and did not feel that she really knew him, but after Jeff's funeral Ronnie phoned her frequently. As Marge put it: 'He kept tabs on me, Gavril and Anna, to see how I was doing and if we were all right. I really came to know Ronnie. I saw a side of him I didn't know existed. We became good friends. He was very sincere, kind and gentle, with a worldly wiseness that cut across all the drafts.'

Marge was a schoolteacher who was due to retire in March 1995. Colleagues at her school knew of her friendship with Ronnie and telephoned him without Marge knowing to ask him if he could arrange something special for her retirement party. Dad had a previous engagement on that date, otherwise he would have had his band play, but he sent Jeff Clyne and a couple of the guys to play. Marge couldn't believe her eyes when she walked into the auditorium and saw the band on the stage. She said: 'It was so fantastic. I hadn't seen any of them for years and it made the whole occasion a memorable one. They played a full set. We all had a ball and I felt very special that day, thanks to Ronnie.'

There had been trouble in paradise periodically for quite some time: Dad and Jo kept breaking up, she would leave London, saying it was completely over and that she didn't want to see him again, then Dad would get frantic and persuade her to come back. They would declare undying love for each other and it would be back on again and Dad would propose. Even though a wedding date was set there never was a ring, and at the last minute, true to form, Ronnie would back out. He just *could not* get married. This happened a couple of times. He wanted to be with Jo but he didn't want to be married. Dad would phone us and say: 'Jo has gone again. We've broken up.' It reached the point where I used to say: 'You should be used to it by now! This is what the relationship is, Daddy. You two have been doing this for a couple of years!'

I saw the highs and the lows of their relationship first-hand. When everything was going well they were on cloud nine, but they were the opposite ends of the spectrum in so many ways that it caused blow-ups between them. I remember one Christmas when I was staying with Daddy we went over to Jo's for Christmas Day, and the only food she served was plates of tiny little hors d'oeuvres that she had bought. I have no idea what they did together on Christmases when I wasn't around, but that year Dad was hungry, disappointed and furious. They had a huge row, and as Dad and I left his parting words were: 'Jesus *Christ*. It's Christmas Day . . . for God's sake. Can't she cook a proper meal for just *one* fucking day out of the year?'

Mum and I had planned a visit to London that October and stayed with Daddy for about a week. Dad's quartet was playing at the club, and on our last night there I was sitting with a group of friends upfront. It was Daddy's second set, and after the opening number he moved to the side of the bandstand so he was facing me and I was sitting right below him. Dad started playing 'You Don't Know What Love Is'. Mum saw what was going on, that he was playing directly to me, but I was chatting to my friends, so she sent us over a note: 'Shut up and listen!' Mum remembered: Daddy was playing especially for you. I *never* heard such moving music. It was incredible.' Dad went on to play our song, 'Send in the Clowns', followed by 'This Love of Mine', 'Every Time We Say Goodbye' and 'Poor Butterfly'. It was the most moving musical evening of our lives, and we never realised that it was the last time we would ever hear him play.

At the end of the set, when Dad left the bandstand, Mum greeted him with: 'That was unbelievable, Ronnie.' He just looked at her over the top of his glasses and said: 'Good, was it?' Mum told me: 'Although he must have realised it was an incredible understatement, we each knew he had just surpassed himself. What he couldn't say with words he just said with music. It is a night that will remain in my memory and heart for ever.' Mine too.

In November of the same year, in recognition of Ronnie's contribution to jazz he was presented with the award of Fellow of the City of Leeds College of Music. Professor Tony Denton, a great fan of my father's, prepared and then read the citation at the awards ceremony. His opening remarks were: 'It gives me great pleasure to undertake this duty today, having listened to the artistry and eloquence of Ronnie Scott for many years.' Professor Denton had planned on bringing Ronnie to the college to talk to the students and to play in the near future. Sadly, because of Dad's health problems, this plan never came to fruition.

It had been clear for several months that my father had major problems with his teeth and he was in the process of trying to make a decision about which treatment would be right for him. He and Mum talked at length about it. He was deeply disturbed, because his embouchure, which he had nurtured, protected and done facial exercises for since he was fifteen years old, was suddenly in serious jeopardy. Dad had consulted some dentists in London, and they had recommended implant treatment. Dad telephoned and asked Mum what she thought, knowing that Aunt Fran had implants but that only a couple of teeth were involved. Dad's dentist was recommending that *all* his teeth, upper and lower, be done, and that both upper and lower restorations should be completed *together*. This type of dental work is done in stages, the first stage taking from four to six months before they can proceed to the next phase, which takes three to four months. All this would add up to a year of intense discomfort and excruciating pain and not being able to play.

Dad also discussed his dental problems with his good friend George Coleman when he was in New York, explaining the whole procedure and asking him what he thought. George, who was all too familiar with the nightmare at hand, having had the same problems himself, did not like the treatment plan that had been proposed to Ronnie at all. George explained

MY HERO: PART TWO

to Ronnie that his dentist was able to do implants in such a way that he always had special temporaries in his mouth and *never* went through a period when he could not play. They discussed Ronnie's plight in depth and at length. George felt deeply concerned about the treatment that Ronnie was to receive, so much so that he finally persuaded him to telephone George's dentist, Dr Kenneth Judy. For some reason Ronnie did not actually go to see Dr Judy; they only spoke on the phone. Instead, Dad decided to stick with his dentist in London, a decision that turned out to be a bad one. George is left with a deep conviction that Ronnie's ultimate and fatal depression was the product of not being able to play as a result of that bad decision. George said: 'Had he been able to play he would have been able to overcome the other pains and disillusionment that he was plagued with at the time.' *Everyone* who knew and loved my father is in total concurrence with George.

In January 1995 Ronnie proceeded to make the necessary arrangements to begin his dental treatment, and on Friday 24 February the first of the procedures was performed. Little did he know, but things were about to go drastically wrong.

I came home to New York in May 1995 and Dad was coming for his usual visit. He never forgot Pincus, the doorman who used to stand outside the Three Deuces and in later years worked for many other establishments, and he would ask Mum: 'Have you seen Pincus? Is he still around?' In the past we had always managed to find Pincus, and he and Dad would chat, always getting a chuckle out of Dad, but this time we could not find him. Dad and I walked from midtown Manhattan to Washington Square Park where there were thirty or so chess tables and you could watch all kinds of people playing chess, from champions to bums. He would explain the game to me as we watched the players. He loved it and we often spent a couple of hours there. I told him all about Woodstock. The previous summer I had gone with a few friends to the Woodstock revival. Mum had given me a beautiful woollen hand-made shoulder bag with a dove woven on one side and the peace sign on the other. Dad had brought the bag back from Poland for Mum in the 1960s. I told him about the whole adventure, and that Mum had kept the bag for all those years and I actually took it to Woodstock. He was knocked out. He thought it was just the greatest thing.

I have a propensity to miss my flight when travelling, and Dad and Mum were always teasing me about it. Once on my way to Florida I had missed the flight and was stranded at Newark Airport in New Jersey, a story we always dubbed 'the birth of the whoopee cushion'. We were dining in Kaplans reliving the event. When I found I was stranded I called Mum so that she could call Dad and let him know I had to wait five hours for the next flight. I walked around and found a little novelty store where they sold tricks and jokes, and I thought, Ah, a whoopee cushion, great! This should entertain me for a while. So I bought one and also picked up a newspaper to hide it and proceeded to walk around the airport occasionally letting one go! It was hilarious, all the people rushing around in the airport could not tell where the sound was coming from. The expressions on their faces had me in stitches for the duration.

Of course I had it with me the whole time in Florida, and when I told Daddy about the airport he was doubled up with laughter. Wherever we went I took the cushion and the newspaper and every now and then, when he was least expecting it and at the worst moments, I would let it rip and then hide behind the paper, peeking over the top to see the expressions on people's faces. Dad was rendered helpless and laughed until the tears ran down his face. He thought it was just brilliant! After that I always took it with me when I went to visit Dad. On one occasion, when he took me to Heathrow Airport to put me on the plane for New York, Dani, Jo's daughter, was with us, and we found a nice restaurant where we could have something quick to eat. We were all sitting around the table talking; there was a group of very posh English people at a table next to us, and behind us was a young couple who seemed very nice and were also English. Everyone was talking and I pulled out the whoopee cushion! Dad said: 'No, no, no, Rebecca, *please*! *Don't* do it! Don't *do* it!' Dani ran off from the table in the opposite direction, making sure she was a safe distance away but could still see everything that was about to happen! I discreetly blew up the cushion and stuck it under my leg and just let it rip! The lady from the group of upper-crust people next to us was absolutely horrified and let out in a high-octave voice: 'Oh! Oh! My goodness! Whatever was that?' They all started exclaiming about it. I could not see the table behind us because I was hiding my face behind the paper, I was laughing so much. Daddy could see them and they apparently jumped about six feet in the air, by which time Dad was just hysterical, he could not stop laughing. There was a little bit of air left in the cushion, so I waited for everyone to quieten down, the posh table going off, saying, 'Oh, my! It's so revolting, my goodness . . . well, I never . . .', when of a sudden I just let it go again and the cushion went *bruuumpt . . . bup bup bup . . .* Daddy was falling out of his chair, doubled up with laughter. The snobby bunch was just mortified by this second assault, but the couple behind were by now helplessly laughing too!

We just loved fart humour. Dad gave me a book that he and Mum had bought years ago, the story of a Frenchman, Joseph Pujol. His stage name was Le Pétomane. He lived from 1857 to 1945 and performed at the famous Moulin Rouge for great sums of money, drawing gates of 200,000 francs. Le Pétomane had the unique gift of being able to retain vast amounts of air in his intestines and would appear on stage with a long tube protruding from the seat of his pants, through which he would proceed to emit sounds that ranged from a rapidly firing machine gun to musical notes, and he could blow a candle out from the distance of a foot! So hysterically funny were his performances that ambulances waited outside the theatre to cart off ladies who had laughed so hard their stays had caused them to faint. Needless to say, this was our favourite book.

During the engagement of the marvellous Brazilian band, Airto Moreira and Flora Purim, at Ronnie Scott's, Sydney Gotlieb brought two young music students, Dan Wallfische and his girlfriend, to listen to the music. Dan came from a long line of classical musicians. His father is a very well-known cellist and his grandmother, Anita Wallfische, a very well-known violinist who still plays in symphony orchestras today. Anita Wallfische survived the terror of the Nazi concentration camps because of her great artistic talent as a musician. Sydney told my father the story of how she started an orchestra inside the concentration camp. The commandant happened to be an ardent admirer of classical music and frequently had them play concerts for him. Through her ingenuity and musical prowess Anita Wallfische managed to save the lives of many musicians. The story brought tears to my father's eyes.

After Airto finished his set Sydney brought Dan and his girlfriend into the inner sanctum to meet Ronnie. Drinks were offered. Dan thanked Ronnie and asked for two beers. Ronnie replied: 'Wouldn't you like a real drink? Like a brandy or something?' They gladly accepted – a student's allowance doesn't permit such luxuries. Within minutes the young students and Ronnie were deeply engrossed in a discussion about music. Dan had asked Ronnie about improvisation. No longer able to play, Ronnie started humming a straight version of 'Blue Skies', turned to Dan and said: 'Now, what would you do with that?' Then he hummed short phrases. Dan understood immediately what Ronnie was teaching him, and they spent at least two hours together, Ronnie sharing his wealth of musical expertise with the young couple. About a week later Sydney received a letter from Dan thanking him for such a wonderful evening, expressing how marvellous it had been to sit in the office with Ronnie sipping brandy and discussing music for a couple of hours. He said it was an evening he would cherish for the rest of his life.

I could see that Dad was trying very hard to be optimistic about his teeth, but the fact that he could not play was getting him down. I started talking to him about Australia, and I tried to get him to consider again the semi-retirement he had thought of in 1991. George Coleman told me that during some of their many conversations, Ronnie shared with him how much he really liked Australia and how he would have liked to spend more time there. But although Dad talked about it and considered the idea he never followed it through: it was one of those things that slipped away from him.

One day in the summer Dad telephoned and told Mum that Jill was renting a luxury trailer in the beautiful, peaceful Wye Valley. He was feeling a little down and thought a change might help him to feel better. My mother agreed that it sounded a great idea. Dad made the arrangements with Jill and went for a week's holiday. Jill's magnificent trailer was huge; they called it 'the penthouse'. Jill remembered: 'Ronnie drove down from London, and when he arrived he got out of the car and looking across the valley said: "It looks like *The Archers*!" ' They had a good time, and on the last night after dinner they were sitting reminiscing when Jill pulled out a huge box of photographs. She recalled: 'There were lots in there from our holidays together in Florida and New York, Becky. Your dad really enjoyed seeing them again.' Ronnie had decided to drive back to London after midnight so that he could avoid the traffic.

My father, who had always done broadcasts, was doing many more now. He also did seminars, judged contests and, of course, there was the nightly routine at the club. But his life at this time was reminiscent of the two other occasions when he hadn't been able to play: back in the 1960s when he was struck with Bell's palsy, and again in the 1970s, when he broke his little finger. Now, as then, nothing could take the place of playing. It was his support, and Dad was worried about whether he would ever be able to play again, a concern that was always with him.

Much as he hated the idea of becoming seventy, one of the rewards his senior years won him was reduced airfares in America. He loved this and made the most of it. I was due to meet him in Florida on one occasion, but he telephoned Mum to say that as there was a hurricane on its way he was going to fly to Las Vegas for a few days until it was all over. The mecca of gambling did little to excite my father; the thing that impressed him most was a hotel built entirely out of black glass in the shape of a gigantic pyramid. As far as Vegas was concerned, he said: 'I suppose everybody should see it once, but that's enough.'

When Dad got back to London, sometimes he would hang out with Critch and Martin in the back office. They played at the club as a trio now, and occasionally they would make it a quartet with Mornington Lockett. Martin remembered: 'Ronnie was not a tactile person, but on occasions, when he wanted to pay a compliment, he would put his hand on my arm and say: "That was great, Martin." It meant the world to me because he was genuine and didn't give praise lightly.' John Dankworth concurred. On occasions when he was working opposite Ronnie or playing with him, John recalled: 'It couldn't have happened on more than three occasions when he came up to me and said, "That was beautiful, John" or "Great playing". If he ever said anything like that it was the greatest prize I could ever have in the world. He was very sparing when it came to that, but when he said it you knew he meant it. It was the highest praise you could get. That's what I loved about him, and I know that a lot of other musicians feel the same way.'

CHAPTER FIFTEEN

SAND THROUGH THE HOURGLASS

Life does not cease to be funny when people die any more than it ceases to be serious when people laugh.　　　GEORGE BERNARD SHAW

The doors of Heaven and Hell are adjacent and identical.　　　NIKOS KAZANTZAKIS

I T WAS JANUARY 1996 and my mother and I were looking forward to Daddy coming to New York. Dad, who usually came to visit us in the springtime, had been asked by the BBC to take part in a series called *Sentimental Journeys*. Dad's sentimental journey was to revisit legendary 52nd Street between 5th and 6th Avenues and reminisce with Arthur Smith about clubs such as the Three Deuces, the Famous Door and Jimmy Ryan's, telling stories about his innumerable visits to the jazz mecca of New York. He stayed at the Edison Hotel on 45th Street, which was a favourite of his, and we were there to meet him in the lobby when he arrived. He was in good spirits even though his thrombosis was giving him a bit of trouble at the time. He was, as he put it, 'starvaration', and we immediately went into the hotel restaurant, which was another favourite haunt of his. Dad pulled out his schedule so we could make plans to be together when he wasn't working with the BBC crew. It was quite a severe workload and all of it outdoors. The weather was brutal and bitingly cold. My mother expressed concern because he had no hat, suggesting that we should get one before the crew arrived, and he said he would pick one up on his way to 52nd Street.

It was time to go. The BBC crew had arrived and wanted to get a head start on their project. It turned out that they were going to take Ronnie on the Staten Island Ferry as part of the journey. My mother and I exchanged glances. Dad wasn't that well, and it couldn't have been any colder in Siberia than it was that day, especially on a boat. We did persuade him to at least go back upstairs for his scarf, and when he came back down the producer of the show, a young lady, extracted a Russian fur hat from one of her many containers and handed it to Dad, saying: 'This might help!' We were very grateful. Dad took the hat and with a huge grin on his face unbuttoned the ear flaps and pulled it down until it rested on his eyebrows, proceeding to indulge us all with his favourite sport of gurning. Dad was irrepressible, his body language fitting the insane facial expressions, his eyes darting this way and that, making an occasional unintelligible utterance in a strangled voice, until we were in hysterics. There was a coachload of people milling about the lobby waiting to be checked in, and they didn't know whether to laugh or look the other way. He put on such a pantomime that must have lasted for a minimum of ten minutes. Dad and the crew left for the journey and we agreed to meet him for dinner after it was all over.

I wanted to go to Planet Hollywood for dinner, but my father declared: 'I'm not standing in any bloody lines, you know!' Mum knew of a famous Jewish restaurant called Wolf's that was very close to Planet Hollywood, and it was agreed that if there were lines then we would go to Wolf's. We all jumped in a cab and found that, much to my chagrin, cold or not there was a very long line outside Planet Hollywood, so we walked the few blocks to Wolf's (which has since closed). My father wasn't too happy because by now he was tired and his legs had begun to bother him, so we were anxious to get inside a nice warm atmosphere and enjoy some hot food. Mum had not been to Wolf's for a couple of years and had no idea that the management had changed. Big mistake, we all ordered chicken, and when it arrived it was cold, greasy and pasty-white and just generally unappetising. My mother was furious. Knowing that Dad wasn't feeling very well, she called the waitress over and when Mum complained the waitress said: 'This is how we serve it. It's this or nothing.' Livid, my mother said: 'Who the hell have you got in the kitchen, or maybe I should ask *what* have you got in the kitchen?' She got up from the table and said: 'We're leaving.' Apologising like mad to my father, she went out to hail a cab so that when we came out we could step straight into it without hanging about in the cold. As soon as the three of us, with Dad in the middle, were in the cab, the cabby said: 'Where to?' My mother and I started to name a street but my father said: 'Don't listen to *either* of them. They've *no idea* what they're doing. From now on I'm in charge!' And he proceeded to give the cab driver directions. Turning to us, he said: 'That's it. From now on when I come to New York *I* choose the restaurants. Do you both understand?' Good humour prevailed, and once again we were soon all laughing.

Dad's last night in New York on that trip was a Monday, and he planned to take the BBC crew and my mother and me to the Village Vanguard. Monday night is big band night and the Thad Jones–Mel Lewis Big Band was playing. This was another tradition of my father's: he always went to hear the band if he happened to be in New York on a Monday night. He was on good form all evening, keeping everybody laughing with his stories and graciously playing host in that special unassuming way of his. The next day we went with Dad to the airport to see him off, none of us quite sure when he would be back because of his thrombosis. Dad knew that he had to have an operation on his legs within the next few weeks and thought he would come back once he had recovered.

I went back to Rhode Island for just a couple of weeks. I had spent Christmas 1995 with Mum and had arranged with Dad to spend his birthday with him in London on 28 January. I actually arrived in London several days before so that I could spend some extra time with Dad. When I got there he was somewhat downhearted, and we used to sit up and talk into the early hours of the morning. He told me that things were again not working out with Jo and that she didn't want to see him any more, that she had cancelled coming to his birthday dinner, so I decided that I would try to do something extra special to cheer him up. I phoned Mum in New York and told her what was going on and that I wanted to do something that Daddy would really enjoy. I asked her for Spike Milligan's number, explaining that I wanted to try to get them together. Mum thought it was a fantastic idea, guaranteed to succeed in cheering Daddy up.

It was Dad's sixty-ninth birthday, which turned out to be his last. I knew that Spike was one of Dad's best friends and remembered that he had told me that he had not seen Spike in quite some time. I was a little nervous about phoning Spike, because although Dad and Mum talked about him a lot I had never actually met him, and I am very shy when it comes to meeting new people. When I got up the courage to call I actually spoke to Shelagh, Spike's wife, who was very warm and welcoming. I explained my plan, letting her know that the birthday dinner was to be held at Little Italy, which is opposite the club and was one of Dad's favourite restaurants. He loved the food there and was great friends with the proprietors. I thought it would be the best birthday present ever, and it would make him feel better to be with an old friend.

Dad had all of Spike's books. Mum had Spike sign *Small Dreams of a Scorpion* for me the year I was born. She often told me about the Goons. Mum and Dad were avid fans, and to this day when something Mum has been working on comes out right she yells: 'Ying tong.' My friends love it; she says it's a sound of glee and has people in stitches when she sings it all the way through. Dad couldn't talk about Spike without chuckling, always remembering one or other of his jokes. I never really understood how famous he was, just as I never really saw Dad as being famous, I suppose. Peter Sellers was very well known in America, so when Dad told me he was a part of the Goons too I began to realise what was going on. The guests were Spike and Shelagh, Dani (Jo's daughter) and her boyfriend Ivan, a young saxophonist who admired my dad.

Daddy, myself, Dani and Ivan arrived at the restaurant. Daddy had no idea what was going on. I had asked Shelagh and Spike to arrive a little late, and Shelagh was happy to arrange that. They had hired a car to bring them into London from Rye. We had a set menu, and the guys at the restaurant were great in helping me to make the selections. It was an evening I will never forget. Our table was upstairs, which was perfect because it was more private, and the waiters were really excited that Spike was going to be there too. Ivan's mother had made a really delicious chocolate cake that was in the shape of a saxophone. My chair was positioned so that I could see people coming up the stairs. Dad couldn't see from his seat. Although I had never seen Spike or Shelagh before, I knew it was them the moment they came up the stairs. I looked over at Dad, and the expression on his face when he saw Spike approaching the table was one of total disbelief and surprise breaking into sheer joy! He started to cry a little when he realised he was going to spend his birthday with his old friend whom he had not seen for a couple of years (although they had spoken to each other on the phone many times). Daddy and Spike just talked all night, they reminisced and shared jokes, they had a marvellous time and laughed a lot; the evening was everything I had hoped it would be for my father. The menu was signed by everyone there, and I had it framed for Daddy (we still have it). My father was elated with the way I had managed to pull the evening together. He telephoned Mum, saying: 'You'll never believe what our daughter did for me last night . . .!' In fact he told everybody about it. I owe Spike for life for that night, because it made a very special memory for Dad, and now for me too.

Daddy and Spike had traded jokes for years. Whenever Mum and I were in London together, Daddy would phone Spike to tell him we were in town, and within seconds Dad would be collapsing with laughter because Spike was doing a nutty speech for him. Then Dad would hand the phone to Mum and she would be rendered helpless too. Spike's spontaneous humour is incredible, the improvisation . . . there is definitely a connection between it all and music. He is a musician too. He could have been a professional if he had wanted to. When Mum and I went to visit Spike and Shelagh after Dad died, Spike put on a tape of himself playing the trumpet. I was knocked out; it was really great. My father truly loved Spike. They had a special friendship, and, just by being able to listen to him talk about Dad, in a way I was able to see how if Daddy had chosen to he could have been a professional comedian, something I never really thought about before. It's funny when I think about it, because it's almost as if Spike and Daddy were the two sides of a coin, Dad choosing to be the musician and Spike choosing to be the comedian – and each of them could have been either one.

For some reason that I could never understand, my father got it into his head that his relationship with Jo was his last chance. He was very conscious of his impending seventieth birthday and believed that no one else would want to be with him. Why he suffered from this delusion I will never know. He never looked his age. He was always handsome, charming and funny, and I'm sure that plenty of women would have loved to have been with him. Dad had a brilliant mind – he could converse on any subject; his interests were very diverse – he was very generous, and although he did not tolerate fools gladly he was extremely kind, and people never got bored with him. But he could not see himself any more. He was going through a very bad time. Even then depression was slowly taking him over. He tried very hard not to let me see it, but there were times when there was a deep, deep sadness about him.

One day in spring Mum rang me up, saying: 'Daddy's been trying to reach you. He and Jo have broken up again. She has gone to Boston.' Mum told me that he had made an appointment to get his legs operated on but was postponing the procedure because he wanted to come to New York; he wanted to see Jo. I spoke to Dad on the phone and he said he wanted me to come to New York, but it was a bad time for me. The Strand had big shows coming in and I could not get any time off. So Mum went to meet him when he arrived, and he was quite unhappy because things had gone from bad to worse between him and Jo, and she was going through a period when she refused to talk to my father. My mother said: 'Now you're here, give her time and she'll talk to you.' Sure enough, after a couple of days Jo agreed to come to New York. She had some friends she wanted to see too, but she agreed to meet my father. It was obvious when Dad walked that he was in pain, and my mother was quite concerned and urged him not to delay surgery for much longer; he agreed to go back to London after he had seen Jo. Although they spent time together the relationship was still on the rocks. Jo was making plans to move to California and had returned to her friends in Boston. Dad did not know when he would see her again. However, he kept his promise and was booked on a flight to England the next day. I spoke to him late that morning, and he told me that he was going to have lunch with Mum and then she would see him off at the airport.

My parents talked at length. Although Dad was going in for surgery on his legs, his main concern was his teeth. He had battled valiantly with the slow and painful process of having implants. The problem at the time was that his upper jawbone was too weak to hold the teeth, and they were a little loose. He said: 'The top ones are loose and when I play I bite *hard* on the top of the mouthpiece.' Mum said: 'There must be *something* that can be done to correct it, Ronnie.' Dad explained that the dentist was trying to work something out but that it did not sound too hopeful. He was afraid that even if it could be fixed, it wouldn't be satisfactory. As he said: 'You see, Mary, the problem for me is that it's not as simple as can I *play* again. It's much deeper than that. If I can't play the way I *want* to play, with the *sound* that I want, then it's all over for me. I couldn't *stand* it if I couldn't play up to my standards.'

All his life, each time my father got up on the bandstand he tried to play better than he had ever done before. His was a constant, relentless search for the 'perfect' reed, the 'perfect' mouthpiece, the 'magic' horn, the facial exercise to maintain his embouchure so that he could achieve the elusive sound he spent his life looking for — even though there were times when he *was* pleased with his playing. These occasions were rare. Ronnie and Dizzy discussed this very thing on more than one occasion, and when Ronnie asked Dizzy how many times he thought a musician could reach his pinnacle Dizzy's response was: 'Maybe half a dozen times in your *life* if you're lucky.' During one of Ronnie's many discussions with Robert Graves, they were talking about the same kind of thing and Dad said: 'Robert came out with this Spanish word *duende*. It's like the spirit of inspiration that just touches you for a moment.' It's hard to understand the incredibly high standards that these guys set for themselves. Their music is who they were. As Charlie Parker said: 'Music is your own experience, your thoughts, your wisdom. If you don't live it, it won't come out of your horn.'

My mother came home from the airport that day deeply troubled. She feared for my father; his whole existence was being threatened. Dad was being very stoic about the impending operation on his legs, and at this point he even seemed to be handling the situation with Jo in a kind of philosophical way. But the fears that Dad had voiced about his dental problems filled my mother with an inescapable feeling of foreboding.

On 13 March 1996 the news media on both sides of the Atlantic were filled with the dreadful tragedy that happened at Dunblane Primary School in Scotland. Sixteen children and one teacher had been shot and killed by a madman with a gun. My father was so distressed by this appalling act of violence against little children that he was beside himself. Dad telephoned Mum and then me. He was in tears on the telephone, deeply disturbed by the heinous act. Sydney Gotlieb clearly remembers the incident and Dad's telephone call to him. Dad used to phone him up and say, 'Can I speak to the saint, please?' knowing that Sydney had answered the phone. But on this occasion Dad's distress was such that they had quite a lengthy discussion, and it took some time before my father, with Sydney's help, found a way of living with the horror of it all.

Dad went to the hospital in Lisson Grove in May. Marge Ellison went to see him, taking her daughter with her. Seeing his old friend Jeff's daughter must have made him think of me, because Marge told me: 'Your dad talked about you the whole time we were there. He said: "Let me tell you what Becky did for me." And he proceeded to tell us all about his sixty-ninth birthday and how you had arranged for Spike Milligan to be there. He gave us all the details, saying it was the best birthday he had ever had. I couldn't help thinking, wow, this is one proud Dad!'

Uncle Pete, who was in Washington with Stella, did not know that Dad was in hospital. It was their wedding anniversary and they were planning to come on to New York. Bonnie – Ronnie's and Pete's assistant – telephoned him to let him know. Uncle Pete immediately phoned Lisson Grove. The lady who answered said: 'Oh, just a moment. I'll try to find Mr Scott for you.' They couldn't find him! Eventually they found him in the kitchen having a cup of tea. Uncle Pete spoke to him and Dad, who was over-discreet about any illness he had, kind of laughed it off, saying: 'Oh, yeah. You know me, Pete, I'll be all right.' And Uncle Pete said: 'In fact he *was* all right, and he saw to the important business bits while I was away. All was in order when I returned.'

After Dad came home from the hospital, one of the incisions on his leg was not healing properly. Dad phoned Mum and asked her what she thought he should do. Terrified of infection setting in, she urged him to go back to the doctor in case he needed antibiotics. Dad struggled with the problem, and eventually of course it all healed, but it was a tiresome, uncomfortable process. Everything that was happening to him fed his depression. He was filled with anxiety about more than one situation. The medication that he was taking was not having the effect that he wanted, he began to drink more and more, hoping the alcohol would act as an anaesthetic, his tumultuous thoughts robbing him of sleep. The dentist gave him barbiturates to help him sleep, but the combinations of everything only exacerbated his distress. Dad could not play. He had tried practising but was unhappy with what he heard, which added to his already escalating state of depression. Jo was now involved with another man on the West Coast and forbade Ronnie to phone her, which of course made him want to phone her all the more. He sent her flowers; she returned them. Dani was always there, at his beck and call, happy to talk about her mother as long as she was alone with my father, although if anyone else were present she refused to talk about Jo. The frustrations, fears, the mental anguish festered inside him with no outlet; he was in agony. Had Dad been able to play, a lot of the steam would have been released, but robbed of his saxophone there was no release. It was like a whirlwind, spinning him around and around, sucking him down in the spiral. Nothing helped.

I had *never* seen my father drink anything but an occasional beer, but now life became a nightmare on both sides of the Atlantic. Dad would telephone me at work, drunk and upset. My boss at the Strand was great. He understood that Dad was ill and never once did he or the rest of the staff give me any grief about taking his phone calls, sometimes as many as five or six in a night. Dad had never done this before. He would just cry as though his whole insides were crumbling. But the next day he had no recollection of who he had called or what he had said. I phoned my mother, and for the first time she explained my father's illness to me and how it affected him. Together we tried to handle it, to calm him down. I am very grateful that my father never exposed me to his illness as a little girl, insisting that my mother protect me from it. I think it would have really screwed me up. At least now I was an adult with some of life's experiences under my belt, as difficult as it was, I was learning how to cope. The most shattering part of it all for me was that this man, who was a legend in his own time, who in my mind I had put on a pedestal, who never seemed to let anything faze him, who had *always* been my rock when I felt like my world was coming apart, came crashing down into my lap and suddenly, desperately, needed my help. The worst part was that he would tell me he felt so worthless, so useless, so lost, and so dreadfully alone.

In London Uncle Pete had worked out a system, which Dad contributed to because he used to do the same thing every day. He'd have his phone turned off to get some sleep, because he never went to bed until very late. As soon as he got up, he'd have a shower and then he would phone the office somewhere between one and two in the afternoon. If he didn't phone, Uncle Pete got worried. It reached the point that if Dad did not call, Uncle Pete told everybody: 'When Ronnie phones, or when he gets here, let me know. I want to talk to him.' Then it got to a stage where if the phone was engaged for very long, Uncle Pete remembered: 'Ronnie used to get into these enormously long phone calls with whomever: Mary, Jill or Jo. Then after a certain time the red light would go up and I used to jump into a cab and go over there.' It reached the point where Uncle Pete told Dad: 'Look, Ronnie, I've taken the liberty of making a copy of your door keys so that I can get into your flat at any time. I didn't like to, but it was a necessity.' On more than one occasion Uncle Pete got there in the nick of time and rushed Dad to hospital. Uncle Pete said that when he went to pick Dad up from the hospital, the way he bounced back was incredible: it was as though nothing had happened. They walked back to Dad's flat, and Uncle Pete said: 'Have you got your keys?' Ronnie replied: 'Use your own fucking key!' Together, they went up to the flat and Ronnie made them both a cup of tea. Pete left for the club while Ronnie showered and changed, and Uncle Pete said: 'He was really an amazing man. When Ronnie walked into the club you would never imagine in a million years that he had just come out of hospital.'

The guys at the club affectionately called Ronnie 'Mission Impossible' in true Scott humour. For a man who had been practically teetotal all his life, and who hated seeing people get drunk, who could never understand why anyone would want to render themselves useless, the dichotomy of his present behaviour was very difficult to comprehend for most people, impossible for others.

The fact of it was that it came with the territory. On the previous two occasions when the reactive depression had taken hold of Ronnie's life, exactly the same behaviour pattern manifested itself. Like anyone else in pain, a person who suffers from depression seeks relief. When the medication does not bring the longed-for reprieve, it's a well-documented fact that depressed people frequently turn to alcohol and cocaine in a desperate search for immediate relief from their agony. The dreadful irony is that the 'effect of relief' from each substance is a complete delusion. They both actually exacerbate the condition, and then each day is worse than the one before. The women in Dad's life became his obsession. In the past, after he had recovered, when he looked back Dad shook his head in disbelief at the way he had pursued the women in question. Remembering little or nothing of the chaos that always ensued during one of these periods, Dad was filled with incredulity at himself when people told him what had happened after the fact. Out of desperation, Ronnie always begged the women who were caught up in this frenzy to marry him, promising them anything their hearts desired, spending small fortunes on them, travelling halfway around the world in pursuit of them, even if he had to borrow the money or go into debt to do so. I do know that it is well documented in publications pertaining to depression that obsession is part of it: with some people it's money, with others it's objects, or cars; the list goes on ad infinitum. When you are close to the person and live through the depressive phases that vary tremendously in their level of intensity, tending to increase and last for longer periods of time as the depression takes hold, at times one becomes almost inured to the disease. Grey areas develop and it becomes impossible to distinguish between the real person and the effect of the depression.

The only things different this time, as Dad repeatedly told my mother, was that he was older and that he could no longer play his saxophone. He said to her: 'You know me, Mary. I'm not a drunkard. This is not me. I'm out of control, and I don't like what I'm becoming.' My mother always marvelled at my father's amazing ability, even when really ill, to step outside himself and discuss his illness with an unbelievable level of rational objectivity. During one of these discussions he asked her what it took for him to recover from one of these periods of depression. My Mother replied: 'Ronnie, you've done it before, and you can do it again. It takes treatment.' He persisted: 'Yes . . . and what else. Come on, Mary, what else?' Mum responded: 'Ronnie, we both know, it takes time.' The reply came: 'Ah! But that's just it, you see! How *much* time, Mary? That's just the point. I'm going to be seventy in January, for Christ's sake. How much time can I possibly have left that would be worth living, assuming that I can get through this?' My mother's response to that was: 'Look at George Burns.

What an active life he had. The man lived to be a hundred!' And so the dialogue would go on.

Although normally a very private man, my father, who always under-stated any physical problem that he had to cope with, during his bouts of depression went through periods when he spoke to the people around him. The ever-increasing severity of my father's dental problems were discussed with a variety of friends; occasionally the thrombosis was referred to. Things that became troublesome fixations – the break-up of his relation-ship and his deep-seated belief that there was no hope of a new one, and turning seventy – fell into this category. We all knew he had a dread of old age. People who knew him could not understand why, because Ronnie was a timeless kind of person. When in his company you were oblivious of his age; he was for ever young, mentally not an old man.

Back in Rhode Island, myself and two friends had started our little company, Pastie Productions. We had landed our first big job in May, which was to coordinate a special event for WBCN River Rave which was being held at Great Woods, Massachusetts, in June. Great Woods is a massive outdoor venue catering for 20,000 people with the facilities to present ten or fifteen bands at the same time. It's an all-day affair, space is rented out to vendors and caterers, and it takes a massive amount of work to put it all together and to keep everything running smoothly on the day itself. My mother and her partner had recently purchased a catering truck so they could expand their business to on-location catering and agreed to be one of our vendors.

We were very worried about my father at the time, and it had reached the point where every time the phone rang we were filled with dread that the call would be from Uncle Pete with bad news. The day before River Rave, my mother had the catering truck all packed up and ready to go, and she was just about to walk out of the house when the phone rang. It was Dad. He was very down. When he felt like this Mum knew that the con-versation could take an hour or more. What to do? She was on a tight schedule. She explained to Dad about River Rave, but he had forgotten everything that I had told him, and she arranged to call him when she got to Rhode Island. We both phoned him, several times, but each time the phone was busy and we never reached him. Very early the next morning, as we were leaving for River Rave, the phone rang and it was Uncle Pete. Daddy had been taken to hospital and was in intensive care and was very, very ill. What a dilemma. Both my mother and I were in a position where we could not just drop everything and run; we *had* to take care of our business. Mum immediately made flight reservations for me to fly out of Boston the next day. She had to go back to New York and fulfil a commitment she had there before leaving herself, so we agreed that we would meet in London a couple of days later. By the time I got to London, Daddy's physical condition had improved dramatically, and the doctors at the hospital had insisted that he be transferred to the Priory, a psychiatric treatment facility in Roehampton, London.

Back in New York, as Mum was packing for her trip to London the phone rang. It was Daddy: 'Mary, how soon can you get here?' Mum responded that she was flying out that day and would be there the next day. 'Good. Well, get here as *fast* as you can, would you. I *have* to get out of this place, and you're the only one who can help me do it.' From door to door, my mother had about thirteen hours of travel ahead of her, time enough to ponder what was the best way to handle this. She had already spoken to the doctors at the Priory, and Uncle Pete, of course, and all of us were of the same opinion: that Dad needed some time in the Priory. It was also a brief respite for all of us. We could go to sleep at night knowing that he was going to be there in the morning.

Joe Green, one of Dad's oldest friends, ran a small cab company, and Uncle Pete made arrangements for his son Cain to drive us back and forth to the Priory. Cain was at the airport to meet my mother and drove her straight to the Priory. It was a bright, sunny June day, and as the car turned the corner into the long driveway, it looked nothing like a hospital but more like a huge sprawling white-painted mansion, surrounded by magnificent grounds, gigantic hydrangeas laden with heavy blooms, roses scrambling up the walls, well-kept lawns with some of the patients stretched out sunbathing. Dad's room was on the ground floor with roses right outside his window, a single room with a separate bathroom, the floor covered in plush carpet, a single bed with bedside table and lamp, a wardrobe, a small desk and a couple of chairs, and of course a television.

All his life Dad had appreciated the beauty of nature, and was a sun-worshipper, so my mother tried to interest him in his surroundings, suggesting that he could get a marvellous tan during his stay. But Dad was beyond appeasement. I tried to engage him in conversation about music, and the fact that I had been presented with an opportunity to be a part of a catering company that a band called 311 was trying to work into their touring budget. They were booked to do a long tour the following September. I saw it as an opportunity for me to make some good contacts and strike up business relationships for Pastie Productions, not to mention the fact that I loved 311. All the guys in the band are very positive people. Their music was still quite new then, a unique combination of a trip, hip-hop, groovy, funk and jazz, a bit of everything; they were very popular in the States. The drummer Chad is amazing, and Dad always said that as far as he was concerned the most important person in a band is the drummer. I tried to get Dad interested like he used to be when we were on holiday together and we would talk for hours about music. Everything was to no avail. He was obsessed with setting up meetings with the doctors and Mum and me so that he could get out of the Priory and go to see Jo in California.

The relationship with Jo was officially over. Jo had met up with an old friend in California and they had become lovers. She had made it clear to all of us via letters and telephone calls that this man was the new love of her life, surpassing any relationship she had ever had before. She had at long last found the 'right' man; she was very happy.

Everyone in London who was directly involved with Dad at this time unanimously agreed that if it could be arranged Dad would be better off in the Priory, at least until his new medication had a chance to take effect, hopefully relieving him of the need to drink copious amounts of alcohol. Since Jo was immersed in a new relationship, what possible benefit could there be in his going to California?

One of the things that my mother and Uncle Pete clearly remembered about Dad's major breakdown in 1974 was the fact that the doctors were adamant that he would not recover if he returned to the same environment that he had been living in. So while he was in the nursing home they had completely refurbished his apartment. Mum checked with his doctors at the Priory, and they agreed that to do the same thing this time would certainly be to Dad's benefit. Uncle Pete made sure she had all the help she needed, and my mother set about redoing Dad's whole apartment. It was freshly painted, newly carpeted throughout, and some new furniture was bought, staying within the framework of Dad's preference. I stayed with Danni while all this was going on, because it was impossible for both Mum and me to sleep at the flat. Right in the middle of it all Jo starts phoning. It turned out that the man she had met in California was not the right man after all. It was over, and she wanted to talk to Daddy.

The doctors allowed Dad to come out on weekends as long as my mother and I took responsibility for him. They did not want him to drink. Cain picked us all up in his car. It was Father's Day, and we told Daddy that the day was his and that we would do whatever he wanted. He looked over the top of his glasses at us sitting in the back of the car and said: 'What I would *really* like to do is go home, watch all the games, maybe a couple of races, on TV and have a nice home-cooked dinner!' So that was it. He asked for lamb stew, and while my mother was in the kitchen fixing it he ran out and put on a couple of bets. Dad was very relaxed, cracking jokes; he was like his old self again. When it came time to go back to the Priory, Dad looked at his watch and said: 'Come on, it's time to go. I mustn't be late back.' He really was getting better. We rode back with him. Things seemed to be working out.

On one of Dad's days out we went to the club and Jo called while Dad was there. They talked, and that was it: he was going to go to California just as soon as he could get himself discharged from the Priory, which happened a couple of days later. I explained that I had to return to America myself and was booked on a flight that was leaving in three days' time, so instead of flying straight off to California he waited and left the same day as me. Dad was so thrilled with his new bedroom, bathroom and freshly painted living room, which was still in progress, that he asked Mum to stay and finish the flat for him. My mother did not think that this was a good idea, stating that if he and Jo did get married, then surely Jo would prefer to do the flat herself. However, Dad persuaded her to stay, so Mum finished off the basics, leaving the details for my father to finish when he came home.

Dad was in California, in Santa Barbara. Uncle Pete was handling all the business at the club, and Mum and I were back in America. We spoke to Daddy quite often on the phone. He had rented a practice room so that he could practise his saxophone in private to try to get his embouchure in shape. He said it was slowly improving and things might be all right. He was feeling better, swimming a lot and sunbathing. By the middle of August Daddy came back to London. He telephoned me from the club and said; 'Rebecca, guess what?', and I said, 'What, Daddy?' He said, 'Jo and I are getting married!', and I said, 'Really. When is this going to happen?' They had set a date at least twice before, Daddy never able to make that final commitment, then all the trouble would start and they ended up being hateful to each other. When he was down, which he often was over that past couple of years, Jo could not handle his illness at all — not many people could. Dad was a different person when he was ill. He became very possessive, had an extremely short fuse and could be very irritable, intensely sensitive, easily crushed, but would lash out in retaliation to a remark that displeased him, and bitter exchanges were often the outcome. He hated himself when he lashed out, and was often instantly filled with remorse and quick to apologise once the storm had passed. But it was not always so easy for the recipient to be as forgiving. During these phases he felt that the whole world was against him and completely lost sight of those who loved him, often feeling as though he had been abandoned by everyone. Dad would call my mother and say: 'You haven't abandoned me, too, have you, Mary?' After she had reassured him he would say: 'No, no, of course not. I never really believed you would.'

Daddy and Jo couldn't be with each other for any length of time. Give them six weeks and they were at each other's throats. Due to Jo's dislike of my father's smoking, he bought fake cigarettes that he used to hold when he was with her, but he would excuse himself and go outside, or wherever, and sneak a real cigarette, swearing musicians to secrecy so Jo would not find out. It was just as he told us when he eventually returned from California: 'There is not going to be a wedding. We have both agreed that we are incompatible.'

Before my father came back to London, he helped Jo to find a new apartment in Los Angeles, helped her to furnish it and made sure that she was settled in properly. Dad always tried to do the right thing. My business partner Michelle and I were in Los Angeles on business while the move was in progress. We were there for only three or four days. I had phoned Dad to let him know I was coming so that we could spend some time together. When we arrived it was to discover that Jo had arranged to do shopping for her new apartment on the days we were in Los Angeles and she needed Dad with her, so the only time I saw him was for dinner one night.

Shortly after Dad arrived back in London, when he was practising he noticed that his front teeth were beginning to come loose again. After eighteen months of hell with his mouth and now this, it was intolerable, devastating. Dad phoned Mum and told her that the problem was serious and there was not much that could be done. He said that when he played he was afraid the pressure would eventually push them out, and he could not stand the sound he was getting from the saxophone. This time he sank into a deep depression. Uncle Pete and everybody at the club were constantly worried about Ronnie. Now, when Uncle Pete arrived, his first question was always the same: 'Has Ronnie rung in yet?' This was something Dad had done all through the years: once he was awake he would call the club to check on the mail or to see if any important calls had come in.

Things went from bad to worse. His drinking escalated again, the phone calls started once more, my mother and I were constantly checking with him and each other and Uncle Pete to see if he was OK. By the time December came around I followed through on plans to go to London to spend Christmas with Dad, one time he could not be alone. As had happened many times in the past when Dad called her, Jo refused to speak to him on the phone, telling him not to call her any more, and that she wouldn't call him. She tried to make a clean break. Uncle Pete and everybody at the club were so glad to see me, saying: 'It's great that you came over, Becky. Your dad's going to be all right now that you're here.' Dad had even bought a side of smoked salmon for us for Christmas. Wendy, the chef, was keeping it in the kitchen downstairs until it was time for us to take it home. My father had really tried. Knowing how much I hated the cold, he had bought new heaters for my room. He had bought some new bits and pieces for the flat, too, and had made arrangements to have a carpenter come in to build some new shelves to hold his books and records. He wanted to change a couple of the lampshades Mum had bought. I could see that he had been working on his embouchure. The devices for facial muscle exercise were on the table next to his chair, and also on his bedside table.

Dad had tried to warn me that he was really ill, but nothing could have prepared me for what I was about to witness. He was drinking so heavily that there were bottles of Rémy Martin all over the flat, and when we came home from the club he would drink brandy with ginger ale, one after the other, saying to me over and over: 'I don't want you to see me like this.' Dad constantly berated himself, blaming himself for everything, filled with self-loathing. I just could not understand how he could feel this way, when he had so many friends and people who really cared about him and loved him. I felt so sorry for what he was going through and everything that he had to deal with. It was almost in a selfish way that I said: 'Come on, Dad, you're my dad, you can work through this. It will be all right. You'll be fine.' It was very hard for me to see him drunk. There was a time when I had to undress him and put him to bed, and it was so weird and sad. He had taken care of me all my life, as much as he could, and here I was taking care of him.

I was very grateful for the fact that my mother had protected me from Dad's previous bouts of depression. At least now I was able to have the compassion and understanding to cope with the nights when he talked endlessly about things that I guess I really shouldn't have been hearing, but thank God I was old enough to deal with them.

As Christmas drew nearer, so came a frantic escalation of the depression, everything spinning out of control. The intensity of my father's anguish manifested itself in verbal outbursts that were like an electric storm. Sparks flew, igniting my own emotions, and in spite of myself I was suddenly caught up in the midst of his rage. Dad did not want me to be there while he was going through this turmoil; he told me enough times for me to believe that he wanted me to go. The worst and final storm was in the early hours of the day before Christmas Eve. My father died later that morning. It felt as though he had slipped through our fingers like sand. All of us went down in that whirlpool, involuntarily finding ourselves staring blindly, numbly into the void that remained.

The ripples of shock waves rapidly spread around the world, via the media. Thousands of people were stunned at my father's passing and deeply saddened by it. Fans, musicians of every category, actors, comedians, business colleagues, politicians, professors, writers, cartoonists, acquaintances, staff from years before, a vast eclectic pool of friends and family members all living in different parts of the world. Within hours of the news, telegrams of condolence began to pour into the club, the beginning of what became several weeks' worth of mountains of cards, letters, some poetry, an irrepressible stream of expressions of love and respect for my father. Some of the letters were from people who had met him only once, describing what a positive impact that encounter had had on their lives. For all of us who were reeling from the ravages of Dad's illness, it was a reawakening, to see the way each one of the writers had in his or her own way put into perspective who my father *really* was. When put together collectively, their testimonies were an overwhelming affirmation of his humanity, generosity of spirit, kindness, wisdom, ability to make people laugh, compassion, his musicianship, and his tremendous courage. The word 'courage' comes from Latin and Old French and means 'heart'. My father's heart was so big he made everybody feel that he had personally given them a little piece of it. A part of him belonged to everyone.

I had spent the night with Dani and Laurie, who had picked me up from the Mansions the evening before. We were all staying at a friend's flat. I was in a daze and anxiously awaiting my mother's arrival. Uncle Pete and Auntie Stella met Mum at the airport on Christmas Eve and telephoned me immediately, saying they would be on their way to Daddy's flat in about an hour. Nothing had been touched since the morning of my father's death, and Auntie Stella and Mum quietly cleaned the flat up together. Uncle Pete had to make a few phone calls. They had a cup of tea and tried to work out what should be done first. I was top of the list, and they headed out to get me.

When they arrived, we went into the living room for a cup of tea. I was full of apprehension about returning to the flat. Uncle Pete was very calm and gentle, and we sat and reminisced about Dad until gradually I began to relax. Uncle Pete slowly came round to the subject of my going back to the flat with Mum. I really did not want to face it, even with Mum there.

I will always remember Uncle Pete that day. He was like a rock, strong, steady and firm but gentle at the same time. He said to me: 'I'll tell you a story, Becky. Once, when I was driving racing cars, I had a very bad accident. I was seriously injured and it took a long time to recover. Quite frankly it scared me shitless – pardon the expression – but that was how it was. When I was fully recovered I went back to the track and I knew that if I didn't get in the car right then and do a run I would never get in a racing car again. So, terrified as I was, I got into the car, and in a very short space of time regained my nerve. Now, this is what you have to try to do with the flat. You can come back with Auntie Stella and me and your mum. We'll all go into the flat together, and if after half an hour or so you still feel that you have to leave then we'll bring you back here.' I was immediately able to relate to the wisdom of what he was saying. His story was an example of the principle that I learned in my first riding lesson, which is if you fall off you must get right back on the horse.

And so we went back to the flat. I was surprised to see that it looked like the cosy, warm and welcoming little flat that I had grown to love over the years. Uncle Pete was absolutely right, and within a short space of time my apprehension subsided. He and Auntie Stella left, and Mum and I set about trying to cope with everything that had just happened. There were the basic things that we needed, like milk for tea, and although we did not feel like eating maybe later we would, so we had better do some shopping. I really was in deep shock and misery, and we walked in silence towards the King's Road. We turned the corner and I was absolutely stunned to see my father's face on the front page of the newspapers and the glaring headlines. As we walked down the street the newspapers were outside the shops, in stacks, in piles, on display racks, it seemed like Daddy was suddenly everywhere I looked. It was too much. I thought I was going to break down right there in the street. My mother quickly bought some milk and that was it, we turned around and went straight back home. Then there were the announcements on the TV and the radio. For us they were too painful, and we never had the TV or the radio on after the first few bulletins.

We went to the club that night. It was the most comforting place to be, with Uncle Pete and the staff, who were just as shattered as we were. Uncle Pete and Mum and people who were close to Dad were amazed at the amount of press coverage. To us Ronnie was a father, a friend, a partner; none of us had really taken into consideration how well known he really was. Uncle Pete started to share the telegrams and letters with us. Right then for me it was overwhelming, and I could not handle all the outpouring of feelings from hundreds of people. I remember thinking, He was my dad, that's who he was . . . he was my dad. I needed to be alone with my grief and my thoughts of him. Suddenly having to share my father with the rest of the world was more than I could handle. But a few days later, Uncle Pete would read the letters and cards out loud to Mum and me in the office, and just hearing the beautiful things that people had to say about Daddy began to really help me.

I had to telephone The Strand in Rhode Island. I said: 'I don't think I shall be coming back for quite some time because Daddy died.' I ended up losing my job because of it; they just weren't able to hold my position open for me for the length of time that I was away. They were very apologetic about it, and we remained on very good terms. I was still able to work with them on occasions through Pastie Productions.

People were still trying to have Christmas. Gifts were exchanged in keeping with the tradition of previous years. There was even laughter. It's hard to remember my father without a chuckle creeping in somewhere. Since our attempt at shopping had been thwarted, Wendy filled a shopping bag with food from the kitchen for us. Uncle Pete and Auntie Stella had invited us to spend Christmas Day with them, and we accepted their invitation. In fact we received many invitations that night. We were surrounded by kindness and love.

When we got home from the club, we sat in the living room talking about everything. I was in my father's chair, Mum on the couch. I could not get the image of my father lying on the floor out of my mind. My eyes were drawn like a magnet to the place where I had found him, so much so that my mother became aware of the fact that I kept glancing over at the floor. Although she didn't speak about it, she knew exactly what was happening and coaxed me into going to bed, another thing that was hard to do that night. I slept with the lights on.

After I went to bed, my mother shampooed the entire carpet in the living room. There was a wooden box next to the fireplace that I had never opened, but my mother knew that if nothing had changed there were some small Christmas decorations in there from previous years. They were still there, so she hung the red and silver balls on the plants, hung a star in the window, put little star candleholders on the mantelpiece, windowsills and tables, and in the kitchen drawer found candles that fitted them. I woke up late on Christmas morning. My mother had fallen asleep on the couch but was awake when I pushed the living room door open. The transformation warmed my heart. It was, after all, Christmas Day, and now it looked like it. I could see that the carpet was clean, and I said: 'Mum, what did you do in here? It all looks so fresh.' Quietly she replied: 'I shampooed the carpet, sweetheart, and cleaned up. I thought it would help us feel better.'

The last couple of days had been long and hard. It was already well into the afternoon and we decided to call Uncle Pete, who lives in Elstree, Hertfordshire, and explain that it might be better if we stayed quietly at home. Uncle Pete was laughing. 'Good judgement call,' he said. 'You'll never believe it, but we're all sitting here waiting for our Christmas dinner, which supposedly has been cooking since early this morning, but we've just discovered that Auntie Stella forgot to turn the oven on!'

The next couple of weeks proved rough on all of us. Death is never easy to deal with when it comes, but the way my father died, and the fact that it was right on top of the holidays, definitely compounded the situation. The coroner's office was, of course, closed until the New Year. When we were finally able to meet Mr Stocking, his quiet efficiency, compassion and kindness left their mark on all of us. A day or two later, when we had to meet the undertaker, my mother's back had 'gone out', and the club's doctor had given her a prescription so that she could move around, albeit at a strange angle. Uncle Pete, Wally, my mother and I struggled to get out of the small car that had transported us to the undertaker. It was another bitterly cold day. Uncle Pete and Wally were ribbing Mum about her back, reminding us of occasions when Dad's back went out. As we walked across the street, Wally said: 'You know, the funny thing is, the undertaker's name is David Grainger.' He went on to say: 'Remember when Ronnie was about to win a game of chess, he would chuckle, look across the board at Jeff, and say, "David Grainger is in grave danger"?' We all burst out laughing, suddenly able to see the humour that Ronnie would have found even in this scenario. It was as though he was right there with us, helping us get through it.

At a time like this it is only natural that emotions run high and people's feelings are raw. Jo was still in California and was telephoning Uncle Pete, asking if she should come to the funeral. That was a decision that could be made only by her, and eventually Jo made the decision not to come. As Laurie said: 'My mother is halfway round the world, six thousand miles away.' We did what we had to do, and the funeral director went ahead with the arrangements. There were to be several limousines, and we made sure that Dani and Laurie, who would also be representing their mother, had seats in one of them, and a place in a front pew in the hall at Golders Green Crematorium was reserved for them.

The weather forecast confirmed that the day of the funeral, 7 January 1997, was the most bitter, coldest day that London had experienced in decades. The biting wind penetrated the thickest of coats. The cortege assembled outside Ronnie Scott's Club. Mounted on the roof of the hearse was a large floral tribute in the shape of a saxophone made of white chrysanthemums with tiny gold roses for the keys. It was from Uncle Pete, his oldest and closest friend and partner. All the flowers that were waiting in the club were put inside. A tribute made of red roses spelling out his name was from the staff and placed along the inside of the window. The wreaths from my mother and me, a heart and a circle of yellow and white roses with laurel leaves, were on top of the coffin, with many other gorgeous floral tributes surrounding it. We all climbed into our respective limos, the family, Uncle Pete and Auntie Stella in the first car. Cold as it was, each side of Frith Street and all around Soho Square and beyond were lined with merchants, restaurateurs, shopkeepers, waiters and waitresses, all the people whom it took to make Soho, standing three deep, as we slowly pulled away. The men in the crowd removed their hats in respect to Ronnie as the cortege crept past, Mr David Grainger, in keeping with tradition, walking in front of the hearse.

I don't know what any of us really expected, but to see the crowds of people, all very quietly standing, a mark of sorrow visible upon them, paying tribute to my father, whom afterwards the press so aptly described as 'son of Soho' and 'Soho's favourite son', temporarily froze my own grief as I gazed in respect at theirs.

Once out of Soho, David Grainger got into the front seat of the hearse and we headed towards our final destination, Golders Green Crematorium. As the cortege turned into the entrance there were throngs of people who had to move back to allow the cars through. As I looked at the people outside, they ranged in age from between twenty and ninety. Because of the crowds, we had to wait in the car while the funeral director worked out how best to handle the situation. The original plan had been for the pallbearers to carry Dad's coffin in through the front of the hall with all of us following, but this was no longer possible, so they had to take my father's coffin through the back door to its resting place, then we were able to enter. Once again my grief was held in check as I felt the tremendous level of respect and love that came from all these people, determined to pay homage to my father, and listen to the service through rather inadequate speakers outside, unable to fully protect themselves from the harshness of the cold on that cruel January day.

As we took our seats to the sound of a tape of my father's sweet tenor sax, and Rabbi Hall began the service, I sat between Uncle Pete and my mother, numb enough to be able to appreciate the tributes that were paid to Daddy, grateful to hear his old friend Joe Green intone Kaddish, the prayer for the dead, and another old friend of Dad's who was sitting right behind us – we did not know who he was but he realised who we were – who leaned forward and, in a voice just loud enough for us to hear, quietly translated the Aramaic. An act of thoughtful kindness that I will remember for the rest of my life. The service came to an end, we walked past Dad's coffin and placed one hand on it in a final farewell, and headed for the limousines that were waiting to take us back to the club.

As you walk into the foyer of the club there is a table flanked by a couch and a chair. In the centre of the table was a glorious floral tribute from Paul and Linda McCartney. Every single day since then patrons of the club, Uncle Pete and the staff have always kept a vase of fresh flowers on the table.

The club was packed. The thing that touched me most and I will always cherish is the way so many people, musicians and other friends of Dad's, showed so much concern for me. They went out of their way to come over to me and tell me how proud Dad was of me and that he loved me very much. How much he used to talk about me from the time I was a little girl and would tell them stories about things that happened, and things I was involved with as I grew up. Everyone knew about Shenanigans! It surprised me each time and really made me feel quite humble.

CHAPTER SIXTEEN

A GIFT OF LOVE

*Listening to Ronnie play always reminded me of flocks of birds – his music
held so much promise.*   MARIAN MONTGOMERY AND LAURIE HOLLOWAY

> *He doubted; but God said, 'Even so:*
> *Nothing is lost that's wrought with tears:*
> *The music that you made below*
> *is now the music of the spheres.'*

JOHN DAVIDSON

Y MOTHER AND I prepared ourselves for another journey to
England, my best friend and business partner Michelle
accompanying us. This time it was to attend my father's
memorial service at St Martin-in-the-Fields, Trafalgar Square.
We arrived in London a few days before, settling into the little flat in
Chelsea. In contrast to the cruel, bitter cold of January, the city was
bathed in sunshine, and carried on the breeze was the heady fragrance of
wisteria and lilacs, which abounded in gay profusion wherever we went.
Private and public gardens proudly displayed an array of all the glorious
colours and textures of spring, the faces of pansies smiling and bobbing
amid trailing ivy from window boxes on nearly every sill. It was indeed a
celebration of life, which was why we were in London, to celebrate the life
of my father.

Michelle and I had made arrangements to spend the evening before the
memorial service with my friend Alison, Tony Crombie's daughter, and
Mum had arranged to have dinner with Wally Houser and his wife Geraldine
at a favourite Italian restaurant of ours on the King's Road. My mother

noticed that Wally, although charming as always, seemed to be a little on edge and once in the restaurant was anxious to get the food ordered as soon as possible. Finally he took the bull by the horns and said: 'Mary, there's something that I have to discuss with you. It directly involves you and Becky, and I must tell you about it.' Sensing that the information he was about to share with her was of great import, Mum gave Wally her full attention as he began to explain . . .

A young man named Selwyn Curtis wrote a letter to Ronnie in the middle of November 1996, explaining that he had been adopted in 1956 and had finally made the decision to find out who his biological parents were. The adoption documents listed the father as Ronnie Scott, orchestra leader, at the address in Edgwarebury Gardens. Wally was a little apprehensive about how my mother would handle the news and hastened to add: 'I've spoken to Selwyn on the phone. He is a very likable young man, and I'm sure he really is who he says he is.' Wally went on to explain to Mum that he had sent Selwyn an invitation to the memorial service the following evening and that Selwyn would come down to the club afterwards so we could all meet. My mother's immediate response was one of pure delight, assuring Wally that I would be equally thrilled.

Mum returned to the flat to find myself, Michelle, Alison and her mother Beryl all waiting for her in the living room. Alison and I were talking, looking at photographs of her father and mine when they were young musicians together. Beryl followed Mum into the kitchen, where she was making tea for everyone. They chatted and Beryl remembered: 'Your mum said to me: "Come on, Beryl, let's take the tea into the living room. It's getting really late and there's something I *simply must* tell Rebecca tonight." ' We sat with our tea and my mother began: 'Rebecca, darling, Wally told me something tonight that I think will turn out to be a wonderful thing. There is a young man whom none of us knew about until now. His name is Selwyn Curtis. He was adopted as a baby and he's Daddy's son.' As my face froze into a look of incredulity, Mum hastened to assure me: 'This is a good thing, Rebecca. Wally says he's a very nice young man, charming in fact.' Beryl was stunned and so was Alison. For a few seconds everybody looked at each other saying nothing, then Alison said: 'Wow! Becky, now you have two brothers you've never seen before that you have to meet. It's going to be some day tomorrow.' I remember saying: 'Yeah, I always wanted a brother. Now all of a sudden they're coming out of the fricking woodwork!' We all laughed, asking Mum a million questions, most of which had to remain unanswered until we met Selwyn. We chatted about the infinite possibilities that lay ahead. Alison's reference to 'two brothers' of course included Nicholas. Although I had been told about him while I was growing up, not having seen or spoken to him since 1974 I had no memory of him at all. The following day was indeed going to be a long and revealing one.

On Monday 7 April at 6 p.m. we all filed into the church of St-Martin-in-the-Fields, the sound of my father's saxophone through the speaker system filling the great hall, one of the tunes the haunting ballad 'All about Ronnie'. A thousand people were present. Before the service started I briefly met Nicholas, who was sitting with his mother. Both of us were naturally quite shy and few words were exchanged. Mum and Ilsa referred to the time we had played together all those years ago, although back then Nicholas had no idea I was his sister. He remembered the brief meeting since he was twelve at the time. Then it was time to take our seats, and we agreed that we should see each other again at the club after the ceremony was over.

Sitting alone up in the front of the balcony to the left of the stage was Selwyn Curtis, a dark-haired, handsome man, his blue eyes reminiscent of Jock Scott's. Selwyn had arrived early and watched people come in and take their seats. It must have seemed so surreal, looking down at all the people, hundreds of them, knowing none of them and yet realising that, in one way or another, they had all known his father and that among them were people who were related to him. Selwyn's thoughts drifted back to the morning of Christmas Eve. It was just after 8 a.m. when he woke up and turned on the radio in the bathroom and the first words he heard were: '. . . and that was John Prescott, deputy leader of the Opposition, speaking about jazz legend Ronnie Scott, who died last night.' In disbelief he ran downstairs and put on Teletext. Confirmation was immediate, and his eyes welled up with tears. Although he had never met Ronnie, this man was his father, he had been so close, just a breath away from the yearned-for connection. As Selwyn sat in the church the feeling of isolation and loss swept through him again, but the sound of the vicar's voice making the introduction brought him back to the moment as he brought on stage Benny Green, Master of ceremonies, who shared some of his memories of earlier days and introduced the first musical tribute, which was played by American James Moody, one of Dad's favourite tenor players, and Ronnie's rhythm section.

Next came Marian Montgomery and Laurie Holloway, her husband, who accompanied her on piano. She began to sing Johnny Mercer's and Hoagy

Carmichael's 'Skylark'. As Marian's spellbinding delivery of the awesome lyrics swept everyone in the hall along with her on the flight of the skylark, her velvety, breathy voice softly caressed every note and nuance, wistfully unfolding the story with such grace you could have heard a pin drop. Selwyn listened in rapt attention, caught up in the beauty of the singing and the message it carried. He experienced possibly the emptiest feeling he had ever had – it brought home to him what was never going to happen – his chance of knowing Ronnie, of experiencing for himself the one thing that everyone else in this hall was remembering, their own unique experience of spending time with Ronnie, which was, for Selwyn, lost for ever. As he sat in a sea of strangers he ached for someone to share his thoughts with.

The celebration progressed, and Benny Green shared his thoughts and stories, sometimes funny, other times touching and insightful. And in between the music Jimmy Parsons, long-time friend and fellow prankster of Ronnie's, opened with a slightly edited version of one of Ronnie's sketches: 'It's good to see the place so full. You should have been here last night . . . somebody should have been here last night. We had the vergers chucking them in. Someone called the vicar and asked him what time the service was tonight and he said, "I don't know. What time can you get here!" Thank you, Ronnie.' The familiar lines were each greeted with laughter, and ultimately a thunderous round of applause. Jimmy went on to read telegrams from such notables as The Right Honourable Kenneth Clark, Chancellor of the Exchequer, Sir David Steele, and the Blue Note in New York, all paying tribute to my father's unique saxophone playing, his humour and to the world-renowned club that he and Uncle Pete built, saying that the world of jazz owes a great debt of gratitude for his contribution.

The musical tributes poured straight from the hearts of the Tommy Whittle Quartet, Jack de Johnette, piano, Stan Tracey, piano, and Peter King, alto sax, Martin Taylor, guitar, the Ian Bellamy Quartet, the John Critchinson Quartet, and Ian Carr, each performer receiving a warm round of applause. The service was brought to a close by Rabbi Guy Hall, who brought the house down when he told the audience that he was greeted by one of his co-religionists, saying: 'Jesus, Rabbi, what are you doing here?' My father would have really enjoyed Rabbi Hall. The words he had to say even when being serious were sprinkled with humour, and in good tradition he ended on a humorous note, saying: 'You had the vicar speak at the beginning to welcome you, and that is right and proper, that's his job, it's his house, he has to get everybody in. But I am a Rabbi . . . my job is to get you all out!' He went on to offer people the alternatives of staying at the church, where they were serving a variety of refreshments, or going to the club, so he said: 'If you're Christian and religious, stay here. If you're Jewish and anything else, go to the club!'

Like those of everyone else in attendance, Selwyn's emotions fluctuated, and as the service drew to a close, even though he had not met Ronnie, an unexpected feeling of pride began to permeate his senses. That so many people thought so much of Ronnie meant that he obviously had affected many lives in positive ways. To experience the outpouring of genuine love, affection and admiration first-hand made him feel very proud of his heritage. Selwyn's thoughts wandered, and he recalled how as soon as he had found out that Ronnie was his father he went straight to the local library and Waterstones to search through every book he could find about jazz, hungry to learn everything he could about Ronnie. Eventually, Waterstone's ordered John Fordham's book *Jazz Man*, which he read with great interest. It told him about some of the family members, and now he couldn't help but wonder how the family would respond to meeting him. Would they reject him? Or would they accept him for who he was? He hoped that they would welcome him, but if they didn't he comforted himself with the thought that at least he had attended the memorial service and soon he would be in the most famous jazz club in the world and, no matter what happened, nothing could change the fact that Ronnie was his father, and just knowing that right now meant the world to him.

The music that evening was described by Joe Joseph in *The Times* as being '. . . a two-hour cocktail of glorious jazz'. The service brought forth laughter and tears and was indeed a great tribute to and celebration of my father's life.

The service over, Selwyn made his way through the crowds, hoping to make contact with Wally, but by the time he reached the exit ushers informed him that Wally had already left. Anxious to keep the memorial service programme in good condition, he decided to drop it off at his hotel before walking to the club.

The club quickly filled with friends and family who had attended the memorial service. There were uncles and aunts and cousins, many people to meet and greet, a veritable whirl of activity. Wally let us know that Selwyn had not arrived yet but that he was on the lookout for him. After my father's funeral in January, Ilsa had asked my mother for pictures of Dad's family, so in the meantime Mum had them copied and specially framed for Nicholas. We chatted. Nicholas, who, with dark brown hair and eyes strongly resembles his mother, is a member of the Magic Circle in London and enjoys his profession, particularly when performing for children. It was not easy for either of us to be suddenly thrown together after so many years of silence between us. There was a feeling of awkwardness, and after a while we were lost for words.

I met my cousins, Auntie Ella's sons Tom and Joel, then there was Uncle Markie's and Auntie Rosie's daughter Josie, who made me laugh a lot with her stories about Dad and Uncle Mark. Cousin Jack, who all those years ago had attended Grandfather Jock's and Grandma Cissie's wedding. So many of Dad's friends came up to me and told me how they knew all about me and had seen pictures of me growing up, how Dad always carried my picture in his inside pocket and was so proud of me. They all helped me so much. The cause of Dad's death was described by the coroner as 'an incautious overdose', so despite press speculation due to the fact that Ronnie did sometimes suffer from depression, the coroner's verdict was death by misadventure. I was still wrestling with a feeling of guilt but now, thank God, with the support of all Dad's friends, who reached out to me and my mother, I know that it really was not my fault at all, or anyone else's. What happened to my father was an accumulation of illnesses. I don't know which was the worst: the problems that ultimately robbed him of his lifeline, the ability to play the saxophone, or the deep pit of depression that had engulfed him. If he had still been able to play, the chances of his surviving the tentacles of depression would have been much higher. It was certainly what had saved him in the past; without his playing he was completely lost.

I couldn't help wondering what my father would have felt about everything that had happened since his death. I think he would have felt the same way about all the messages and outpouring of love and respect, all the people who came first to the funeral and now the memorial service, as he did about getting the OBE. A little embarrassment and sheer disbelief at first, then shy recognition of what was happening and eventually delight and joy that so many people thought so highly of him.

Wally was so kind that night. Selwyn arrived and Wally seated him at a table, found me and took me to his table and introduced us. There was an immediate connection between us. We were instantly comfortable in each other's company. The witty humour that I had shared with Dad so many times was as natural to Selwyn as it was to Dad and me, and we could make each other laugh just as Dad and I used to do. Wally had gone to find Mum, and when he brought her to the table Selwyn was turned towards me, talking, so Mum saw him in profile. Wally began the introductions and Selwyn turned to face my mother, who was standing in front of the table. She was rendered speechless, momentarily frozen in a time gone by, completely stunned as she recognised instantly the same striking features that had been passed from Morris Schatt to Jock to Ronnie and now from Ronnie to Selwyn. My mother and father had lived together from the time Dad was thirty-seven until he was forty-eight and now Selwyn was forty. Finding her voice, Mum said: 'It's uncanny. You even have the same haircut that Ronnie had at your age!' I joined in and said: 'Look, Mum, look at Selwyn's hands and fingers. They're exactly the same as Daddy's!' I had always loved my father's hands and his long, elegant fingers. Selwyn was as fascinated with this discovery process as we were. If any doubts had been floating at the back of his mind about Ronnie being his father, they were erased for ever.

There were so many questions that each of us needed answers to, the most urgent of course from Selwyn. We needed privacy so retreated to the inner sanctum of the office. Selwyn is an intelligent, soft-spoken, sensitive man, somewhat shy, but he comes straight to the point. There is a large desk in the office, with a high-backed black leather chair with arms behind it and a smaller chair in front. In front of the desk to the right is a large TV, which was always on. I showed Selwyn how Daddy used to sit in the high-backed chair with his feet up on the desk, ankles crossed, watching TV, so we switched places and Selwyn sat with his feet on the desk just as our father had done. At first, we chatted about Dad, but then people came into the office. Auntie Ella and my cousins Tom and Joel, Ilsa and Nicholas, Josie (Uncle Mark's stepdaughter), Tony, Beryl and Alison and, of course, Uncle Pete and several of the musicians were among the people who met and chatted to Selwyn. Everyone was delighted to meet him. As Selwyn said: 'I had a fantastic evening. Everyone was really friendly and interested in my story. I felt very welcome.'

By now everyone was very hungry and we pushed tables together and shared a family dinner, along with memories and jokes. The music at the club that evening was memorable, musical tributes being paid to my father. Chico Freeman took the stand and spoke for a few minutes, dedicating to Dad a tune called 'Tear Drop in the Rain' that he had written for another dear friend of his who had died suddenly. He lifted his saxophone, and the haunting refrain gently touched the hearts of all of us. Tears silently filled the eyes of many, the melody a reminder of Ronnie's gentle side, the softness, the kindnesses, his humanity and the laughter that we would never forget.

Later in the evening everyone was mingling again, so Selwyn and I quietly slipped away into the privacy of the office. I knew that he needed to know what had happened to our father and so as we sat together I told him all I knew of the hours preceding Dad's death and how I had found him at the flat. Although we had known each other for only a few hours, there was a natural closeness between us. We were very comfortable with each other, and as painful as the memories were I found myself able to share with him the details of my own personal trauma. We welcomed each other for what we are, half-brother and half-sister, and each of us was able to take great comfort in our new-found relationship. Selwyn told me that he had discovered that Dad was his father in May 1996 but before approaching someone as well known as Ronnie he wanted some other confirmation to support the paperwork. So he set about trying to find his birth mother, but all his efforts were to no avail and eventually, after six and a half months of searching unsuccessfully, made the decision to contact Ronnie anyway. He vacillated over what approach to take to contact Ronnie: should it be through someone else or should he be direct? My mother, who had now joined us, and I were fascinated to hear how Selwyn contacted Dad. One night, on 14 November 1996, Selwyn wrote his first letter to Ronnie. The next morning, about to post it, he stood by the postbox still wondering if he was doing the right thing, fearing the possibility of rejection, but finally he dropped the envelope into the box. His letter was slightly apologetic and tentative yet reached out to the reader in a way that could not fail to touch his heart. Two nights later, while dozing in his armchair at around 10 p.m., the sharp ring of the telephone woke him with a start. In that moment he knew intuitively it was Ronnie. He reached out and picked up the telephone: 'This is Ronnie Scott. Could I speak to Selwyn Curtis, please?'

Selwyn recalled: 'My legs went weak when he told me who he was. Christ, this was not only the world-famous Ronnie Scott ringing me, but he was my father! I must have sounded like a complete imbecile at first, but I managed to buy myself a few seconds' grace by having to go upstairs to get the paperwork about the adoption.' The two men chatted for about half an hour and Selwyn remembered Ronnie saying: 'So, are you saying that you think I'm your father?' Selwyn responded that the papers he had received indicated that this was the case. Ronnie never denied the possibility for a second; instead, he asked Selwyn a few questions and then said: 'Tell me, Mr Curtis, do you *feel* Jewish?' Selwyn was quick on the uptake and responded: 'Well, I like a bargain.' Ronnie laughed at that. They chatted some more and agreed to meet once the Christmas holidays were over, Selwyn promising to bring all the paperwork and some photographs with him. Never dreaming that this was to be the one and only conversation that he would have with his father, Selwyn hung up the phone that night with the feeling that they had got along pretty well.

Selwyn is the first to admit that he never had any inclination to play an instrument, but there is no doubt that there were areas of common ground between him and Dad, especially sports. They certainly had football, rugby and cricket in common, and although Selwyn is not a horse-racing man he enjoys placing a bet now and then with the same singular lack of success that Ronnie often experienced!

My mother asked Selwyn if it would be possible for him to stay for a few extra days. Selwyn was delighted with the idea of spending more time with us and quickly made the necessary arrangements.

During the next few days we learned a lot about my half-brother as Selwyn's story unfolded. He was born on 5 June 1956 in Croydon, Surrey. Shortly after he was adopted into the Curtis family and was their first child. They moved to Taunton in Somerset, and when Selwyn was just two years and nine months old Mr and Mrs Curtis, who were delighted with their small son, decided to complete their family by adopting a baby girl, a sister for Selwyn. The new house was large and spacious but the town of Taunton lay low in a valley. Gradually Selwyn became ill, and the family doctor advised Mr and Mrs Curtis that the valley was detrimental to Selwyn's health and suggested that they should move. The Curtises had always wanted to live in Bournemouth, and the doctor agreed that the sea air could only improve Selwyn's health. Fortunately, Mr Curtis, who worked in a large department store, was offered a promotion at a store in Bournemouth, and in 1963 the family moved into a new home in the borough of Poole, very close to Bournemouth.

Although the first winter was a harsh one, and they got their full share of the blizzards that swept across the country, young Selwyn's health rapidly improved. Selwyn recalled: 'Over the years my father was offered promotions away from Bournemouth, but he turned them all down for the sake of my health as well as a love for the area. It was a sign of the sacrifice made for my sake. I was very fortunate to have been adopted by such a considerate and caring family.' One day when Selwyn was about seven his father had taken him to the local park. They were kicking a ball around when suddenly all the colour drained out of Selwyn's face and he collapsed.

Mr Curtis quickly aroused him sufficiently to pick him up and carry him on his shoulders back to the house. A doctor was summoned and by the evening Selwyn was rushed to hospital, seriously ill – somehow he had contracted meningitis. Fortunately, he made a full recovery and was soon back attending primary school, which was within a few minutes' walk of their home. Selwyn went on to pass the eleven-plus exam, gaining entrance to Poole Grammar School. His mother and father were completely successful in providing a secure and loving environment for him, so much so that when they made the decision that the time had come to tell him that he was adopted it had no negative effect on him. Selwyn told me: 'They were my mum and dad and that was that. However, I can never remember the subject ever being talked about in the home since then. Perhaps if it had been, I might have been prompted to start searching for my biological parents earlier. Who knows?'

When the summer holidays came around Selwyn always took a summer job. His favourite was selling ices in a booth outside the café on Bournemouth Pier – the perfect place for meeting girls! Selwyn and I ribbed each other about grammar school when he told me that he did not do as well as he should have done because of his preoccupation with sports, excelling at football. Like Dad, he was captain of the school football first XI, and he played for his school at both under-fifteen and under-nineteen age levels. At cricket, he played for his school and for Dorset School at the under-fifteen level. Needless to say, all this extracurricular activity took its toll on the academic side of Selwyn's life, and when the time came for him to take his mock A-levels he was not prepared and his results were somewhat poor. Seventeen at the time, he decided that the likelihood of his passing the exams was slender, and rather than waste another year he opted to leave school and get a job.

Selwyn's first job was with Barclays Bank Trust Company, paving the way for a position with a firm of accountants. Always involved with the financial end of things, Selwyn went on to work for the City Council, which is where he met his wife, Kris. Kris is strikingly pretty with blonde hair and blue eyes. They married on 22 June 1985, and Kris moved into Selwyn's one-bedroom flat, which he had bought a couple of years earlier. About nine months later they moved into a three-bedroom semidetached house, and on 23 April 1989 my nephew, Ashley, was born. His arrival was a great source of joy to his grandparents, and Selwyn's dad thought the world of him. Three years later, in June 1992, Selwyn and Kris moved again, this time to a three-bedroom detached house, which is where they still live today.

Just four months after they moved, in October 1992 Selwyn's father suddenly died of a heart attack. It was devastating. He had no history of heart trouble so the shock was immense. In the space of ten short months another tragedy was to strike: in August 1993 Kris, who was six months pregnant, lost the baby girl she was carrying. She had always wanted a little girl, and they both felt the loss deeply. Selwyn had to take care of the formalities and register the death. They named the little baby Holly, and she is buried in the local cemetery, which is just a short walk from their home in Bournemouth. Selwyn said: 'I think it was a combination of these events, plus the fact that I was approaching forty, that made me decide that I should look for my natural parents before it was too late.' Happily, in 1994 Kris became pregnant again, on 22 November giving birth to a healthy, bouncing baby boy called Ben. Selwyn proudly showed us photographs of the boys. Ashley looked a lot like his father, except for the blond hair that came from Kris's side of the family, and has blue eyes just like his mum and dad and Grandfather Jock. Little Ben, although he has blond hair, has dark brown eyes just like Ronnie, his grandfather. Selwyn said that he and Kris had never been able to fathom out where those brown eyes came from before, since everyone in Kris's family has blue eyes.

We chatted about music and discovered that, while we were growing up, a common factor between us was our mutual appreciation of the popular end of music. Selwyn's favourite musicians were Eric Clapton, Van Morrison, the Beatles, Steely Dan and a band called Little Feat. Old Tamla Motown held a fascination for him too: the Temptations and Four Tops, etc. We both have a love of blues, which is of course part of the foundation of jazz, and quickly agreed that Billie Holiday, undoubtedly, is our favourite singer – interesting, because while we were discovering her, each in our own time, worlds apart, neither of us knew that she was also Dad's favourite singer. It wasn't until I was about fifteen that Dad and I really discussed music.

In the two and a half years since my father's death, Uncle Pete has done a phenomenal job of picking up the pieces and has breathed new life into the club, most recently putting together a fabulous programme of events for the fortieth anniversary of Ronnie Scott's, a terrific celebration of everything that he and my father achieved together and of Uncle Pete's determination to keep the flame alive. As Paul McCartney said, 'Nowadays, the club thrives and goes from strength to strength, and in doing so Ronnie's spirit lives on. Only recently I was down there for another late night session where I caught a fabulous Brazilian band rocking the roof off the club.'

We have grown closer as a family, spending time together when Mum and I go to England, Selwyn and the family coming to London to see us and us going to Bournemouth to visit them. Kris has welcomed us with open arms. Knowing Mum would love to have grandchildren, when Kris watched her play with the boys she told her that she made a great grandmother. In the meantime our telephone bills could buy us a ticket across the Atlantic! My nephews Ashley and Ben clearly carry some of the distinctive Schatt and Messias features, but it seems apparent that Ashley has inherited some of the other genes too. At only ten years of age he is very musical and when the music teacher at his school asked him what instrument he would like to play he selected the alto saxophone, his great-grandfather Jock's instrument of choice. We cannot help but think how proud Ronnie would have been of his son and grandsons. My father is remembered in so many ways: through the club, his music, his place in the history of jazz, his humanity, his idiosyncratic humour and the endless pleasure that he gave to so many people, and through his children and grandchildren. The Jewish faith believes that you live on for as long as there is someone to remember you. My father is going to be around for a long time to come, living in the hearts of future generations.

Death is nothing at all. I have only slipped into the next room. I am I and you are you ... Why should I be out of mind because I am out of sight?

REVD HENRY SCOTT HOLLAND

APPENDIX 1: BIBLIOGRAPHY

Jazz Man: The Amazing Story of Ronnie Scott and his Club, John Fordham, Kyle Cathie Ltd

Some of my Best Friends Are Blues, Ronnie Scott with Mike Hennessey, W. H. Allen

52nd Street: The Street of Jazz, Arnold Shaw, DaCapo

Notes and Tones, Arthur Taylor, self-published

APPENDIX 2: DISCOGRAPHY

T HE FOLLOWING IS not a full-scale discography but is a listing of every recording and its date, where known, under Ronnie's own name and two or three under someone else's name. Ronnie recorded with Johnny Claes, the Ted Heath Band, the Jack Parnell Band and the Jazz Couriers (Ronnie Scott and Tubby Hayes), the Kenny Clarke/Frances Boland Big Band, etc. and as a guest on several sessions for groups such as the Beatles, Tommy Steele, Phil Collins, etc. There is no complete discography of every recording he ever played on, but if you would like a more comprehensive account, discographies of Ronnie Scott, the Jazz Couriers (Ronnie Scott and Tubby Hayes), including the band's itinerary, and Johnny Claes's Clae Pigeons are available from Tony Middleton, 32 Quentin Road, Lewisham, London SE13 5DF.

Ronnie Scott Boptet
Recorded King George's Hall, London, 9 April 1949
Dennis Rose (tp), Johnny Rogers (as), Ronnie Scott (ts), Tommy Pollard (p), Lennie Bush (b), Tony Crombie (d), Ginger Johnson (bgo)

Wee Dot	Esquire (E)10-036, (E)S315
Coquette	
52nd Street Theme	
Ow!	
Don't Blame Me (DR, JR out)	(E)12-011
Stoned	
Scrapple from the Apple pt 1	(E)10-038
Scrapple from the Apple pt 2	
Donna Lee	

Note: Rest of Esquire (E)S315 see LP entitled *Bop at Club 11*, page 329

Ronnie Scott Quartet
Recorded London, 28 February 1951
Ronnie Scott (ts), Tommy Pollard (p), Lennie Bush (b), Tony Kinsey (d)

Too Marvellous for Words	Esquire (E)10-131, ESQ-303

Have You Met Miss Jones?
September Song   (E)10-125
Flamingo

Ronnie Scott Boptet
Recorded London, 21 April 1951
Jimmy Deuchar (tp), Spike Robinson (as), Ronnie Scott (ts), Vic Feldman (p),
Lennie Bush (b), Tony Crombie (d)
    Chasing the Bird   Esquire (E)10-141, ESQ-303
    Little Willie Leaps
    El Sino   (E)10-154
    Crazy Rhythm

Ronnie Scott with Ronnie Ball Trio
Recorded London, 13 October 1951
Ronnie Scott (ts), Ronnie Ball (p), Pete Blannin (b), Tony Kinsey (d)
    Close Your Eyes   Esquire (E)10-185, ESQ-303
    I Didn't Know What Time It Was
    The Nearness of You   (E)10-197
    All of Me

Ronnie Scott — Kenny Graham
Recorded London, 3 December 1951
Ronnie Scott (ts), Kenny Graham (ts), Vic Feldman (p), Lennie Bush (b), Tony
Crombie (d), Judy Johnson (maracas), Ginger Johnson (bgo), Bob Caxton (cga)
    Not So Fast   Esquire (E)10-211, ESQ-311
    Battle Royal   (E)10-195
    Fast   (E)10-211
    Twin Beds   (E)10-211

Ronnie Scott Quintet
Recorded London, 16 September 1952
Ronnie Scott (ts), Dill Jones (p), Lennie Bush (b), Tony Crombie (d), Tony Kinsey
(timb)
    Smoke Gets in Your Eyes   Esquire (E)10-265, ESQ-311
    Scott's Expedition   (E)10-255
    Avalon   (E)10-265
    Love Me or Leave Me   (E)10-255

Ronnie Scott Jazz Group
Recorded London, 1 December 1952
Jimmy Deuchar (tp), Ken Wray (tb), Derek Humble (as), Ronnie Scott (ts), Benny
Green (bar), Norman Stenfalt (p), Lennie Bush (b), Tony Crombie (d)
    All the Things You Are   Esquire (E)32-001
    Pantagrulian
    Mullenium
    Nemo

Got the Message
The Nearness of You
The Champ

Ronnie Scott Quintet
Recorded London, 13 December 1952
Ronnie Scott (ts), Harry Klein (bar), Norman Stenfalt (p), Lennie Bush (b), Tony Crombie (d)

Nomo	Esquire (E)10-275, ESQ-311
Trouble Air	(E)10-279
Eureka	
Seven Eleven	(E)10-275
All the Things You Are	(E)20-006
Great Scott	

Ronnie Scott Jazz Group
Recorded London, 2 February 1953
Jimmy Deuchar (tp), Ken Wray (tb), Derek Humble (as), Ronnie Scott (ts), Pete King (ts), Benny Green (bar), Norman Stenfalt (p), Lennie Bush (b), Tony Crombie (d)

I May Be Wrong	Esquire (E)32-001
On the Alamo	
Day Dream	
Stringin' the Jug	
Seven Eleven	
What's New?	
How Am I to Know?	
Just One of Those Things	

Ronnie Scott Orchestra
Recorded London, 13 April 1953
Same as preceding but Marie Korchinska (harp), Geoffrey Gilbert (fl), Johnny Grant (vcl) added

Have You Heard?	Esquire (E)5-088
Indian Summer	

Korchinska (harp) out, same date

Lover, Come Back to Me	Esquire (E)10-291
Compos Mentis	

Ronnie Scott Quartet
Recorded London, 18 June 1953
Ronnie Scott (ts), Rocky Coluccio (p), Lennie Bush (b), Tony Crombie (d)

Tangerine	Esquire (E)10-311
Tangerine	(E)EP1
How Am I to Know?	
How Am I to Know?	(E)10-335
Night and Day	
Night and Day	(E)EP2

| I Cover the Waterfront | (E)EP1 |
| I Cover the Waterfront | (E)10-311 |

Ronnie Scott Orchestra
Recorded London, 13 August 1953
Jimmy Deuchar (tp), Ken Wray (tb), Derek Humble (as), Pete King (ts),
Ronnie Scott (ts), Benny Green (bar), Norman Stenfalt (p), Lennie Bush (b),
Tony Crombie (d)

Double or Nothing	Esquire (E)10-331
Hard Feelings	
Stompin' at the Savoy	(E)10-321
Body Beautiful	

Ronnie Scott Orchestra
Recorded London, 1 February 1954
Same as preceding but Vic Feldman (p) replaces Stenfalt

I Get a Kick out of You	Esquire (E)10-361
Cymbalism	(E)10-351
Humble Pie	(E)10-361
Dear Old Southland	(E)10-351

Ronnie Scott Orchestra
Recorded London, 17 March 1954

Fast and Loose	Esquire (E)32-003
Body Beautiful	
Yardbird Suite (1)	
If I Should Lose You	
In the Land of Nimbupani	
Laura (2)	
Oo-shoo-be-do-be	
This Can't Be Love (3)	
Dear Old Southland	
El Sino (4)	
I Wished on the Moon	
Nemo	

Note: 1) Jimmy Deuchar (tp), Derek Humble (as) + rhythm only; 2) Ronnie Scott
(ts) + rhythm only; 3) Vic Feldman (vib), Lennie Bush (b), Tony Crombie (d) only;
4) Pete King (ts), Benny Green (bar) + rhythm only

Ronnie Scott Quartet
Recorded London, 28 April 1954
Ronnie Scott (ts), Vic Feldman (p), Lennie Bush (b), Tony Crombie (d)

Sunshine on a Dull Day	Esquire (E)10-371
Fools Rush In	(E)10-395
Poor Butterfly	(E)10-371
Perfidia	(E)10-395

Ronnie Scott Orchestra
Recorded London, 17 May 1954
Jimmy Deuchar (tp), Ken Wray (tb), Derek Humble (as), Pete King (ts), Ronnie
Scott (ts), Benny Green (bar), Vic Feldman (p), Lennie Bush (b), Tony Crombie (d)
| | |
Perdido — Esquire (E)10-391
Cherokee
In the Land of Nimbupani — (E)10-381
Fast and Loose

Ronnie Scott Jazz Group
Recorded London, 7 September 1954
Jimmy Deuchar (tp), Mac Minshull (tb), Derek Humble (as), Pete King (ts), Ronnie
Scott (ts), Benny Green (bar), Vic Feldman (p, vib, cga), Lennie Bush (b), Phil
Seamen (d)
Fine and Dandy — Esquire (E)32-006
Bouncing with Bud (1)
Things Ain't What They Used To Be
Serenade in Blue (2)
Humble Pie
'Cuse These Blues
Perdido
Tenderly
Fuller Bop Man
Nice Work (2)
Tin Tin Deo
Fools Rush In (3)
In the Land of Nimbupani
Note: 1) Jimmy Deuchar (tp), Derek Humble (as) + rhythm only; 2) Vic Feldman
(vib), Lennie Bush (b), Phil Seamen (d) only; 3) Ronnie Scott (ts) + rhythm only

Ronnie Scott Quintet
Recorded London, 15 October 1954
Jimmy Deuchar (tp), Ronnie Scott (ts), Vic Feldman (p, vib), Lennie Bush (b), Phil
Seamen (d)
Falling in Love with Love — Esquire (E)10-435
I Remember You
Influence — (E)10-415
Flying Scott

Ronnie Scott Orchestra
Recorded London, 2 November 1954
Henry Shaw (tp), Ken Wray (tb), Derek Humble (as, cl), Pete King (ts),
Ronnie Scott (ts), Benny Green (bar), Vic Feldman (p, cga), Lennie Bush (b),
Phil Seamen (d)
Taboo — Esquire (E)10-411
Second Helping
Seamen's Mission — (E)EP31
Lester Leaps In

Recorded London, 4 January 1955
    Evening in Paris   Esquire (E)10-431
    After You've Gone
    But Not Me   (E)10-432
    Serenity

Recorded London, 23 February 1955
    Parisian Thoroughfare   Esquire (E)EP61,
                           Barclay (F)EP74018
    Don't Worry 'bout Me
    Quicksilver   (E)10-451
    Quicksilver   (E)EP61
    Time after Time   Esquire (E)EP61, 10-451

Ronnie Scott Quintet
Recorded London, 9 March 1955
Henry Shaw (tp), Ronnie Scott (ts), Vic Feldman (p), Lennie Bush (b), Phil Seamen (d)
    Fidelius   Esquire (E)10-441
    Fidelius   (E)EP65
    They Can't Convince Me
    Short Circuit   (E)10-441
    Short Circuit   (E)EP65
    Don't Take Your Love from Me

Ronnie Scott Orchestra
Recorded London, 13 April 1955
    S'il Vous Plaît   Esquire (E)10-461, EP81
    Jordu
    Pearl   (E)10-462
    This Heart of Mine

Ronnie Scott Quintet
Recorded London, 8 June 1955
    Split Kick   Esquire (E)EP94
    It Don't Mean a Thing
    Caravan   (E)10-465
    I'll Never Smile Again

Ronnie Scott Orchestra
Recorded London, 11 October 1955
Stan Palmer (tp), Henry Shaw (tp), Dave Usden (tp), Jimmy Watson (tp), Jack Botterill (tb), Robin Kaye (tb), Mac Mishull (tb), Ken Wray (tb), Joe Harriott (as), Dougie Robinson (as), Pete King (ts), Ronnie Scott (ts), Benny Green (bar), Norman Stenfalt (p), Eric Peter (b), Phil Seamen (d)
    Bang   Esquire (E)EP85
    With Every Breath I Take
    A Night in Tunisia
    The Big Fist

Ronnie Scott Orchestra

Recorded Royal Festival Hall, London, 18 February 1956
Jimmy Deuchar (tp), Les Condon (tp), Ken Wray (tb), Derek Humble (as), Pete King (ts), Ronnie Scott (ts), Benny Green (bar), Stan Tracey (p), Lennie Bush (b), Tony Crombie (d)

    Basie Talks   De FJ10712, LF1261
    It Might As Well Be Spring
    I Want You to Be My Baby (unissued)
    Drop Me off at Harlem
    Ting-a-ling
    Straight Life
    Don't Worry Me (unissued)
    Flying Home

Ronnie Scott with the Dizzy Reece Quartet

Recorded London, 3 July 1956
Dizzy Reece (tp), Ronnie Scott (ts), Terry Shannon (p), Lennie Bush (b), Phil Seamen (d)

    Out of Nowhere   Tempo TAP9
    Scrapple from the Apple

Ronnie Scott New Quintet

Recorded London, 29 October 1956
Jimmy Deuchar (tp), Ronnie Scott (ts), Terry Shannon (p), Lennie Bush (b), Alan Ganley (d)

    I'll Take Romance   Tempo (E)TAP17
    Speak Low

Ronnie Scott with the Victor Feldman Trio

Recorded London, 3 January 1957
    I Surrender, Dear   Tempo TAP19
Note: This was a Victor Feldman date with various sidemen; this one number featured Ronnie as soloist with the rhythm section

Ronnie Scott Sextet

Recorded London, 9 January 1957
Jimmy Deuchar (tp), Derek Humble (as), Ronnie Scott (ts), Stan Tracey (p), Kenny Napper (b), Phil Seamen (d)

    Bass House   Philips (E)BBL7153
    You Leave Me Breathless
    Squeeze Me

Ronnie Scott Sextet

Recorded London, 10 January 1957
As preceding but Norman Stenfalt replaces Tracey
    It Don't Mean a Thing   Philips (E)BBL7153
    Give Me the Simple Life

Polka Dots and Moonbeams
All this and Heaven too
This Can't Be Love
Phil's Tune
IPA Special
Avalon
Pittsburgh Opener

The Jazz Couriers
Recorded London, 8 and 15 August 1957
    Through the Night Roared the   Tempo TAP15
       Overland Express
    Royal Ascot
    On a Misty Night*
    Cheek to Cheek
    Oh, My!
    Plebus
    Reunion
    A Foggy Day
    The Theme
Note: *An alternative take issued on a Tempo anthology TAP17

The Jazz Couriers
Recorded London, 16 February 1958
    What Is This Thing Called Love?   Tempo TAP22
    Some of My Best Friends Are Blues
    The Serpent
    Guys and Dolls
    Time Was
    Speak Low
    Cheek to Cheek

The Jazz Couriers
Recorded London, November 1958
    Mirage   London LTZ-L15188
    After Tea
    Stop the World, I Want to Get Off
    In Salah
    Star Eyes
    The Monk
    My Funny Valentine
    Day In, Day Out

The Jazz Couriers
Recorded London, 26 June and 3 July 1959
    If This Isn't Love   Tempo TAP26
    Easy to Love
    Whisper Not

Autumn Leaves
Too Close for Comfort
Yesterdays
Love Walked In

The Jazz Couriers
Recorded London, unknown date 1958 or 1959
    Monk Was Here   Top Spot Tunes (unnumbered)
    Last-Minute Blues   (45 rpm)

Ronnie Scott – The Night is Scott and You're so Swingable
Recorded Ronnie Scott's Club, London, 14 November 1961
Jimmy Deuchar (tp), Ronnie Scott (ts), Stan Tracey (p), Kenny Napper (b), Jackie Dougan (d)
    The Haunted Jazz Club   Font (E)TFL5176
    Suddenly Last Tuesday

Ronnie Scott Quartet
Recorded London, 3 July 1964
Ronnie Scott (ts), Ernest Ranglin (g), Lennie Bush (b), Tony Crombie (d)
    Sweet Lotus Blossom   Font (E)TL5332

Ronnie Scott Quartet
Recorded London, 3 July 1964
Unknown string section added to preceding
    What's New?   Font (E)TL322
    They Can't Convince Me
    All About Ronnie
    Once Upon a Summertime

Ronnie Scott Quartet
Recorded London, 11 November 1965
Ronnie Scott (ts), Stan Tracey (p), Rick Laird (b), Bill Eyden (d), strings out
    Baubles, Bangles and Beads   Font (E)TL322
    For Heaven's Sake
    The Night Is Young (and You're
       so Beautiful)
    The Night Has a Thousand Eyes
    Treat it Lightly

Ronnie Scott and the Band
Recorded Ronnie Scott's Club, London, 25–26 October 1968
Kenny Wheeler (tp, flhrn), Chris Payne (tb), Ray Warleigh (as, fl), Ronnie Scott (ts), John Surman (bar, sop), Gordon Beck (p, org), Ron Mathewson (b, el-b), Kenny Clare (d), Tony Oxley (d)
    Recorda Me   CBS/Realm (E)52661
    King Pete
    Second Question
    Marmasita

Too Late, Too Late
Lord of the Reedy River
Macumba

At Ronnie's
Recorded Ronnie Scott's Club, London, 3 and 4 August 1973
Ronnie Scott (ts), Mike Carr (org), Bobby Gein (d), Loughty Amao (cga-l)
    Sombrero Sam   RCA (E)LPL1-5056
    Lou's Piece
    The More I See You
    Midnight Blue

Serious Gold
Recorded London, 18 October 1977
Ronnie Scott (ts, sop), John Taylor (keyboards), Louis Stewart (g), Ron Mathewson (b), Martin Drew (d)
    Invitation   Pye (E)NSPL18542
    Lazy Afternoon
    Forty Colours
    Hey-oke Suite Ballad
    Send in the Clowns
    Interfusion

Ronnie Scott Quintet — Never Pat a Burning Dog
Recorded London, October and November 1990
    Contemplation   Jazz House JHR012
    I'm Glad There Is You
    White Caps
    All the Things You Are
    This Love of Mine
    When Love is New
Note: JHR012 now available as a CD with an additional track: Little Sunflower

Ronnie Scott Orchestra
Esquire 85

Couriers of Jazz!
Carlton 116

Live at Ronnie Scott's
CBS 52661

Ten Years at Ronnie Scott's — Jazz Decade, London
CBS 63742

Great Scott! Studio Recordings Vol. 1
Esquire 303

Battle Royal
Esquire 311

Bop at Club 11 – 1949 Concert
Esquire 315

Live at the Jazz Club Vol. 1
Esquire 328

Never Pat a Burning Dog
Jazz House 12

Message from Britain
Jazzland 34

Serious Gold
Pye 18542

Scott at Ronnie's
RCA 5056

Re-releases

When I Want Your Opinion I'll Give It To You
Recorded Ronnie Scott's Club, London

Ronnie's Blues	Jazz House JHAS610
I'm Sick and Tired of Waking Up Tired and Sick	
What's New?	
Easy Living	
Blues in B and B Flat	
Bye Bye Blackbird	
One Night at Ronnie's	

The Night Is Scott and You're so Swingable
Ronnie Scott (ts), Ernest Rangin (g) Lennie Bush (b), Tony Crombie (d), Stan Tracey (p); some tracks Rick Laird (b), Bill Eyden (d)

Baubles, Bangles and Beads	Redial 558-888-2
For Heaven's Sake	

Sweet Lotus Blossom
The Night is Young (and You're
    so Beautiful)
The Night Has a Thousand Eyes
What's New?*
They Can't Convince Me*
All About Ronnie*
Once Upon a Summertime*
Treat it Lightly

Note: *Includes string section. String arrangement by Richard Rodney
Bennett

The Night Has a Thousand Eyes
Ronnie Scott and Sonny Stitt
  Sonny Speaks (This Is Sonny   JHAS614
      Speaking)
  The Night Has a Thousand Eyes
  A Sonny Day for Ronnie
  Bye Bye Blackbird

Ronnie Scott and the Band Live at Ronnie Scott's
Ronnie Scott (ts), Kenny Wheeler (tp, flhrn), Chris Payne (tb), Ray Warleigh (as, fl),
John Surman (bar, sop), Gordon Beck (p), Ron Mathewson (b), Kenny Clare (d),
Tony Oxley (d)
  Recorda Me (Remember Me)   CBS/Sony 1494439 2
  King Pete
  Second Question
  Marmasita
  Too Late, Too Late
  Lord of the Reedy River
  Macumba

Ronnie's Compositions
Fast and Loose
Scott's Expedition
Theme for Pawnshop Blues
Double or Nothing
I'm Sick and Tired of Waking Up
    Tired and Sick
Ronnie's Blues
Treat It Lightly (with Stan Tracey)
The 1612 Overture
Theme
A Sonny Day for Ronnie (with Sonny Stitt)

Musical Tributes to Ronnie Scott

Excuse Me, Do I Know You? A Tribute to Ronnie Scott
John Critchinson Quartet, featuring Pat Crumley (saxes, fl), Mark Fletcher (d), Leon Clayton (b), with guests Georgie Fame and Flora Plurim

This Heart of Mine	Jazz House JHCD056

Let Me Count the Ways
Turned into You (featuring Georgie Fame)
You Don't Know What Love Is
Excuse Me, Do I Know You?*
Carib Blue
Little Tear (featuring Flora Plurim)
Nippon Soul
Back in Love Again
Weaver of Dreams*
Seven Steps to Heaven
Ssh! Ronnie's Talking
Note: *Martin Drew replaces Mark Fletcher

Barbara Jay – Just Friends. Dedicated to the Memory of Ronnie Scott and Benny Goodman
Accompanied by Dick Pearce (flhrn), Roy Williams (tb), Tommy Whittle (ts), John Critchinson (p), Brian Dee (p), John Shorter (p), Bill Le Sage (vibes), Martin Taylor (g), Andy Clyndert (b), Lennie Bush (b), Dave Green (b), Bobby Orr (d), Martin Drew (d)

Just Friends	Spotlite Jazz SPJ-(CD)557

Speak Low
East of the Sun
All About Ronnie
Come in from the Rain
I'm Glad There Is You
The Nearness of You
Willow Weep for Me
New York State of Mind
Stomping at the Savoy
The Lady's in Love with You
You Turned the Tables on Me
These Foolish Things
If Dreams Come True
The Man I Love
Memories of You
A Smooth One
Moon Glow
Goodbye

Got a Match?: A Tribute to Ronnie Scott
Martin Drew Quartet, featuring Laurence Gottle, Mornington Lockett, Gareth
Williams, with tributes from George Coleman, Dick Morrisey, James Moody and
Oscar Peterson

    Softly as in the Morning   Jazzizit Records JIT CD9919
      Sunrise (short)
    Blue Monk
    Got a Match
    I Didn't Know What Time it Was
    The Nearness of You
    Easy to Love
    Think on Me
    The Doctor
    Softly as in the Morning Sunrise (long)

APPENDIX 3: CONTACTS FOR PEOPLE SUFFERING FROM DEPRESSION

The National Depression Campaign (UK)
35 Westminster Bridge Road
London
SE1 7JB
England

Tel: 020 7207 3293
Fax: 020 7633 0559

The Manic Depression Fellowship is a 'user-led' organisation which aims to challenge stigma, promote awareness of manic depression and provide support and advice to their members.

Members receive a quarterly newsletter, advice and information on the latest research, medication and self-management techniques, as well as legal advice and support with employment and benefit issues.

Contact numbers for MDF:
Tel: 0181 974 6550
Fax: 0181 974 6600

Overseas information

Manic Depression and Mood Disorders Support and Information
Sydney, Australia
Tel: 2 98 165 688

Crisis 24-hour Helpline for all Depressives
Auckland, New Zealand
Tel: 0 800 800 717

MDSG Support for Manic Depressives, Depressives, Family and Friends
Manhattan, New York, USA
Tel: 212 533 6374

INDEX

Eddie Thompson Trio 108
Edison, Harry 90
Eldridge, Roy 199, 207
Elizabeth, Queen 223–4
Elizabeth, the Queen Mother 31, 32
Elkin, Adolph 30
Ellington, Duke 26, 95, 232
Ellington, Mercer 67
Ellis, Herb 226
Ellison, Jeff 128, 158, 204, 211, 233, 274
Ellison, Marge 274–5, 289
Ellson, John 253
Emerson, Keith 180
Emerson Lake and Palmer 171
ENSA 44
Esquire Records 73, 85, 94
Establishment Club 114, 115
Evans, Bill 123, 137–8
Ewart, Bill 115
Eyden, Bill 128, 237

'false fingering' 90, 91
Fame, Georgie 258
Famous Door 17
Fangio, Juan Manuel 75
Farmer, Art 150
Farron, Ramon 106–7
Feather, Ray 78
Feldman, Victor 29, 85, 92, 97
Feldman Club 34, 50
Ferguson, Maynard 136, 154, 158, 162
52nd Street 17, 63, 65, 66, 74, 207, 283
Fitterman, Basil 35
Fitzgerald, Ella 72, 89, 159
Flack, Roberta 198
Flamingo Club 101
Flick, Harry 254
Fordham, Jack 107
Four Freshman 213
Fox, Charlie 37
Fox, Ilsa 117, 121, 122, 166, 192–3, 218, 307, 309
Frampton, Peter 155
Frank, Aubrey 47
Frazier, Joe 165–6
'free jazz' 144, 145, 164
Freeman, Chico 246, 247–8, 311
Freeman, Earl Lavon 246, 247
47 Frith Street 124
Fullado Club 42, 58, 64

Gallagher, Noel 270
Ganley, Allan 76, 99, 100, 168
Garland, Judy 152
Gary Burton Quartet 137
Gensel, Dr John Garcia 235, 236
George (club employee) 128–9, 143, 170, 172–3, 180, 198–9, 200, 203–4, 215
George, Norman 47
39 Gerrard Street (Old Place) 107–8, 127, 155, 156, 267
Getz, Beverly (McGovern) 160, 184, 195–6, 260, 261
Getz, Pamela (Raynor) 160
Getz, Stan 73, 90, 100, 117, 152, 160, 161–2, 166–7, 184, 195–6, 197, 200, 203, 204, 221, 260–1
Gien, Bobby 179, 185
Gilberto, João 184
Gillespie, Dizzie 58, 59, 63, 66, 67, 71, 74, 85, 161, 176–7, 200, 203, 204, 207, 221, 225, 234, 251, 258, 268–9, 288
Giuseppe ('Joe': club chef) 204, 211
Gojkovic, Dusko 150
Gold, Harry 45–6
Goldberg, Dave 42, 54, 58
Goldrich, Manny 66
Golson, Benny 114, 127
Gonzales, Babs 113
Goodman, Benny 26, 189
Gordon, Cynthia 28, 30–1, 34, 35, 39–40, 48–9, 50–1, 55–7, 205
Gordon, Dexter 113, 114, 145, 202
Gorman, John 153
Gotlieb, Dr Sydney 137, 139, 161, 162, 191, 279, 289
Gourley, Jimmy 146
Graham Collier Sextet 156
Graham, Kenny 86
Grant, Johnnie 92
Grantz, Norman 89, 90
Grappelli, Stephane 169, 188–9
Graves, Robert 107, 135, 136–7, 147, 168, 169, 197–8, 288–9
Gray, Johnnie 59
Green, Benny 87, 101, 109–10, 199, 223, 251, 260, 264, 307, 308
Green, Dave 212, 237
Green, Joe 81, 82, 294, 304
Greene, Joe 113

Griffin, Johnny 133, 150, 151, 226
Gruvis Malt 270–1
Gunstock, David 35
Gypsy Larry 129

Half Note Club 117, 201
Hall, Rabbi Guy 308–9
Hampton, Lionel 156
Harris, Kenny 20, 98
Harris, Max 85
Harry, Uncle 9
Hawaiian Serenaders 31
Hawkins, Coleman 17, 58, 66, 78–9,
    130, 138–40, 145, 207
Hayes, Edward ('Tubby') 101, 108, 111,
    156, 170, 177, 258
Heath, Albert 172
Heath, Percy 172
Heath, Ted 54–5, 56, 57, 59, 60, 81, 88
Hendricks, Jon 156
Henebery, Terry 156
Henriques, Basil 28
Henshaw, Laurie 155
Herman, Sonny 27–8, 29, 32, 36, 37,
    38, 42, 48, 64
Herman, Woody 26, 63, 66, 136, 154,
    184, 189, 200, 201, 221
Hey Hey Club 17
Hicks, John 200, 224, 225
Higgins, Billy 226
Hill, Graham 175
Hill, Vince 158
Hines, Earl 162
Holiday, Billie 63–4, 66, 90, 120, 202,
    207, 315
Holland, Dave 150
Holloway, Laurie 305, 307
Horne, Lena 112
Houser, Wally 109, 113, 157, 200, 303,
    305–6, 309, 310–11
Houston, Bob 167
Houston, Clint 226
Hoyle, Linda 155
Hubbard, Freddie 133, 176
Hulin, Barbara 153, 242
Hulin, Cyril 149, 241, 242
Hulin, Richard 257
Hulin Artists Management 199–200
Humble, Derek 86, 87, 98, 109, 136,
    150, 162, 164

Hunt, Jim 91
Hylton, Ennis 12, 18
Hylton, Jack 12, 26, 139
Hymen, Phyllis 232

Ind, Peter 231
International Jazz Festival 159
Israels, Chuck 123

Jack, Cousin (Rosenbloom) 9, 10, 312
Jackson, Frances 220, 262
Jackson, Jack 60
Jackson, Milt 172, 199
Jacquet, Illinois 95
James, Harry 26, 136, 154, 162
Jarreau, Al 213
Jasper, Bobby 114
Jay, Barbara 92, 93, 95–6, 113
Jazz Couriers 101, 105, 107
Jazz Journal 201, 202
Jenna, Auntie (Whidden) 214, 229,
    231, 254
Johnson, J.J. 95
Jones, Jack 169–70
Jones, Jo 189
Jones, Selena 150
Jones, Thad 109, 136, 154, 227, 285
Josie (Barber–Auntie Rosie's daughter)
    53, 93, 95, 149, 310

Kay, Connie 172
Keefer, Rick 150
Keith Prowse Organisation 30
Kenton, Stan 96, 97, 136, 154
Kessel, Barney 153, 226
Kevin, Bobby 70
King, Alan 66
King, Pete (friend and partner) 6, 72,
    79, 86–8, 94, 97, 101, 109, 111,
    116–117, 123, 132, 162, 163, 168,
    174, 175, 179, 180, 185, 191, 192,
    193, 197, 200, 204, 222, 223–4,
    234–5, 251–2, 289–90, 291, 293, 295,
    297, 299–300, 301, 302, 302, 304,
    315
King, Peter (saxophonist) 264, 308
King, Stella 101, 193, 223, 234–5, 300,
    302
Kington, Miles 176
Kirk, Roland 113, 115–17, 127, 133, 159

New Musical Express (NME) 87–8
Nistico, Sal 226

Oakes, Michelle 270, 297, 305
O'Day, Anita 162
O'Doherty, Jill 237, 240, 243, 244–5,
    246, 256, 259, 264, 265, 280, 297
Oliver, Jack 72
Orlando, Tony 170–1
Osborne, Mike 144
O'Toole, Peter 122–3
Oxford and St George's Club (the
    Settlement) 27–8, 29, 34–5
Oxley, Tony 145

Page, Leoni 81
Parker, Charlie 42, 58–9, 61, 65, 66,
    67, 71, 74, 76, 77, 95, 96, 130, 146,
    207, 289
Parnell, Jack 54, 57, 81, 85, 86
Parsons, Jimmy 139, 157, 211, 272–3, 308
Pass, Joe 199, 203
Pastie Productions 270–1, 294, 295, 301
Pat Smythe Trio 202
Patrick, Johnny 221
Pauer, Fritz 144
Pearce, Dick 226, 253, 259–60, 273
Peck, Nat 150
Persson, Åke 150, 151, 163, 174, 179
Peterson, Oscar 89, 90, 156, 176, 200
Phillips, Esther 213
Pike, Dave 150
Pincus, Gilbert 65–6, 277
Pitch, Harry 27, 39, 49
Plexico, Lonnie 246
Pollard, Tommy 70, 73, 76, 80, 85
Posner, Henry 21
Posner, Leon 20–1
Poulton, Linda 180–1, 185, 188, 191, 192
Powell, Bud 67, 79
Priory, the 294, 295
Pullen, Don 225
Purim, Flora 253, 279
Pyne, Chris 145

Quaye, Cab 47, 75

Rafie, Uncle 9, 13–14
Rainbow Corner 36
Ranglin, Ernest 118

Riccio, Dr 193
Rich, Buddy 48, 63, 136, 148, 156, 170,
    176, 213, 258
Rivera, Mario 226
Roach, Max 58, 205, 206
rock 'n' roll 100–1
Rogers, Johnny 76
Rollins, Sonny 81, 105, 122, 127,
    130–1, 161, 164, 258
Ronnie Scott All Stars 85, 86
Ronnie Scott Directions 139, 157
Ronnie Scott Orchestra 87–8, 96
Ronnie Scott's Club 108–10, 113–14,
    122, 124–5, 127–30, 143–4, 145,
    147–8, 150–1, 152–8, 162–3, 168–9,
    172, 176–7, 198–9, 203–4, 213,
    221–2, 225–6, 243, 253, 258
Ronnie Scott's Record Productions 206
Rosa, Lita 158
Rose, Denis 39, 47, 49, 50, 51, 61, 71,
    72, 76, 233
Rosenbloom (Ross), Mark (Uncle
    Markie) 8, 9, 10, 21, 53–4, 95, 106,
    149, 175
Rosenbloom, Solomon 8, 57, 106
Rosie, Auntie (Ross) 53–4, 106
Ross, Annie 156, 170, 235, 258
Ross, Arnold 112
Ross, Ronnie 117
Rouse, Dougie 124
Rowles, Jimmy 195
Royal Tottenham Dance Hall 42
Rubin, Natalie 53, 84
Rubini, Joe 32

Sassoon, Vidal 29
Scaffold 152, 153
'scat' singing 72
Schatt, Dave 31
Schatt, Philip 7, 18, 67, 68, 94, 149
Scott, Jock (Joseph (Jock) Schatt) 7, 8,
    9, 10–11, 12, 18, 40, 41, 45, 46,
    67–8, 69, 77, 78, 83–4, 94, 102–3,
    106, 139, 148–9
Scott, Mary (née Hulin) 2, 3, 6, 117–
    18, 119–20, 121–3, 128, 134–5,
    136–7, 138, 142, 143, 144–5, 146–7,
    148–9, 151–2, 153, 154–5, 163, 166,
    170, 171, 173–6, 177–8, 180–2, 183,
    184–5, 186, 187, 189, 190–2, 194–5,